DATE DUE

~~DEC 19 1968~~			
~~FEB 10 1970~~			
MAY 7 1973 R			
GAYLORD			PRINTED IN U.S.A.

MEASUREMENT
Definitions and Theories

New York · John Wiley & Sons, Inc.

LONDON

MEASUREMENT
Definitions and Theories

IIIIIIIIIIIIIIIIIIIIIIIIIIIIIIIIIIIIIIIIIIIIIIIIIIIIIIIIIIIIIIIIIIIIIIIIIIIIIIIIIIIIIIIIIIIIIIIIIIIIIIIIIIIIIIIIIIIIIIIIIIIIIIIIIIIIIIIIIIIIIIIIIIIIIIIIIIIIIIIIIIIIIIIIIIIIIIIIIIIIIIIIIIIII

EDITED BY

C. WEST CHURCHMAN

UNIVERSITY OF CALIFORNIA

AND

PHILBURN RATOOSH

UNIVERSITY OF CALIFORNIA

SECOND PRINTING, NOVEMBER, 1962

LIBRARY OF CONGRESS CATALOG CARD NUMBER: 59–11796
PRINTED IN THE UNITED STATES OF AMERICA

PREFACE

The December 1956 meetings of the American Association for the Advancement of Science included a five-part symposium on measurement. The purpose of the symposium was to enable the participants to examine and discuss important fundamental problems of measurement that have arisen in the disciplines of science. The papers of this symposium are included in this volume.

The symposium was designed to present contrasts in approaches to the problems of measurement. For this reason, the participants were chosen from different disciplines: e.g., physics, psychology, economics, accounting, philosophy. Furthermore, the participants were chosen because it was known that they had different viewpoints on the meaning and significance of measurement.

The result is a book of contrasts. This volume does not constitute a series of connected discourses on measurement. It is not a textbook on the subject of measurement. But it may present as good a picture as possible of what the workers in the foundations of measurement are concerned about in the middle of the twentieth century.

The editors have made no concentrated effort to maintain consistency among the contributors. But they have on occasion suggested revisions of manuscripts, and they have regrouped some of the papers in order to place them in a more congenial setting. The editors are grateful to the authors who responded quickly and obligingly to suggestions that were made.

In Part I of this volume we have grouped together the papers that are primarily concerned with defining the concept of measurement—or at least with trying to characterize the meaning of the concept. Here the contrasts are quite noticeable. "Measurement" clearly means a number of things. It is probably wise to point out that differences in opinion about what measurement means do not necessarily constitute confusion on the part of science. What something really means is the result of many different reflective viewpoints, as Hegel pointed out. In effect, the entire section on meaning should present a better picture of the meaning of measurement than any of the writers could have given by himself.

Part II is entitled "Some Theories of Measurement." The difference between "meaning" and "theory" is not intended to be striking; either of the theory papers could have been included in the first part. But these papers do try to construct the concept of measurement within the framework of a formal language, and in this sense represent distinguishable efforts.

Part III deals with the problems of measurement in physics and includes papers of more direct concern to one group of scientists. The contrast with Part IV (on the problems of measurement in the social sciences) is obvious enough. Perhaps the most obvious aspect of the contrast is that the physicists are concerned with problems of measurement arising from accepted models, whereas the behavioral scientists are concerned with problems of measurement arising from proposed empirical studies.

The original symposium was under the general guidance of C. W. Churchman. The separate sessions were designed and chaired by the following:

Measurement in the Physical Sciences	Henry Margenau
Measurement in the Social Sciences	Paul Lazarsfeld
Measurement in the Value Sciences	Donald Davidson
Formal Aspects of Measurement	Philburn Ratoosh
General Aspects of Measurement	Sebastian B. Littauer

The editors are grateful to the other chairmen who contributed so much to the success of the meeting. The paper by Suppes was invited, but the author could not read it at the meeting.

C. West Churchman
Philburn Ratoosh

June, 1959

CONTENTS

I

SOME MEANINGS OF MEASUREMENT

1

DEFINITION AND MEASUREMENT
IN PHYSICS

Peter Caws

ASSISTANT PROFESSOR OF PHILOSOPHY
UNIVERSITY OF KANSAS

1. Measurement presupposes something to be measured, and, unless we know what that something is, no measurement can have any significance. Physics accordingly requires definition also, if measurement is not to be left hanging in the air. Yet a great deal of the discussion of definition, in recent years, has made reference to measurement. Physics has been described by Campbell [1] as the science of measurement, and there seems to be a general feeling that no physical property can really qualify as such unless we know how to measure it, i.e., unless we know how to describe situations involving it in mathematical terms.

Definition and measurement certainly have functional similarities which make it almost inevitable that a discussion of one should sooner or later involve the other. They both have the character of leading to relations which set the entities of science in order with respect to one another. The kinds of order that they establish can be broadly differentiated, but they run together in many cases, so that there are times when the two procedures seem to amount almost to the same thing. Definition, in general, is concerned with the systematic order of the conceptual schemes of science, and with the nature of the relations between different entities. Measurement has a more limited function, that of establishing metrical order among different manifestations of particular properties, and of making scientific events amenable to mathematical description. Often the relation between two *different* properties is not clear unless measurements have been carried out on both in some case where they appear together; nowadays much definition is expressed in a mathematical form which presupposes measurement.

In this paper we will seek to clarify the differences between definition and measurement and the way in which they affect one another, but it is first necessary to pay attention to some of the confusion which has arisen out of inadequate definitions of the two words, and to stipulate definitions in terms of which the subsequent discussion will be conducted. In the case of measurement, first of all, it has not always been clear whether the term means an *operation* involving an observer and a more or less complex apparatus, or whether it means the *number* that emerges as the result of such an operation—whether, in other words, a measurement produces a result or an operation produces a measurement. To say that the measurement resides in the operation is to make the same number, expressing the same state of the same system, a different measurement depending on the means by which it was obtained. On the other hand, to ignore the operation may be to ignore an interaction which itself affects the result. This is one problem. Then, if measurement does have a relational function, what exactly are the entities that the relation relates? I am speaking now of the relation involved in a single measurement and not of functional relations established by series of measurements. This question is sometimes answered by saying that the result of a measurement is a proposition expressing a relation between a number and an object to which it is assigned, e.g., that the proposition "the length of this rod is 2 meters" can be expressed as

$$2(\text{length in meters})\text{this rod}$$

which has the form xRy [2]. This has the disadvantage of using uncritically a category—object—which is itself the subject of some controversy, and of using as a relation something that one might expect to stand as the terminus of a relation, namely length. Furthermore, such formulations have led to the belief that measurement really has one foot in the outside world, and that it can, therefore, give us information about the link between the external and the theoretical.

When we come to definition the situation is not much better, although the topic is considerably older. The traditional distinction between real definition, which captured the essence of a thing, and nominal definition, which gave equivalences for its name, has been replaced in science by a distinction between what may be called operational and constitutive definitions—operational definitions being those that link theoretical entities with the world of experience, and constitutive definitions being those that link such entities with each other. The problem of the nature of the entities thus linked is encountered here also. Operationism adopted a fallacy that was almost a reversion to the idea of real definition—the principle that the physical entity in fact *is* the set of operations by which it is measured. Logical empiricism, on the other hand, has tended toward a different but equally unfortunate extreme, which in its most exaggerated form consists in reducing the physical entity to a name or linguistic symbol. The kind of definition to which the latter approach leads—that is, the discovery of expressions which can be substituted for the defined expression without altering the truth or falsity of any statement in which it occurs—provides perhaps a psychological reinforcement for operationism, for it brings to light one of the most striking similarities between definition and measurement. Definition requires the replacement of one symbol in an expression by another symbol or symbols; measurement requires the replacement of a symbol by a number, itself also a symbol. It is not far from this point to an identification of the two processes.

The essential function of measurement—to turn to more constructive considerations—is the setting in order of a class of events with respect to its exhibition of a particular property, and this entails the discovery of an ordered class the elements of which can be put in a one-to-one correlation with the events in question. The most obvious available ordered class is that of finite real numbers. I am not sure that we always ought to demand a number; certainly, as I hope to show later, we are not *bound* to use one. The definition that I would adopt is this:

Measurement is the assignment of particular mathematical characteristics to conceptual entities in such a way as to permit (1) an unambiguous mathematical description of every situation involving the entity and (2) the arrangement of all occurrences of it in a quasi-serial order.

I use "quasi-serial order" in Hempel's sense [3], to mean an order which determines, for any two occurrences, either that they are equivalent with respect to the property in question or that one is greater than the other. The mathematical description of a situation involving an entity u might take the form

$$u = a,$$

as it does when the measurement yields a number, or it might take the form, for instance,

$$a \leq u \leq b,$$

or

$$P(a \leq u \leq b) = c \qquad (P \text{ is a probability function})$$

which, while yielding a numerical value (of P) ought still to be regarded as a measurement of u and not simply of P—indeed, in some cases, this is the only way in which a value can be obtained.

This definition makes no reference to the means whereby the mathematical characteristic is arrived at—it simply says what measurement *is*, objectively. The operational procedure necessary may be called a *technique* of measurement; it has been shown to involve not only the observation of a state but often as well the preparation of the state to be observed. Even as thus defined, measurement does not become entirely self-contained. To it, as objective, must be added what Cassirer [4] calls a "subjective index," stating the conditions under which it has validity. This impotence of mathematical statements alone will be encountered again when more general aspects of theory are discussed.

Just as a restrictive definition of measurement is, if possible, to be avoided, so it is best not to make the definition of definition itself too restrictive. Unlike measurement, definition has often been divided into two or more types, together covering all possible cases, which have been defined separately. Reference has already been made to nominal versus real definitions, and operational versus constitutive definitions; a recent treatise specified three kinds—word-word, word-thing, and thing-thing [5]. I agree that it is not easy to find a single definition of definition, but I think these categories unfortunate. Although my definition involves some terms that will require further explanation, it may as well be stated immediately:

An internal definition is any statement which sets an entity in unambiguous relation with one or more entities of the same group, and an external definition is any statement which sets an entity in unambiguous relation with one or more entities of another group.

The word *unambiguous* means not merely that the form of the relation shall be unambiguous but that no other entity shall enter into the same relation with those to which the defined entity is related by its definition.

Both these definitions have been formulated with a view to maximum generality compatible with the necessary rigidity of science. Nothing has been said concerning the question whether the measurements are exact or the definitions true. The form prescribed is simply that which anything must have if it is to be called here a measurement or a definition, and the question of the truth or falsity of either is a later consideration. The discussion of the relations between them may now be entered upon.

2. Definition enjoys a priority, both historical and logical, over measurement. Science grew out of a situation in which the former was freely practiced without any thought of the latter. One would have to place this state of affairs before Hipparchus, perhaps, or before Archimedes, in order to be strictly accurate, although in fact there was little progress after that era until the Renaissance. Definition, it is true, was carried on in rather vague ways, usually *per genus et differentiam,* but still it served to make more or less clear many ideas which have been fundamental to the advancement of science. The understanding of these ideas in a form which provided a basis for argument did not depend on the existence of any technique of measurement. Aristotle did not, as far as I know, *measure* motion, lightness or heaviness, or heat, yet he discussed them in a fashion which is still intelligible to us. That he frequently came to the wrong conclusion points to the inadequacy of his method but not to the illegitimacy of his concepts, which indeed were not very different from those with which laymen still approach science. Quantity as it exists in physics is not easily discoverable in the world of common experience, although quantities are perceived, in varying degrees, as reflected in the adjectives of comparison.

The logical priority is apparent in the historical discussion. It makes perfect sense to speak of definition without measurement, and most popular expositions of physics, and some more serious ones, are constructed on this basis. Techniques of measurement have today become so complicated that, if definition depended on an understanding of them, it would be impossible even to begin to explain to the man in the street what science is doing; yet this is agreed to be an exceedingly important task, on the successful accomplishment of which, perhaps, the life of science depends. I believe that it is possible to make clear the relations between scientific entities, for explanatory but not for quantitatively predictive purposes, without any reference to measurement. A definition that does this may be understood better by a non-scientist than one which involves more mathematics, but that does not make it an unscientific form of definition, and the scientist himself needs it to interpret the results of his measurements. On the other hand, as was indicated at the outset, it is meaningless to speak of measurement unless there is already available some form of definition.

The question that now arises is this: Assuming that definition of a kind can be carried out in the absence of measurement, what is the nature of the entities that are defined in this process, and how can we be sure, when measurement comes along, that what is defined and what is measured are the same thing? The last part of the question expresses the problem for which operationism hoped to provide a solution. Impressed with the mathematical character of physics, and realizing—as few physicists seemed to realize—the importance of measurement as the basis of all *mathematical* description of nature, the early proponents of this doctrine insisted that all definitions should be derived from the operation of measurement. This is a neat solution to the problem of the identity of the measured and the defined, since the same operation serves for both processes. But it leaves the problem of the nature of what is measured and defined untouched. Suppose we measure a length by the familiar device of putting a standard measuring rod against it, and obtain a numerical result; does this tell us anything about length as such? What it does yield is something that may be called a "specific length," by analogy with specific gravity; but when the process is complete we know nothing about length as it applies to the case in question that we did not know about it as it applied to the standard measuring rod that we used. We would know something about length operationally only if the measuring rod itself had no length.

In fact, such an operation might never be performed unless there were some antecedent idea of length, and an interest in making it more exact, in the mind of the experimenter. Cassirer [6] makes the point that all measure has to be "conceived and sought" before it can be found in experience, i.e., one has first a concept of some quality and looks afterwards for quantitative expressions of it. It is true that some numerical relationships have been discovered by chance, but it is remarkable how quickly, in such cases, a conceptual meaning of the relation has been sought. This tendency has been deplored by some philosophers on the ground that the meaning of the relation is exhausted in its analysis on its own grounds, and that it only confuses things to introduce quasi-metaphysical "concepts." Their fear seems to be that there is a temptation to hypostatize the concept as something external. This, however, is a trap into which only the most naive are likely to fall. Concepts may safely be used if they are understood, and in fact they are a most useful tool in the organization of experience, possessing in themselves thinglike properties which enable them to be manipulated as if they were external.

We have to explain how these conceptual entities are defined, if not operationally. The mental equipment of ordinary men provides them as they mature with a large number of concepts, generalized, by a process that is largely automatic, from the diverse presentations of sense. These presentations are originally in apparent chaos, but are organized into simple concepts, which are irreducible and cannot be analyzed, by an involuntary neural mechanism. The process of concept formation acquires a direction with the learning of language and is influenced by the accumulated knowledge of society. At this stage, most concepts are unsuitable for any activity that might be called scientific; but the mind has a reflex action upon itself and perceives the need for a more precise organization to simplify and extend its grasp of reality. This is the scientific impulse, and leads to a new category of conceptual entities. A concept deliberately changed or modified to provide a better interpretation of the sensed world I call a *construct;* and a scientific construct, in particular, is a concept deliberately modified or invented with a view to erecting or improving a theory.

The entities with which philosophy deals have more or less close connections with one another and form what I shall call, for want of a better word, *groups*. Constructs fall into groups according to the kinds of experience they interpret—there are groups for physics, anthropology, mathematics, etc. But not all entities are conceptual, and there are two other important groups distinguishable on nonconceptual grounds, namely, language and sense data. Any empirical science must start with sense data, and external definitions have first to be established between this group and constructs, between this group and language, and between constructs and language, as shown diagrammatically in Fig. 1. The sides 1 and 2 of this triangle represent external definitions that have been called *ostensive;* side 3, external definitions that have been called *stipulative*. Within the group of con-

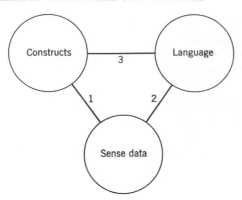

Fig. 1. External definitions.

structs, internal definitions are those that have been called *constitutive;* within language, internal definitions are those that have been called *nominal, implicit, contextual,* etc.

The clarity of constructs is refined by internal and external definition following a pattern of successive approximation. This process, from the point of view of science as a whole, exhibits the historical advancement of the subject; from the point of view of the individual, it is the history of his education. It does not lead to a rigid structure, nor can it be expected to. This flexibility is perhaps its greatest virtue. There must always be room for adjustment, for the introduction of new ideas and for the testing of new hypotheses. I do not deny that at any given time the constructs used by scientists are profoundly influenced by the results of measurement, but to tie them down rigidly to measurement is fatal.

3. Although at this point we are equipped with satisfactory definitions, in the sense that we can explain the relations between our constructs and the world, still the definitions are not complete because greater precision and the possibility of prediction are available. To bring them into the picture, measurement is needed, and the part it plays in refining the scientific structure can best be approached by asking the question: "What does it mean to say that physics is a *mathematical* science?" This is a common phrase. Today one has to be a good mathematician in order to become a good physicist. Professors of physics are constantly complaining that their students are inadequately prepared in mathematics, and, at the other end of the academic spectrum, it has been suggested that research in mathematics ought to be endowed 50 years ahead of research in the other sciences.

But no other science can be reduced to mathematics or to any other kind of calculation. Putting it naively, mathematics lacks the physical part of physics. The reason why it is found to be applicable to physics is this: the functional relations between the entities of physics appear to be of the same form as functional relations in mathematics. What makes the greatest difference between the two disciplines is not that the statements of mathematics are analytic and those of physics synthetic, for this criterion breaks down in some recent views of physics. The distinction is best made between the variables that enter into those statements. Mathematics receives its confirmation in virtue of the fact that any equation becomes a tautology if numbers, related to one another in the way prescribed by the functions involved, are substituted for the variable elements in it. We can say then that the variables of mathematics constitute the class of numbers. The equations used in physics must satisfy this requirement too, i.e., they must be valid mathematically before they can hope to be valid physically. But they are confirmed *as physical statements* in virtue of the fact that they reduce to tautologies, not when the numbers substituted for the variables already have the prescribed functional relation but when they are selected on other grounds. This refers to the classical case; we have suggested that occasionally what is substituted may be something other than a simple number. The variables of physics, as Menger [7] has shown, cannot be regarded as the class of numbers but must be described as classes of pairs, such that for each pair one member is an element of a class of physical entities and the other member is a number. Thus a subclass of numbers is selected from the whole class of numbers by a physical principle of selection.

There is nothing about the physical member of such a pair necessitating its linkage with a *number;* the construction of the pair in this way is a matter of convenience. This point may be emphasized by considering whether it might be possible to make the other member of the pair something other than a number and still have a practical science of physics. Suppose that, in some world other than ours, there are intelligent beings who have not discovered mathematics but whose organs are so constructed as to give them an enormously heightened sensitivity to color, so that they can distinguish many distinct shades within what is to us a narrow spectral band.[1] Suppose that they have discovered fire and the metallurgical arts. Their fundamental metric

[1] In view of recent criticisms of traditional theories of color vision (Edwin H. Land, "Experiments in Color Vision," *Scientific American,* **200,** no. 5, May, 1959, p. 84), it may be as well to emphasize that the possibility or impossibility of this program for human observers is irrelevant to the illustration.

then might be the color scale of temperature. This provides unambiguous relations of coincidence and precedence; our phrase "greater than" would be rendered "bluer than," and there would be other changes of a similar kind. A calculus of colors could be worked out, for the combination of two particular colors determines a unique third, and a standard color might be selected the combination of which with any other would be an operation analogous to "+1" in arithmetic. The color system would not be simply linear, of course, but that might be an added advantage. I do not say that their physics would be any more successful than ours, although a few thousand years of civilization would presumably lead to improvements in the system, but at least it would be possible. Temperature would be a "fundamental" quantity; length could be defined in terms of it via thermometer readings, time by means of some periodic phenomenon such as the passage of heat waves through a long metal rod, work (and, derivatively, force, mass, etc.) via the Carnot cycle, electrical properties via thermocouple phenomena. The inhabitants of this world would have quite clear ideas of these other things on their own grounds, but somebody would probably tell them, sooner or later, that their concepts had no meaning apart from a technique of assigning to each occurrence of them one and exactly one real color, i.e., defining them operationally.

The purpose of this diversion has been to stress the contingent nature of the link between physics and mathematics. It happens that mathematics is at the moment the most highly organized of the sciences, and it is natural that physics should, where possible, seek to benefit from this organization. But this involves a further danger. Even if it is clear that physics cannot be reduced to mathematics, still the hope may be entertained that both can, in some fashion, be reduced to logic. This reduction, however, is exactly what cannot be done.

Logic is concerned with the presuppositions of any knowledge, but with the content of none. It always has to act upon some content, even if this is provided only by the p and q of the logic book, but it is indifferent to the nature of this content. Now mathematics seems at first glance to have this quality too; every child knows that two and two make four whether one uses apples or matchsticks for the demonstration. The use of apples, however, involves a physical-type variable and not a mathematical-type one, and calculations in terms of them must rank as applied mathematics. For the formal quality, one must go back a step further; mathematics deals with number, and what modern mathematical logic really does is to impart substance to the idea of number, as Dedekind cuts or classes of classes—something *on which* the logical operations may be performed.

The function of definition is to state particular relations between qualitative entities which together constitute a structure whose form is logical. These entities are encountered empirically, i.e., at least in the case of the entities of science, they are wholly derived from sense experience, although they may not be identifiable with sense data. Physical properties, as a group, must have their own links with sense experience, independently of the links belonging to mathematical properties; and clearly, since measurement leads first to the mathematical, it cannot provide a direct path to experience.

The true function of measurement is to link mathematics and physics. Observe that it is not a question of establishing a connection between the empirical and the theoretical, which was what operationism claimed to do, for this has already been done in the manner that I have outlined. What measurement does is to connect two parts of theoretical knowledge, the mathematical and the conceptual, imparting relevance to the one and precision to the other. The mathematical nature of physics is analogical. It is impossible to define one construct in terms of another by means of a mathematical equation alone; one can only say that the relation between them is of a logical form similar to that of the mathematical relation. This is an important point and needs to be stressed. Joseph expresses it well when he says [8]:

Mathematicians and physicists say that momentum is defined as mv, or mass into velocity; but they only mean that it is something varying in this definite relation to variations of mass and velocity. In the same way, the velocity of a moving body is not defined, in the sense that what it is is explained, by saying that it varies directly as the distance and inversely as the time of movement, or $= s/t$. An independent act of the understanding is involved, when we speak of that as velocity which so varies.

And again:

Area and volume are different things from length, and can no more be produced by squaring and cubing length than growth and happiness can be produced by squaring and cubing wealth.

If we wish to attach any meaning to this irreducible qualitative element, we cannot rely on a mathematical theory but must go beyond this aspect of the theory and assume, as Bridgman has said [9], "an intuitive knowledge of the language of ordinary experience," adding to the mathematical equation a text showing its applicability. In no other way can we understand what significance the equation is intended to have apart from its purely mathematical one.

Measurement thus assigns, in a stipulative fashion, mathematical characteristics to conceptual entities, and enables us to apply what we learn about the organization of the world in one realm to the clarification of the other. The logical structure comes to the surface, as it were, in mathematics as it does nowhere else, and this is the reason why mathematical modes of thought nearly always effect an economy of effort when they are applied to other disciplines. If this view is maintained, there is seen to be nothing in classical algebra to make it preferable to statistical mathematics; the fact that there is a calculus of probabilities ought, if not to prepare us for the discovery of statistical situations in physics, at least to mitigate our surprise at their appearance. There is no more reason for consternation at the impossibility of making simultaneously exact numerical measurements of two noncommutative entities than there is for despair at the fact that we cannot see galaxies that have receded beyond the limit of observation. The impossibility is inherent in the structure of the world as understood in the light of our present knowledge; we have a means of describing the situation, but it is unscientific to fret because we cannot change it. Nobody can say that progress in science will not lead to greater clarity there too. Certainly, we have little ground for concluding that an impasse has been reached with the Heisenberg uncertainty principle when we cannot even solve the n-body problem in classical mechanics.

4. All our knowledge has to be expressed in conceptual terms; we can know nothing intelligently about what is external except as it is mediated to us by the neurological apparatus which originally informs us of its existence. We have no sure way of telling whether the logic, which exhibits itself in every department of enquiry, has its root in that unconscious faculty of man which is interposed between what is delivered to his senses and what is received cognitively, or whether it is, in fact, an ontological characteristic of nature. Whatever may be the truth of this matter, one thing is certain: it is inescapable. It is certainly a condition of our thought, whether as a characteristic of our minds or as a characteristic of a world of which our minds are part, and consequently it is to be found equally in the systems invented by us and in those presented to us.

The only way in which a new statement is seen to be coherent with the body of knowledge already established is in virtue of its participation in this logical structure. From the point of view of logic, there are two steps in the demonstration of this coherence. First, the statement must not entail the negation of any previous statement; this grants its provisional admission. Second, it may be shown to be, with respect to some statement or statements already known, a tautology. If this is done, its position is assured. In the case of a statement which has reached only the first stage, a direction for research is indicated, for what is needed is the discovery of another fact the statement of which, together with the first statement and any others that may be appropriate, can be turned into a tautology. This is most clearly seen, again, in mathematics, but it is a general principle of all rational thought, as has been well demonstrated by Wittgenstein [10]:

The fact that the propositions of logic are tautologies *shows* the formal—logical—properties of language, of the world.

That its constituent parts connected together *in this way* give a tautology characterizes the logic of its constituent parts.

In order that propositions connected together in a definite way may give a tautology they must have definite properties of structure. That they give a tautology when *so* connected shows therefore that they possess these properties of structure.

This has particular significance for physics, which, as Whyte [11] has shown, is being driven to the point where the quest for new knowledge becomes equivalent to the quest for dimensionless equations. The tautological nature of the mathematical part of a physical statement is guaranteed by the structure of mathematics, which retains here also its close connection with logic itself; but the conceptual part of physics is far from having attained any such satisfactory status. It requires systematization and reformulation in such a way that nonmathematical statements about constructs can be seen also to reduce to tautologies, i.e., attention must be paid to definition in order to make this the case. Furthermore, the constructs on which measurement is to be carried out must be chosen, and the measurements designed, so that the results can be incorporated into dimensionless equations.

In conclusion, some justification is needed for the emphasis in this paper on the conceptual entities called constructs. Bridgman [12] considers that the use of a nonoperationally defined construct such as length involves "a Platonic view of the world diametrically opposed to the whole operational approach." I am sorry about this, but I see no escape from it. It is a question of faithfulness to the way in which men think. Operationism is, undoubtedly, an extremely valuable aspect of analysis, but it can hardly be made a practicable method of science. One is constantly turning to conceptual ideas in order to understand what operationism is saying. The mind inevitably organizes units, thinglike concepts, on which relations converge. Confronted with unrelated sense data, it creates the category "thing"; confronted with scientific data, it creates the category "construct." The construct is not a visual image, nor is it external to the mind; it is analogous to a piece in a game which thought plays. Chess requires not only rules but also men, and physics requires not only laws but also constructs. One could change the rules in chess, yet still play with the same men; and similarly it is not always necessary to replace the old intuitive construct with a new, rigidly formalized one, even if a new technique of measurement appears, as long as one understands the new relations into which it enters.

I might illustrate this by a more concrete example with which I am familiar. Some years ago I was working, intermittently, in a geochronometric laboratory [13], one in which the age of geological and other specimens is found by a determination of their carbon 14 content. What we were measuring, in fact, was the age of the specimens; although at first we used a constant-pressure counter coated with solid carbon, the process was changed twice—first to the use of acetylene in a proportional counter, then to carbon dioxide in a proportional counter. The age we were measuring throughout had for us the same meaning—it meant the time elapsed since the organism in question had died; as for the operations, they consisted mostly of turning stopcocks and looking for leaks in the vacuum system. All this was set up on a purely theoretical basis. A final quotation from Cassirer [14] therefore seems appropriate. "It is not so much with the sensuous instruments of measurement that we measure natural processes as with our own thoughts."

REFERENCES

1. Norman Campbell, *An Account of the Principles of Measurement and Calculation*, London, Longmans, Green, 1928.
2. Victor F. Lenzen, "Procedures of Empirical Science," *International Encyclopedia of Unified Science*, **I**, no. 5, Chicago, University of Chicago Press, 1938, p. 12.
3. Carl G. Hempel, "Fundamentals of Concept Formation in Empirical Science," *International Encyclopedia of Unified Science*, **II**, no. 7, Chicago, University of Chicago Press, 1952, p. 59.
4. Ernst Cassirer, "Einstein's Theory of Relativity," supplement to *Substance and Function*, New York, Dover Publications (Chicago, Open Court), 1923, p. 358.

5. R. Robinson, *Definition,* Oxford, Clarendon Press, 1950.
6. Cassirer, *op. cit.,* p. 359.
7. Karl Menger, "On Variables in Mathematics and Natural Science," *British Journal for the Philosophy of Science,* **V,** no. 18, 1954, p. 135.
8. H. W. B. Joseph, *Lectures on the Philosophy of Leibniz,* Oxford, 1949, pp. 34, 54.
9. P. W. Bridgman, *The Nature of Physical Theory,* Princeton, Princeton University Press, 1936, p. 60.
10. Ludwig Wittgenstein, *Tractatus Logico-Philosophicus,* London, Kegan Paul, 1947, p. 157.
11. L. L. Whyte, "A Dimensionless Physics?" *British Journal for the Philosophy of Science,* **V,** no. 17, 1954.
12. P. W. Bridgman, "Comments on the Paper of Edward G. Ballard," *Methodos,* **V,** no. 19, 1953, p. 240.
13. The Yale Geochronometric Laboratory, Edward S. Deevey, Jr., director.
14. Cassirer, *op. cit.,* p. 365.

2

MEASUREMENT, PSYCHOPHYSICS, AND UTILITY[1]

S. S. Stevens

PROFESSOR OF PSYCHOLOGY, DIRECTOR PSYCHOLOGICAL LABORATORIES
HARVARD UNIVERSITY

The business of pinning numbers on things—which is what we mean by measurement—has become a pandemic activity in modern science and human affairs. The attitude seems to be: if it exists, measure it. Impelled by this spirit, we have taken the measure of many things formerly considered to lie beyond the bounds of quantification. In the process we have scandalized the conservatives, created occasional chaos, and stirred a ferment that holds rich promise for the better ordering of knowledge. Restrictive definitions of measurement have toppled as the practice of measurement, outrunning legislation, has forced us to broaden and generalize our conceptions. The ultimate, perhaps, is reached by those who claim that whenever we can single out a relation between two things we have a scale of measurement of some sort.

It is no new thing, of course, to find practice outrunning legislation, for that is the nub of the story of mathematics. The irrationals, the

[1] Prepared under Grant *G-2668* from the National Science Foundation and Contract *Nonr-1866(15)* between Harvard University and the Office of Naval Research (Project *NR142-201*, Report *PNR-201*). Several friends and critics have helped the writing at some points and have contested it at others. For their helpful discussions, I am especially indebted to L. J. Savage, John W. Tukey, G. A. Miller, Ardie Lubin, W. H. Kruskal, F. M. Lord, and Garrett Birkhoff.

surds, the imaginaries, and the negatives are numbers that still bear names reminiscent of protest—protest against outlandish practice and against the writing of unauthorized absurdities. But orthodoxy bent to accommodate practice. Mathematicians staved off chaos by rationalizing the use of irrationals, and by imagining a broader domain in which imaginaries and negatives could serve as proper elements. An analogous story can be told of measurement. The reach of this concept is becoming enlarged to include as measurement the assignment of numerals [2] to objects or events according to rule—any rule. Of course, the fact that numerals can be assigned under different rules leads to different kinds of scales and different kinds of measurement, not all of equal power and usefulness. Nevertheless, provided a consistent rule is followed, some form of measurement is achieved.

Perhaps it is unfair to pretend that this liberal and open-handed definition of measurement is the accepted norm, for some practitioners of the physical sciences prefer to cling to the narrower view that only certain of the tidier rules are admissible. This attitude is quite understandable, but just as the acceptance of the absurd, fictitious, and imaginary roots of negative numbers redounded to the enrichment of mathematics, so, too, may the theory of measurement find itself enriched by the inclusion of all orderly numerical assignments. Mathematics has at last freed itself of the earthy perspective under which it formerly sought to justify its laws by manipulations performed upon solid objects, and has taken off into the blue of pure abstraction—where it properly belongs. Measurement, however, must remain anchored here below, for it deals with empirical matters (although it borrows its models from mathematics). On the other hand, there is no requirement that measurement remain confined to the simpler problems of counting which first gave rise to it.

In the beginning, mathematics and measurement were so closely bound together that no one seemed to suspect that two quite different

---

[2] Should we say "numeral" or "number"? N. R. Campbell says numeral. Most other writers say number. Elsewhere I have tried to distinguish among the meanings of these terms and the related terms numerousness and numerosity (see [31], p. 22). It would be nice to adhere to a consistent usage but, as the reader will discover, I have not done so. The term "numeral" in this paragraph refers to an element in a formal model, not to a particular mark on a particular piece of paper. The term "number" sometimes has this meaning, but, in common usage, it also has many others. I have tried to reserve the term "numerousness" for the "subjective" aspect or attribute which we observe when we look at, but do not count, a collection of objects. Numerosity is the "physical" attribute of a collection which we measure by counting, i.e., by pairing off the items in a collection against the successive positive integers.

disciplines were involved. Whole-number arithmetic and scales of numerosity grew up tightly intertwined, and the ancients seem not to have discerned the difference between the formal model on the one hand and the empirical matter of scaling on the other. The numerosity of collections of objects (number in the layman's sense) constitutes the oldest and one of the most basic scales of measurement. It belongs to the class that I have called *ratio scales*. Undoubtedly it was man's early efforts to construct a scale of numerosity that led to his invention of a formal arithmetic, and it is not surprising that many millennia were to come and go before men saw that the test of a formal system need not reside in its ability to reflect what can be done with piles of pebbles.

Modern mathematics, far from concerning itself merely with numerosity, has become so nonquantitative in its abstract reaches that Gödel could suggest that it was purely an historical accident that mathematics developed along quantitative lines [21]. Perhaps this is so. But from another point of view the "accident" has a certain inevitability about it. Striving to deal with collections, be they fish, cattle, or warriors, ancient man seemed destined in the nature of things to have hit upon the concept of number and to have made therein his first triumphant abstraction. It is hard to conceive how mathematics could have begun elsewhere than in measurement.

In recent times, however, it has become clear that the formal system of mathematics, the "empty play upon symbols," constitutes a game of signs and rules having no necessary reference to empirical objects or events. As Hardy says, "It is impossible to prove, by mathematical reasoning, any proposition whatsoever concerning the physical world, and only a mathematical crank would now imagine it his function to do so" [18]. As human history goes, this hard-won understanding is an affair of very recent times. The final divorcement between the formal, abstract, analytic system and the empirical questions that originally sparked its development has clarified the relation between mathematics and measurement. Under the modern view, the process of measurement is the process of mapping empirical properties or relations into a formal model.[3] Measurement is possible only because there is a kind of isomorphism between (1) the empirical relations

---

[3] It is now common parlance to refer to formal, mathematical systems as "models." The recency of the distinction between the formal model and the empirical operations of science impresses me particularly, for as little as two decades ago some of my colleagues expressed surprise that I should refer to a formal system as a "model" that could be used to represent empirical relations [29].

among properties of objects and events and (2) the properties of the formal game in which numerals are the pawns and operators the moves. As Russell put it: "Measurement demands some one-one relation between the numbers and magnitudes in question—a relation which may be direct or indirect, important or trivial, according to circumstances" [23, p. 176].

Before we consider this matter further, let us review some recent history.

THE CLASSICAL VIEW

What I should like to mean by the classical view of measurement is the conception that grew up in the physical sciences and that received its fullest exposition in the works of N. R. Campbell [4, 6, 7, 14]. This is the view that dominated the scene until the 1930's. More recently I have been startled to see some of my own notions described as the "classical measurement theory" [10, 43], but this seems somewhat premature. It is not so much that the term "classical" has the connotation of "out of date and slightly wrong"; it is rather that the point of view I am urging represents a considerable departure from Campbell's tradition. Moreover, its development is still in a state of flux. But more about this later.

The classical "classical theory" grew quite naturally out of the evolution of the number system, which, as we have already noted, apparently began as a primitive project in the scaling of numerosity. The exact history of how this enterprise came about is lost to the record, of course, but our attempts to reconstruct the main features of the story are probably not far wrong. The important point for our present concern is the fact that some long-forgotten genius somehow contrived to build a number system—a formal model—to represent what he did with pebbles, fingers, or cattle. With the aid of this model, he measured the numerosity of his possessions.

Since the formal model was invented for this purpose, it is scarcely surprising that the model turned out to be isomorphic with the empirical operations performable with such things as pebbles (from whose Latin name we derive our word calculus). Thus three pebbles put with four pebbles to make a larger pile is mirrored by the symbolic expression $4 + 3 = 7$. Ultimately, when the axioms of addition were finally exhumed from the long-standing "rules of practice" of whole-number arithmetic, it was readily seen that the property of numerosity "satisfied" these postulates. Thus the commutative law, to take a particular example, which says that $4 + 3 = 3 + 4$ has its analogue in pebble counting, for it makes no difference in what order we take the piles of pebbles.

It was a straightforward matter to extend the scaling procedure developed for numerosity to the scaling of length. Of course, a richer formal model was required for this extension, and the number domain had to be expanded to include fractions and the rest of the rational domain. However, the isomorphism between the model and the physical operations performable with lengths is still close. For example, both the physical addition of lengths and the formal addition of rational numbers are commutative.

The classical view of measurement, as Campbell presents it, is essentially the view that direct or "fundamental" measurement is possible only when the "axioms of additivity" can be shown to be isomorphic with the manipulations we perform upon objects. Only a few properties, such as length, weight, and electric resistance, are measurable in this fundamental way. Most other magnitudes dealt with in physics are measured by indirect or "derived" measurement—a process in which derived magnitudes are defined by means of numerical laws relating fundamental magnitudes. Thus density, the classical example, is measured by the ratio of mass to volume.

Partly as a result of Campbell's masterly exposition, the view has been widely held that the assignment of numerals to objects other than by the procedures involved in fundamental or derived measurement is not measurement at all. The clash of opinion on this issue is well documented by the deliberations of a distinguished British committee appointed in 1932 to consider and report upon the possibility of "quantitative estimates of sensory events" [14, 30]. The particular subject of discussion was the sone scale of loudness [39]. The committee split wide on the meaning of measurement, and some harsh words were written condemning the alleged measurement of sensation. In the Final Report [14], one member said, "I submit that any law purporting to express a quantitative relation between sensation intensity and stimulus intensity is not merely false but is in fact meaningless unless and until a meaning can be given to the concept of addition as applied to sensation."

Campbell himself was troubled. At times he seemed to suggest that loudness measurement might be possible, if based on monaural-binaural loudness matches, or, alternatively, if estimations of half loudness should turn out to be consistent with other estimations, such as one-third or one-tenth loudness. In the end, however, Campbell went along with the conservative wing of the committee and asked: "Why do not psychologists accept the natural and obvious conclusion that subjective measurements of loudness in numerical terms (like those of length . . .) are mutually inconsistent and cannot be the basis of measurement?" Why, he might have asked, does the psychologist not give up and go quietly off to limbo?

This is how matters stood in 1940. In the meantime, unaware that the British committee was trying to settle the issue, some of us at Harvard were wrestling with similar problems. I remember especially some lively discussions with G. D. Birkhoff, R. Carnap, H. Feigl, C. G. Hempel, and G. Bergmann. What I gained from these discussions was a conviction that a more general theory of measurement was needed, and that the definition of measurement should not be limited to one restricted class of empirical operations. There was also an obvious need for an improved terminology. The terms "fundamental" and "derived," as used by Campbell, were clear enough, but much cloudy discourse revolved around certain other distinctions, such as that between "intensive" and "extensive" magnitudes. Like some other authors, I had tried to redefine these terms [28] but had succeeded only in compounding confusion.

The best way out seemed to be to approach the problem from another point of view, namely, that of invariance, and to classify scales of measurement in terms of the group of transformations that leave the scale form invariant. This approach would seem to get to the heart of the matter, for the range of invariance under mathematical transformations is a powerful criterion of the nature of a scale. A fourfold classification of scales based on this notion was worked out sometime around 1939 and was presented to the International Congress for the Unity of Science in 1941. World War II then came along, and publication was delayed until 1946 [30]. A fuller development appeared in 1951 [31].

One consequence of this approach is to make it clear that the classical terms "fundamental" and "derived" describe two classes of operations, not two classes of scales. Both fundamental measurement and derived measurement usually result in ratio scales, which are invariant under multiplication by a constant, or, as is sometimes said, are unique up to a similarity transformation. This is not to deny, of course, that the distinction between fundamental and derived is a useful one in physics, for in many contexts it is important to distinguish between kinds of operations. But there is a sense in which even more powerful distinctions can be made.

SCALES OF MEASUREMENT

Although the definition of measurement could, if we wished, be broadened to include the determination of any kind of relation between properties of objects or events, it seems reasonable, for the present, to restrict its meaning to those relations for which one or another property of the real number system might serve as a useful model. This restriction is implied when we say that measurement is the assignment of numerals to aspects of objects or events according to rule. But even this restriction leaves the concept broader than would be countenanced by the classical view, for all that is required is a consistent rule of assignment. The only procedure excluded is "random" assignment: if there is no criterion for determining whether a given numeral should or should not be assigned, it is not measurement.

Within this framework, we can distinguish four kinds of scales, which I have called nominal, ordinal, interval, and ratio. A fifth kind of scale, called a logarithmic interval scale [37], is also possible, but apparently it has never been put to use. We will return to it in a later section.

The four scales are listed in Table 1. An advantage of this tabulation is that it reveals certain interesting relations among the scales. Thus, the second column is cumulative in the sense that to an empirical operation listed opposite a given scale must be added all those operations listed above it. To erect an interval scale, for example, we need a procedure for equating intervals or differences, plus a procedure for determining greater or less, and a procedure for determining equality or equivalence. To these procedures must be added a method for ascertaining equality of ratios if a ratio scale is to be achieved.

The next column lists the kinds of transformations that leave the "structure" of the scale undistorted. In this column, each group of transformations is contained in the one above it.

The last column in Table 1 lists some examples of each scale.

It is an interesting fact that the measurement of some quantities may have progressed from scale to scale. We can imagine, for example, that certain Eskimos might speak of temperature only as freezing or not freezing and, thereby, place it on a nominal scale. Others might try to express degrees of warmer and colder, perhaps in terms of some series of natural events, and thereby achieve an ordinal scale. As we all know, temperature became an interval scale with the development

TABLE 1.   A Classification of Scales of Measurement *

Scale	Basic Empirical Operations	Mathematical Group Structure	Typical Examples
Nominal	Determination of equality	Permutation group $x' = f(x)$ where $f(x)$ means any one-to-one substitution	"Numbering" of football players Assignment of type or model numbers to classes
Ordinal	Determination of greater or less	Isotonic group $x' = f(x)$ where $f(x)$ means any increasing monotonic function	Hardness of minerals Street numbers Grades of leather, lumber, wool, etc. Intelligence test raw scores
Interval	Determination of the equality of intervals or of differences	Linear or affine group $x' = ax + b$ $a > 0$	Temperature (Fahrenheit or Celsius) Position Time (calendar) Energy (potential) Intelligence test "standard scores"(?)
Ratio	Determination of the equality of ratios	Similarity group $x' = cx$ $c > 0$	Numerosity Length, density, work, time intervals, etc. Temperature (Rankine or Kelvin) Loudness (sones) Brightness (brils)

* Measurement is the assignment of numerals to events or objects according to rule. The rules for four kinds of scales are tabulated above. The basic operations needed to create a given scale are all those listed in the second column, down to and including the operation listed opposite the scale. The third column gives the mathematical transformations that leave the scale form invariant. Any numeral x on a scale can be replaced by another numeral x', where x' is the function of x listed in column 3.

of thermometry, and, after thermodynamics had used the expansion ratio of gases to extrapolate to zero, it became a ratio scale.

Since a more complete description of these scales is available elsewhere [31], we will not discuss them more fully. I would merely point out that the oft-debated question whether the process of classification underlying the nominal scale constitutes measurement is one of those semantic issues that depends upon taste. Whitehead [45, p. 30] calls classification a "halfway house" on the road to measurement. I prefer to call it a form of measurement, because the use of numerals to designate classes of objects, such as items in a catalogue, is an example of the assignment of numerals according to rule. The rule is: Do not assign the same numeral to different classes or different numerals to the same class. This is quite different from a "random" assignment under which no rule would be in force. With no rule in force, the same numeral might be assigned to different classes, and different numerals might be assigned to the same class. A class in this sense may, of course, contain only one member, as when the coach "numbers" his football players.

The forming of classes of equivalent objects or events is no trivial matter. An operation for determining equality is obviously the first step in measurement, but it is more than that. It is the basis of all our categorizing and conceptualizing [2]—of all our coding and recording of information. It underlies the ubiquitous process by which we sort the environment into significant constellations of events and, thereby, take the first step toward systematizing the booming confusion of the universe. Thus, it provides the basis of our identifying, recognizing, and labeling ordinary objects. Without this step, no further measurement would be possible.

In some contexts, what is largely a matter of nominal scaling goes by the heading "detection theory" and a considerable discipline is flowering under this name. A specific issue concerns the determination of a threshold [38], the separation of stimuli into two classes: those that produce a reaction and those that do not. It is true, of course, that the location of the boundary between these two classes is often stated in terms of its position on a ratio scale of some stimulus continuum, but the prior existence of such a ratio scale is not a prerequisite to the nominal process of sorting stimuli into two classes, detectable and not detectable. These are nominal categories, and threshold determination is an instance of nominal scaling.

Another development that has bolstered the scientific importance of nominal scaling is the development of information theory. This theory provides a tool for the treatment of data at the nominal level of measurement [15]. It allows us to deal effectively with categories (alternatives) without regard for any ordinal relations that might obtain among the categories. Thus the measure of transmitted information, T, provides a measure of association at the nominal level of scales. Other measures of association useful with nominal scales have also been the object of recent research [16].

STATISTICS AND MEASUREMENT

The fourfold classification of scales of measurement provides a convenient framework on which to display some of the common statistical measures. Depending on what type of scale we have constructed, some statistics are appropriate, others not. The group of mathematical transformations permitted on each scale (see Table 1) determines which statistical measures are applicable. In general, the more unrestricted the permissible transformations, the more restricted the statistics. Thus, nearly all statistics are applicable to measurements made on ratio scales, but only a very limited group of statistics may be applied to measurements made on nominal scales. A few examples of typical statistics appropriate to the various scales are listed in Table 2.

The fact that a given statistic is appropriate, in the sense used here, does not always tell us whether the statistic is the one we should compute. For example, the median, the arithmetic mean, the geometric mean, and the harmonic mean are all appropriate to ratio scales, but which of them should be used in a given circumstance must be decided by other criteria than the fact that measurements were made on a ratio scale [34]. The type of scale involved provides a necessary but not a sufficient condition for the choice of a statistic.

The criterion for the appropriateness of a statistic is *invariance* under the transformations permitted by the scale, as listed in Table 1. This invariance may be of two principal kinds: the numerical value of the statistic may remain constant when the scale is transformed, or

TABLE 2. **Examples of Statistical Measures Appropriate to Measurements Made on the Various Classes of Scales**

Scale	Measures of Location	Dispersion	Association or Correlation	Significance Tests
Nominal	Mode	Information, H	Information transmitted, T Contingency correlation	Chi square
Ordinal	Median	Percentiles	Rank-order correlation [31]	Sign test Run test
Interval	Arithmetic mean	Standard deviation Average deviation	Product-moment correlation Correlation ratio	t test F test
Ratio	Geometric mean Harmonic mean	Per cent variation		

else the numerical value may change although the item designated by the statistic remains the same [31]. The first type, invariance of numerical value, holds, for example, for such dimensionless statistics as the product-moment correlation coefficient, r, and the coefficient of variation, V, which expresses per cent variability. The second type, invariance of reference, holds for such dimensional statistics as the median, mean, standard deviation, etc. For example, the case standing at the median of a distribution remains at the mid-point under all scale transformations that preserve order (isotonic group), and the case standing at the mean remains there under all linear transformations.

Each of the columns in Table 2 is cumulative in the sense that a statistic listed opposite a given scale is appropriate not only to that scale but also to all scales listed below it. Thus, the mean is appropriate to an interval scale and also to a ratio scale (but not, of course, to an ordinal or a nominal scale).

This cumulative property of Table 2 needs qualification, however, when we go from nominal scales to the other varieties. The nominal scale involves only discrete categories or classes. When the categories are naturally discrete, e.g., *male* or *female*, the problem is straightforward. We can then count men and women and determine which, for example, is the modal class. But when categories are formed by partitioning a continuous variable, like stature, a certain arbitrariness enters in. If we group statures into class intervals 1 inch wide, we may, again, find the modal class for a given sample of people. However, if we change the boundaries of the class intervals, or if we make the intervals different in size, the modal value may change. If we make finer and finer measurements and reduce the size of the class intervals more and more, we may even find that no two statures are the same, i.e., there is no mode.

We see, then, that there is an essential difference between the concept of a mode as applied to naturally discrete classes and as applied to a continuous scale. In the discrete case, the mode remains invariant under all the scale transformations listed in Table 1, but, in the continuous case, the mode is not invariant under increasing monotonic transformations.[4]

Returning now to Table 2, we note that it contains two empty cells.

___

[4] I am indebted to J. W. Tukey, W. H. Kruskal, and L. J. Savage for calling my attention to this point. My earlier discussions neglected the problem and led thereby to some wrong implications (see especially [34]).

This merely reflects the fact that I am not aware of any measures of correlation or tests of significance that apply only to ratio scales. Perhaps such statistics exist and will soon be brought to my attention. If they do not exist, the possibility of their invention presents an interesting problem.

As already indicated, the appropriateness of a given statistic is conditioned by the nature of the scale against which measurements are made. Table 2 suggests, for example, that, when operations are available to determine only a rank order, it is of questionable propriety to compute means and standard deviations. This conclusion, obvious as it may seem to some [25, 1], met with disapproval by others [3]. One author makes his point in a humorous skit on "The statistical treatment of football numbers" [19]. One of the objections seems to be that the implications of Table 2 place too great a restriction on the usefulness of statistics.

As I see this issue, there can surely be no objection to anyone computing any statistic that suits his fancy, regardless of where the numbers came from in the first place. Our freedom to calculate must remain as firm as our freedom to speak. The only question of substantial interest concerns the use to which the calculated statistic is intended. What purposes are we trying to serve? When we compute the mean of the numerals assigned to a team of football players, are we trying to say something about the players, or only about the numerals? Obviously, we cannot say much about the players if the original numerals were passed out under a nominal assignment—the sole rule being "one to a customer." The only "meaningful" statistic here would be N, the number of players assigned a numeral.

Or suppose the assignment were made on some ordinal basis. The coach might line the players up in order of stature, and assign successive integers beginning with the shortest man whom he calls 1. We then compute the mean, and it turns out to be 20. Would the player bearing the numeral 20 stand at the mean of the distribution of statures as measured by a yardstick? Only by accident would this be the case. Plainly, then, if we want to interpret the result of averaging a set of data as an arithmetic mean in the usual sense, we need to begin with more than an ordinal assignment of numerals.

Discouraging as it may appear, the outcome of "statisticizing" is no better than the empirical measurements that go into it. The assertion that "statistical technique begins and ends with numbers and with statements about them" [3] is both true and false. At the formal, syntactical level of discourse, where we are concerned only with the mathematical model itself, we can accept this statement as essentially correct. But when, with the aid of semantical rules, we relate certain aspects of the model to certain aspects of the empirical universe, it becomes another story. For when we use a statistical model to reach conclusions about matters of empirical fact, we are no longer concerned merely with numbers. The question then arises, to what do the numbers refer? This question takes us back to the empirical operations that underlie our measurements and that give the numbers meaning, sharp or vague, as the case may be.

The basic principle is this. Having measured a set of items by making numerical assignments in accordance with a set of rules, we are free to change the assignments by whatever group of transformations will preserve the empirical information contained in the scale. These transformations, depending on which group they belong to, will upset some statistical measures and leave others unaffected. In other words, for guidance in setting bounds on the statistical treatment of empirical measurements, we must look to the principle of invariance. The empirical operations that underlie the scale determine what transformations can be made without the sacrifice of information, and the permissible transformations determine, in turn, the appropriate statistical measures, i.e., those that preserve the requisite invariance.

Some of the statistics appropriate to nominal and ordinal scales are sometimes called nonparametric, or distribution-free. These names express the idea that, in using them, we make no assumptions regarding the distribution of the underlying population from which a sample was drawn. To what extent certain of the so-called nonparametric statistics are, in fact, "distribution-free" is perhaps an open question at this time, and not one to be settled here. The only point I would like to make is that, when our empirical procedures limit us to ordinal measurement, it is obviously proper that we forego assuming knowledge of the parameters of the population because the form of a distribution has meaning only in terms of an interval or a ratio scale. Fortunately, many useful statistical procedures have recently been invented to deal with nominal and ordinal measures, and these various procedures could be added to Table 2 [27].

In making these additions, we must be careful to ask what type of measurement scale is assumed by the statistical procedure. Usually this question has an obvious answer, but, sometimes, it may not be so clear. Thus, although Wilcoxon's "matched-pairs signed-ranks" test is sometimes classed with statistics applicable to ordinal scales, one of the steps involves taking the difference between the two scores of a pair. If the scores in question are measurements made only on an ordinal scale, it seems evident that the numerical difference between them can have no firm meaning. The numerical differences would be determined only by the accidental manner in which numerals were assigned to the original rank-ordered scores, and this assignment could be changed by any increasing monotonic transformation.

THE LOGARITHMIC INTERVAL SCALE

Thus far we have discussed the four classes of scales most widely used in the scientific enterprise. It is an interesting question whether the list in Table 1 is exhaustive of the possibilities, or whether other classes might be devised. Under the broad definition of measurement—the assignment of numerals according to rule—it would seem probable that other rules than those described might be invented.

One interesting possibility would be to base a scale of measurement on the three empirical operations: determination of equality, determination of greater or less, and determination of equal ratios. An empirical operation for determining equal intervals would be assumed to be lacking.

What kind of scale would this provide? Clearly we would be able to identify items, order them, and set them in the relation $a/b = b/c = c/d$ . . . . The term "logarithmic interval scale," suggests itself as a name for this scale, because $\log a - \log b = \log b - \log c$, etc. The mathematical transformation under which the structure of this scale remains invariant I have called the *power group*. Thus, for any numerical value x, we can substitute x', where $x' = kx^n$, and the constants k and n are positive.

With this class of scales added to the list, the hierarchy of scales, together with their transformation groups, would take the form shown in Table 3. The arrangement of this table is intended to suggest that a ratio scale is possible only when empirical operations are available to create both types of interval scales—linear *and* logarithmic. If we can determine both equal differences and equal ratios, we can eliminate the additive constant b and the exponent n, and we are left with only the multiplying constant of the similarity transformation, i.e., we are left with a ratio scale.

If we cannot determine equal intervals, we are left with equal, but unknown, ratios, which limits us to a logarithmic interval scale. The formal properties of such a scale may be interesting, but, like many mathematical models, it has thus far proved useless to the empirical

TABLE 3. Hierarchy of Scales

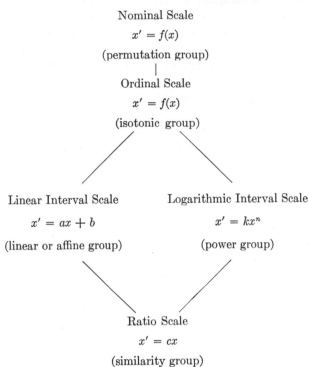

Nominal Scale

$x' = f(x)$

(permutation group)

Ordinal Scale

$x' = f(x)$

(isotonic group)

Linear Interval Scale   Logarithmic Interval Scale

$x' = ax + b$ $x' = kx^n$

(linear or affine group)   (power group)

Ratio Scale

$x' = cx$

(similarity group)

business of science. Scales of equal intervals, however, have had great utility, as witness the scales of temperature (Fahrenheit and Celsius) and the scale of calendar time. There is probably no *a priori* reason why a use could not be found for a logarithmic interval scale built on equated ratios, where the numerical value of the ratio can be chosen only arbitrarily, just as we arbitrarily set the numerical value of a difference on a linear interval scale. Note that both types of interval scales are determined up to two arbitrary constants. In other words, the statement that a scale is determined except for two constants is not always definitive.

As a concrete example of how a set of measurement standards for a logarithmic interval scale might be constructed, let us imagine a situation in which we have an ordinary balance (for determining weight) plus a balance so constructed that the empty pans hang level, but the fulcrum is located at some unknown position, not in the center of the beam. We will also assume that the operation of placing two weights in the same scale pan is for some reason impossible. How then might we proceed? With the balance having the uncentered fulcrum, we could construct a series of weights, A, B, C, . . . , such that $A/B = B/C = C/D$, etc. On the uncentered balance, weight A balances weight B, and then, when weight B is moved to the other pan, it balances weight C placed in the pan formerly occupied by weight B. Whether weight A is heavier or lighter than weight B could be determined by the balance with the centered fulcrum. With these two balances, we could construct an ordered series of standard weights, and to these weights we could assign an appropriate series of numerals. Any two numerals could be chosen arbitrarily, and this choice would fix the values of all the others. Thus, if we set $A = 2$ and $B = 6$, then $C = 18$ and $D = 54$, etc.

It should be mentioned, perhaps, that elsewhere I have attempted to show how, by the addition of a third type of balance with which to create a series of weights spaced by equal intervals, we could proceed to create a standard series of weights answering to the requirements of a ratio scale [31]. The point of that demonstration is to try to show that the *physical* addition of weights—the placing of two weights in the same scale pan—is not required to produce a scale isomorphic with Campbell's "fundamental" scale of weight (or of mass, as he prefers to call it).

The statistics applicable to measurements made on a logarithmic interval scale would include those appropriate to a linear interval scale, except that we would need to work with the logarithms of the scale values rather than with the scale values themselves. For example, under the power group of transformations, the item corresponding to the mean would remain invariant, provided we averaged the logarithms of the scale values rather than the scale values themselves.

There is little likelihood, of course, that anyone is going to express the weight of meat and potatoes on a logarithmic interval scale. Our lack of interest in these scales stems from our greater interest in ratio scales, to which we nearly always resort whenever we can.

It is possible, on the other hand, that in certain areas of psychophysics a use may be found for logarithmic interval scales. There is evidence that, on a certain class of "prothetic" continua (subjective brightness, loudness, heaviness, etc.), observers' judgments of equal intervals or differences are subject to a systematic bias that is not present in judgments of equal ratios [40]. If this is indeed the case, then scales built on equalized ratios are a promising possibility. Again, we would prefer, if possible, to go a step further and construct ratio scales of these psychological magnitudes. As we shall see, ratio scales are possible, provided we assume that the observer can tell not only when two perceived ratios appear equal but also what the numerical value of the ratio is.

There is a further possibility that the outcome of certain well-known scaling techniques (e.g., pair comparisons) may, when applied to prothetic continua, lead most naturally to logarithmic interval scales. This comes about because discriminal dispersion on prothetic continua, instead of being constant (as generally assumed), tends to be proportional to the psychological magnitude in question. The psychological magnitude, in turn, is a power function of the stimulus magnitude (on at least 14 prothetic continua) [37]. It follows, therefore, that psychological values separated by equal units of dispersion on the stimulus scale stand in a constant ratio to each other. In other words, there is reason to believe that some of the "equal-interval scales" constructed by the method of pair comparisons, or by related methods, are, in fact, "equal-ratio scales," i.e., logarithmic interval scales.

OTHER TYPES OF SCALES

The five scales listed in Table 3 would seem to exhaust the possibilities, at least those of scientific interest, except perhaps for the class of scales on which no transformations would be possible. These would be ratio scales having in some sense or other a natural unit, so that not even the similarity transformation (multiplication by a constant) would be admitted.

On the other hand, it has been suggested that certain other scales of measurement, intermediate in power between some of those in Table 3, might be added to the list. The most interesting suggestions along this line are those of Coombs [8, 9, 10]. It is not possible to discuss all his suggestions here, but I would like to try to examine one of his proposed scales, the so-called ordered metric scale. This scale has been the object of considerable interest, and ingenious procedures for generating it have been attempted.

The ordered metric scale is said to lie between the ordinal and the interval scales. It assumes that we have an operation for ordering objects on a continuum and also for ordering the intervals between the objects. In other words, we are able to say that the distance between one pair of objects is greater or less than the distance between another pair. This rank-ordering of intervals gives us more information than does the mere rank-ordering of the objects, but it gives us less information than is contained in an interval scale.

The question that naturally suggests itself is this: if our operations can tell us when one interval is greater or less than another, why can they not tell us when the one interval is not greater or less than the other? Why, in other words, can we not determine equal intervals? The operations sufficient for an ordered metric scale ought to be sufficient to determine an interval scale, for otherwise we would be in the odd position of having to argue that an ordinal scale (on intervals) is possible whereas a nominal scale is not.

In what sense, then, is an ordered metric not an interval scale? As I understand it, the argument seems to be that the outcome is an ordered metric scale whenever a procedure sufficient to determine an interval scale is applied to a finite set of objects that do not happen to be equally spaced on the continuum in question. The failure to achieve interval measurement is not caused by an inadequacy of the available procedures but by a paucity of things to measure.

To illustrate this point, let me try once again to construct an imaginary example in an area with which we are all familiar. Suppose we were to try to scale, in terms of their weights, a set of objects A, B, C, D, ... All we have to work with, let us say, is a well-constructed balance and plenty of fine sand. We will assume that we can put one object and some sand in the same scale pan, but that we are not permitted to use the sand to construct a graded series of weights having interval or ratio properties. In other words, we cannot weigh the objects in the ordinary sense, because we have no series of standard weights. How then might we proceed?

First, we use the balance to determine the rank-order of the objects, which we will assume turns out to be $A < B < C < D$ . . . . Next we place A in one pan and B in the other, and proceed to add to the pan holding object A an amount of sand a required to achieve a balance. We then set aside sand a and proceed to do the same with B and C, adding to B enough sand b to balance; similarly, with C and D, etc. We can then proceed to rank-order the differences between the objects by using the balance to determine the rank-order of the weights of the various amounts of sand, a, b, c, ... In this manner we achieve an ordered metric scale.

It is clear that the operations we have envisaged would really be sufficient to determine an interval scale, provided objects of appropriate degrees of heaviness were available or could be manufactured. We could then set up a series of weights (objects) for which the required incremental amounts of sand a, b, c, . . . would all be equal. Such a series might serve as a set of standards in terms of which unknown weights could be measured on a scale unique up to a linear transformation, i.e., on a linear interval scale.

Why, if we can achieve an interval scale, should we settle for less? It seems probable that, in a really serious enterprise in which the establishment of an interval scale was of sufficient moment, we would not be content to stop short of it. For the particular experimental undertakings [8, 26] that have been presented as examples of ordered metric scaling, it seems possible to suggest ways in which the procedures could be modified or extended to produce interval or ratio scales. This is especially true when the scale in question concerns subjective magnitudes, for then, as we shall see, the position of the stimuli on the subjective scale can be ascertained, even though the stimuli do not happen to mark off equal distances. Under such circumstances, perhaps it is fair to ask for evidence that interval or ratio scaling is impossible before we settle for a weaker form. The ordered metric scale appears in practice to be a kind of unfinished interval scale. It is probably not necessary to regard it as a new class of scale in the sense of the listing in Table 3.

PSYCHOPHYSICAL MEASUREMENT

Let us turn now to another problem: the measurement of psychological or subjective magnitudes. This is the century-old problem that has been both the hope and the despair of the behavioral sciences, and the pursuit of which has sparked new methods of measurement, not only in psychology but also in economics and sociology. Its modern roots go back mainly to Fechner, who first elaborated a theory and a procedure for the measurement of sensation and who bequeathed us the famous but erroneous "law" which states that the magnitude of a sensation is proportional to the logarithm of the intensity of the stimulus. In the following, I will try to show that, when we measure sensation by a variety of methods that are more straightforward and direct than Fechner's, we do not obtain the logarithmic relation. What we find is a power function: the psychological magnitude ψ is related to the stimulus magnitude ϕ by $\psi = k\phi^n$, where k and n are constants. The implication of this psychophysical law is that equal subjective ratios correspond to equal stimulus ratios. (For a fuller account of this matter, see [37].)

The power function turns out to be a good approximation to the relation between stimulus and response on at least 14 different prothetic continua. Values of the exponent n have been found to range upward from about 0.3 for loudness. Typical values for some of the other continua are: brightness 0.33 to 0.5 (depending on area of target, state of visual adaptation, etc.), apparent length 1.1, duration 1.15, numerousness 1.34, heaviness 1.45, velocity 1.77. In an experiment recently completed, we have found that the apparent intensity of an electric shock, produced by a current (60 cps) through the fingers, grows as a power function of the current, with an exponent of the order of 4.

These continua are called *prothetic* to distinguish them from another class of continua called *metathetic*. The class of prothetic continua includes the "quantitative" aspects of things, whereas the class of metathetic continua includes the "qualitative" and positional aspects, such as pitch, apparent azimuth, and inclination. These two classes are defined and distinguished by functional criteria [37], but the names are suggested by the nature of the physiological mechanisms that seem to underlie at least some of the continua. On continua such as brightness, loudness, and heaviness, for example, we seem to progress along the continuum by a process of adding excitation to excitation— a prothetic process.[5] On continua such as pitch and position, we seem to progress along the continuum by a process of substituting excitation for excitation—a metathetic process. The power function seems to be the general law relating subjective and physical magnitudes for prothetic continua, but not necessarily for metathetic continua. Pitch, for example, is not a power function of frequency [41].

So much for the general outcome of the recent work in psychophysical scaling. Let us consider briefly the methods by which these results are obtained. (For additional details, see [38].)

Perhaps it may help to imagine a simple experiment in which we seat an observer before a large blank wall on which we can project a narrow band of light of variable length. The problem is to find how the observer's subjective impression of length varies with the physical length of the band. We are not concerned with the accuracy with which he can estimate the length in feet or inches but only with the form of the function relating his psychological impression to the stimulus magnitude. In other words, we want to establish a ratio scale of *apparent* length.

[5] Better etymology would require the term "prosthetic." In dropping the *s*, I am following a precedent sanctioned by the medical dictionaries (see Gould or Stedman).

Four general classes of procedures might be used, each, of course, capable of many variations [36]. These procedures, together with a typical directive for each, might run as follows.

1. *Magnitude Estimation.* Present a line of a given length and tell the observer to call it some number, say, 10. Then present a line of some other length and say: "If the first line was 10, what would you call the second line? Use any number that seems appropriate—fraction, decimal, whole number—but try to make the number proportional to the apparent length as *you* see it." Then proceed to present other lengths, in irregular order, and ask for similar estimates of apparent length. (Do *not* limit the observer to the use of an arbitrary range of numbers.)

2. *Magnitude Production.* This is the inverse of (1). Instead of asking the observer for numerical estimates, name values in irregular order and ask the observer to alter the length in order to produce magnitudes corresponding to the values named.

3. *Ratio Estimation.* Present a standard length, followed by a comparison length. Ask the observer to estimate the apparent ratio between the lengths. Use comparison lengths longer and shorter than the standard length, in irregular order. (Do *not* change the standard in the course of a given experiment.)

4. *Ratio Production.* Present a standard length. Follow it by a variable length and ask the observer to adjust the variable to make it appear some fraction of the standard, e.g., $\frac{1}{2}$, $\frac{1}{3}$, $\frac{1}{5}$, $\frac{1}{10}$, etc. (This method is sometimes called fractionation.) Also ask the observer to set the variable to various multiples of the standard (method of multiplication).

In bare outline, these are some of the methods that have been used. In a thorough investigation, it would probably be wise to use more than one of these methods, and more than a single version of each. Any one procedure may have certain pitfalls and biases that a multiple attack might reveal. Such biases can often be canceled or corrected in a counterbalanced design [36].

Two of these methods (1 and 4) have actually been used to obtain estimates of apparent length, and both methods produced results suggesting that apparent length varies approximately as the 1.1 power of stimulus length. That the exponent in this case is close to 1.0 is not surprising, for we all know that 1 foot looks about half as long as 2 feet. As a matter of fact, it is sometimes argued that observers are able to make these judgments of apparent length because they learned to do so by making measurements with yard sticks. It is not clear how we could prove that learning does or does not explain the results obtained, but from one point of view the question is irrelevant. For regardless of how the observer got to be the way he is, it is a legitimate, and in many instances an important, matter to determine how he now behaves. His present perceptual judgments are not without interest merely because they may have been conditioned by past experience.

Learning would seem to be a less likely explanation for the form of the ratio scale obtained when observers judge the apparent intensity of an electric current passed through the fingers, where the sensation of shock grows almost as the fourth power of the current. A person may previously have experienced electric shock, but it is hardly probable that he was simultaneously observing a galvanometer in series with himself. Learning also seems an unlikely determinant of the functions governing loudness and brightness, for the stimulus measures underlying these continua are quite unfamiliar to most people. For the typical (median) listener, the loudness of a 1000-cycle tone grows as the 0.3 power of the intensity (energy) of the stimulus [33]. It is a curious and interesting fact that the apparent brightness of a luminous surface in a dark field grows according to a similar law, with approximately the same exponent.

These two continua, loudness and brightness, have been studied more intensively than any of the others (except, possibly, the heaviness of lifted weights). The interest in loudness and brightness stems mainly from the fact that the forms of these two subjective scales are of practical importance to acoustical and illuminating engineering. Loudness scales have been constructed by various methods in at least a dozen different laboratories (in at least four different countries). The agreement among the results is far from perfect, of course, but it has been good enough to lead a committee of the International Standards Organization to recommend a standard scale for the measurement of loudness. The function proposed relates loudness in sones, S, to the sound pressure level, P, of a 1000-cycle tone by the equation

$$\log S = 0.03P - 1.2$$

In this equation, P is a logarithmic measure (decibels). One important use that has been made of this subjective scale is in the development of a procedure by which the loudness of a complex sound can be calculated from a knowledge of the spectrum of the sound [35].

Examples of the results obtained for loudness and brightness by the method of magnitude estimation are shown in Fig. 1. (The experi-

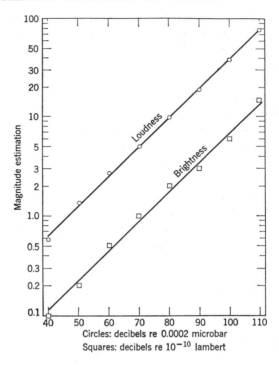

Fig. 1. Median magnitude estimations for loudness and brightness. For loudness each of 32 subjects made two estimates of each level of a 1000-cycle tone in irregular order with no designated standard. Estimates were transformed to a common modulus at the 80-db level. For brightness, each of 28 dark-adapted subjects made two estimates of each level in irregular order. The target subtended about 5 degrees and was illuminated for about 3 seconds at each presentation. Once at the beginning of each session, the subject was shown the level 70 db (14 subjects) or 80 db (14 subjects), and was told to call that level 10. Estimates for all subjects were transformed to a common modulus at 70 db.

ment on brightness was conducted by my colleague J. C. Stevens.) The fact that the median numerical estimates for both loudness and brightness fall close to a straight line in a log-log plot means that, for the typical observer, the stimulus-response relation is a power function. The exponents are determined by the slopes of the lines. The slopes in Fig. 1 are close to 0.3.

In both the foregoing experiments, communication between the experimenter and the observer was in terms of numerical values. The question sometimes arises whether we can dispense with the use of numerical descriptions and still verify the power law. The answer is that in principle we can. The procedure would involve the presentation of two stimuli to define a certain subjective ratio. The observer would then be asked to adjust two other stimuli to produce the same apparent ratio. If it turns out that for all pairs of adjusted stimuli the *physical* ratio is constant, then the subjective magnitude must be a power function of the physical magnitude. The limitation of this procedure is that we could not thereby determine the value of the exponent. We would be limited, therefore, to a logarithmic interval scale.

An actual experiment of this sort, involving two sense modalities, was conducted by J. C. Stevens [37]. He set two spots of light, each to a different intensity, and asked 15 observers to adjust one of two sounds to make the apparent ratio between the loudnesses match the apparent ratio between the brightnesses. The stimulus ratios of the lights were varied over a range of 10,000 to 1, or 40 db. The results were quite interesting. The median observer set approximately the same ratio between the intensities of the sounds as the experimenter set between the intensities of the lights. This of course is the result that would be predicted on the basis of the two functions in Fig. 1. The experiment adds further evidence to the conclusion that the psychophysical law is a power function, and it confirms the approximate similarity of the exponents governing brightness and loudness. By itself, however, the experiment does not tell us the numerical values of the exponents. It appears that only the observers themselves, by one or another form of numerical estimation, can tell us the values of the exponents.

It is of interest to note that in constructing a ratio scale of sensation intensity we are concerned with the dynamic "operating characteristics" of the sensory system. This aspect of sensation may be contrasted with the "static" relations usually determined by matching procedures in which we map certain invariances, such as equal-sensation contours (e.g., equal-loudness contours, luminosity functions, etc.). The mapping of static invariances usually commands the most attention in psychophysics, but, important as these invariances may be, they need to be supplemented by a knowledge of the dynamics involved in the growth of sensation with stimulus intensity. Otherwise we are in the position that would confront a physicist if he could determine contours of equal potential, but had no way of measuring the levels represented by the different contours.

EQUAL-APPEARING INTERVALS AND JUST NOTICEABLE DIFFERENCES

In our study of the relations among the various scales of measurement (Table 3), we noted that it is in principle possible to construct a ratio scale from a series of equated ratios, provided we can also construct an interval scale on the same continuum. Why then can we not determine the exponent of the power function by having people first set pairs of stimuli to produce a given but numerically unknown ratio, and then set various stimuli to produce equal-apparent spacings among them? If both these tasks could be accomplished, it would be a straightforward matter to construct the ratio scale and thereby determine the explicit function relating stimulus and sensation.[6] What I did not know when I first proposed this procedure [31] is that observers are not able to equalize intervals on prothetic continua. On metathetic continua, they apparently can do so, but on prothetic continua it turns out that intervals judged to be equal are systematically larger (in subjective magnitude) at the upper end than at the lower end of the scale.

In making this statement, I am assuming that the ratio-scaling procedures discussed above produce valid scales of sensation. And I recognize, of course, that questions concerning the validity of a scale always reduce ultimately to a matter of opinion: either we think the scale measures what we want to measure, or we think it does not. If we are willing to grant that the foregoing procedures measure what we would like to regard as the magnitude of a perceptual variable, then it can be shown that experiments designed to produce equal intervals via judgments of subjective differences on prothetic continua do not accomplish their purpose.

Studies on a wide variety of prothetic continua [40] have invariably shown that, when a scale of equal-appearing intervals (a category-rating scale) is plotted against the subjective ratio scale of the con-

---

[6] Perhaps we should beware of using the term "sensation." To some readers it may suggest a kind of old-fashioned dualism: mind versus matter. As used here, however, sensation refers to a construct based on the overt responses of human observers. We study and measure sensation by observing the responses that organisms make to the energetic configurations of the environment. We sometimes call these responses subjective, but this is merely to indicate that the reacting system happens to be a human being rather than an inanimate system, such as a voltmeter. From the operational point of view, all that science can know about sensation, it must derive from observations concerning the reactions of organisms [29].

tinuum, the result is a curve that is concave downward.   Figure 2 presents a typical example.   The abscissa scale is proportional to subjective brightness in units called brils.   This abscissa scale was determined by having 10 observers make magnitude estimations of the brightness of a spot of light which was varied over a range of 50 db. Later, the observers were asked to judge the brightness of a series of stimuli on a 7-point scale.   They were shown the faintest level, called 1, and the brightest level, called 7, and were told to judge on a scale of equally spaced units between these two extremes.   In other words, a brightness that looked to be halfway between the two extremes should be called 4.   The stimuli were presented to each observer in a different irregular order.   Two different experiments of this sort were run.

In Fig. 2, where the mean category assigned to each stimulus is plotted on the ordinate scale, we note that the category scales are con-

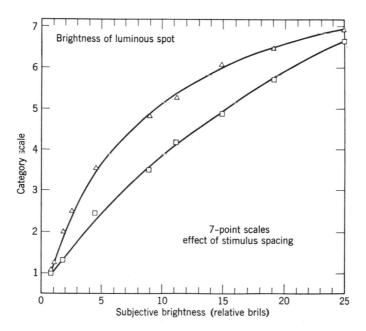

Fig. 2. Category (equal-interval) scales for the apparent brightness of a luminous target subtending an angle of about 5 degrees. The abscissa scale was determined in a separate experiment by the method of magnitude estimation. The curves represent two different experiments on category scaling. The differences in curvature are due mainly to the relative spacings among the stimuli used.

cave downward when plotted against the ratio scale of subjective magnitude. Another important fact evident in Fig. 2 is that the relative spacing of the stimuli has a marked effect on the actual form of the category scale. In one experiment (represented by triangles), the stimuli were bunched relatively close together at the low end of the continuum. In the other experiment (squares), fewer stimuli happened to be used, and they were spread more uniformly over the continuum. From this and many other experiments, we are able to conclude that, whenever stimuli are bunched closer together in one region of the scale, the slope of the category scale steepens over that region.

It is important to note that this sensitivity to stimulus spacing is a characteristic of judgment when observers try to partition a continuum into equal-appearing intervals. On the other hand, stimulus spacing seems to make no difference to the over-all form of the function obtained from judgments of ratios or magnitudes [36]. This we regard as an important point in favor of the ratio-scaling procedures.

We have tried elsewhere [40] to explain the reason for the curvature of the category scale, but briefly, it is this. The observer's sensitivity is not uniform over the subjective scale of a prothetic continuum. A given difference may seem large and obvious in the lower part of the scale, but the same absolute difference is much less impressive in the upper part of the scale. This asymmetry in the observer's sensitivity to differences results in a nonuniformity in the width of the categories. Near the lower end of the scale the categories tend to be narrow, and, by consequence, the slope of the function is steep. Near the upper end the categories broaden and the slope declines.

Let us now turn to a third class of methods that has been used for subjective scaling. This is the class introduced by Fechner. His procedure was to measure just noticeable differences (jnd) along the continuum and to use these measures of resolving power as equal units on a scale of sensation. By assuming (1) that the jnd is proportional to the stimulus magnitude (Weber's law) and (2) that each jnd represents a constant increment in sensation, he derived his logarithmic law. Now it is possible to dispose of this form of Fechner's law by showing that Weber's law is not quite true, but that is a minor matter. The more interesting issue is whether a scale constructed by counting off jnd, as empirically determined, is proportional to apparent magnitude or whether it is not. In other words, does a stimulus 40 jnd above threshold seem twice as great as a stimulus only 20 jnd above threshold? Where prothetic continua are concerned, the answer is "no." By the typical observer the apparent ratio of two such stimuli would be judged greater than 2 to 1, usually very much greater. On metathetic continua, however, the answer is "yes" [32]. As a matter of fact, what is probably the most crucial difference between these two types of continua is that in the metathetic domain the jnd are subjectively equal over the continuum, whereas in the prothetic domain, the jnd grow rapidly larger in subjective size as we go up the scale of the continuum.

The nature of these relations on a prothetic continuum that happens to be simple and easy to judge is shown in Fig. 3, where we see the results of each of the three classes of methods: direct magnitude estimation, category scaling, and jnd measurement [37]. Each of these three procedures results in a different scale. They seem to be meas-

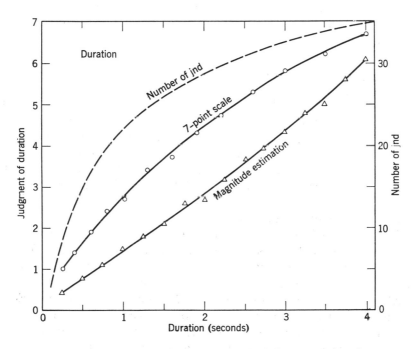

Fig. 3. Jnd scale, category scale, and ratio scale for apparent duration.

Triangles: mean judgments of 12 observers who estimated the apparent duration of a white noise. Stimuli were presented in a different irregular order to each observer.

Circles: mean category judgments made on a scale of "equal intervals" numbered from 1 to 7. Samples of the end stimuli were presented at the outset to indicate the range, and each subject judged each duration twice in an irregular order.

Dashed line: summated jnd, right-hand ordinate.

uring different things. Furthermore, the relative forms of the functions in Fig. 3 have been found to characterize every prothetic continuum thus far investigated. Clearly, we do not obtain a scale that agrees with direct judgments of magnitude either by trying to partition a continuum into equal-appearing intervals or by counting off jnd.

The implications of this last point are rather disturbing, for many modern scaling procedures are founded on the premise that "equally often noticed differences are equal," and that interval scales can be constructed by "unitizing" such things as discriminal dispersions, variabilities, or confusions. But this is just another form of the Fechnerian assumption that jnd are subjectively equal. On metathetic continua, this assumption can often be justified, but, if the continuum in question behaves in a prothetic manner, the assumption can be demonstrated to fail. We are forced to conclude, for example, that such well-known methods as pair comparisons, successive intervals, and the like do not produce interval scales when applied to prothetic continua.

MEASUREMENT OF UTILITY

In this section I would like to turn to a question of lively interest in a field far removed from psychophysics, but which is not unrelated to the issue of subjective measurement. It concerns the subjective value of money (or of commodities in general). Subjective value is what the economists designate by the term "utility," which they speak of measuring in subjective units called "utiles." The question is, can utility be measured in utiles the way brightness is measured in brils, or loudness is measured in sones?

My first introduction to this problem was at dinner with the well-known economist J. A. Schumpeter some two decades ago. I was trying to convince him by means of crude, dinner-table experiments that a person can make meaningful judgments of relative subjective brightness. Whether he was persuaded I cannot say, but he remarked at one point that, if brightness could be measured in this manner, so could utility—and why did we not do it? That is a good question. Before we consider it further, let us try to determine a little more clearly just what we are talking about.

For the sake of simplicity, we will confine our attention to the single commodity known as money. More specifically, as in the concrete instance to be discussed later, we will be concerned mainly with the subjective value of money viewed as a potential acquisition.

Of course, many and varied things have already been said about the problem of utility, and over the past two centuries a flourishing body of doctrine has accumulated, most of it oriented toward the role of utility in human decision making. An extensive and interesting review by Edwards [12] makes it plain that the literature on utility is perhaps a match for that on psychophysics as regards the qualities about which William James so eloquently complained. Both literatures certainly have the "disciplinary value" that James acknowledged, but whether their substantive outcomes are "just nothing" is a question that can lead to long debate. In any case, we are still on the search for a measure of utility. Many subtle and mathematically sophisticated plans for capturing the measure have been proposed, but, as yet, these plans are mostly strategies on paper. Acceptable empirical measurement of the subjective value of money remains an elusive aspiration.

Two major conceptions seem to have dominated the efforts in this field. Under the classical view, money or wealth is regarded as having a subjective value that is at least a monotonic function of dollars. The exact form of this function has not been agreed upon, but it has usually been assumed to be concave downward, i.e., negatively accelerated. The logarithmic form suggested by Daniel Bernoulli has perhaps been the specific relation most widely accepted. Conceived in this manner, utility has no necessary relation to probability or risk. For a first-rate history of this issue, see Stigler [42].

Opposed to this "probability-less idea of utility," which Savage [24] says "has been completely discredited in the eyes of almost all economists," is the conception built on the notion that utility is a function that arithmetizes the relation of preference under conditions of risk or uncertainty. This view has a long history, but its modern form stems mainly from the work of von Neumann and Morgenstern whose treatise gave the theory of utility a shot in the arm from which it is still in a state of high excitement [20].

Although we will return later to a consideration of the older notion of utility, a few remarks are in order regarding the concept of the von Neumann-Morgenstern utility, which, for brevity, I will call the N-M utility. The essence of the notion underlying the N-M utility is that its measurement (on an interval scale) can be derived from preferences or lack of preferences among options involving two variables: commodities and probabilities. We first assume that, if a person shows no clear preference for either of a pair of options, the two options have the same utility for him. In the language of this discussion, this determination of equivalence would get us to the nominal level of scaling (for options). If he prefers one to the other, the options can then be ranked on an ordinal scale. This much seems clear and obvious. The interesting point is the next one. We get to an interval scale of N-M utility by assuming that within equivalent options we can, so to speak, trade probability for utility. How this is done can be illustrated as follows.

Suppose the subject in our experiment says he is indifferent between the prospect of receiving $10 for certain and a fifty-fifty chance of gaining either $25 or $1. Since we are concerned with an interval scale and can, therefore, assign two values arbitrarily, let us say that the utility of $1 is 1 utile and the utility of $25 is 25 utiles. The utility of $10 is then assumed to be determined by an equating of the *expected* utilities of the two options.

$$1.0 \times U(\$10) = 0.5 \times U(\$25) + 0.5 \times U(\$1)$$

$$= 0.5 \times 25 \text{ utiles} + 0.5 \times 1 \text{ utile}$$

$$= 13 \text{ utiles}$$

In this example, then, the utility of $10 is 13 utiles. By starting from these known utility values, and by devising additional options that combine other probabilities and other sums of money, we could proceed to determine, on an interval scale, the utility of other numbers of dollars.

When a procedure based on the N-M model, or others like it, is used to effect an empirical measurement of utility, certain worrisome assumptions have to be made. One of these assumptions is that we know the probabilities by which the utilities are to be multiplied. Since the subject's appraisal of the options with which he is faced depends on his personal appraisal of both dollars and probability, we need to know that the probabilities we assign are, in fact, the subjective probabilities that obtain for this particular subject. So we find that we now face two problems of subjective measurement: subjective value *and* subjective probability. With the added burden of having to measure subjective probability, the theory somehow looks less appealing than it did at first sight.

One way out, perhaps, is to confine our attention to fifty-fifty gambles, where the chance event used to determine the outcome of a gamble is an event, such as the throw of a particular die, for which it can be demonstrated that the subject does, in fact, regard one of two possible outcomes to be as likely as the other. Whatever difficulties may remain, this procedure would seem at least to provide us with the appropriate factor (0.5) with which to multiply the utilities in the N-M equation. This is one of the approaches exploited by Davidson, Suppes, and Siegel [11] in their studies designed to test various mathematical models for decision making.

When the problem is cast in this form, and the subject is confronted with options involving fifty-fifty probabilities, the procedure begins to resemble the psychophysical method of equal-appearing intervals. Thus, in the example given above, the assumption is that the subject's indifference between the two options, $10 for certain and a fifty-fifty chance to gain either $25 or $1, means that $10 is halfway between $1 and $25 on his scale of utility. The question that naturally suggests itself to the psychophysicist is this: if the subject is really being asked about the equality of intervals on his scale of subjective value, why do we not ask him to judge the intervals directly? Why introduce the complicating factor of risk and probability?

Several problems are raised by this question. For one thing, since amounts of money must be stated in terms of the ratio scale of dollars, with which scale the subject is thoroughly familiar, it may be impossible to get the subject to judge in terms of utility rather than in terms of the numerical values of dollars. He may, so to speak, judge the stimulus, not the subjective effect, and commit thereby the "stimulus error." However, this is an empirical question, it seems to me, and one that ought not to be answered *a priori*.

Another contention might be that the economists' interest in utility rests mainly on the role utility plays in the decisions people make under conditions of risk or uncertainty. No doubt this is the interest of many economists. It is conceivably also true, however, that the best way to measure utility might be to remove it from the context of risky decisions.[7] It may be profitable, in other words, to take the view that predicting choices is one problem, whereas measuring subjective value is another. The two problems may or may not be interrelated in some simple way. We will return to this question of a direct and independent measure of utility after some remarks on what seems to be the motivation behind the N-M conception of utility.

There are certain interesting parallels discernible in the history of the concept of utility and the history of the concept of sensation. Sensation and subjective value are both aspects of human reactions

---

[7] Another nasty problem arises in experiments involving risky decisions. It stems from the fact that gambling itself may be liked by some and abhorred by others. Hence, to the problem of measuring utility and subjective probability is added the further difficulty of assessing the utility of gambling.

to the external states of the world, and they are topics about which men have thought for many centuries. They both exist, in an obvious sense, and they both seem to vary in degree or magnitude. This much seems clear. Consequently, when the flowering of modern science had demonstrated the power inherent in quantification, it was only natural that some men's thoughts turned to the problem of measuring what other men had held to be unmeasurable. But how to do it? Where to look for the handle on the problem?

There has never been much question that an ordinal scale of utility is possible—derivable directly from people's expressed preferences. From their lack of preferences it is possible to construct "indifference curves" expressing how much of one commodity can be substituted for another while the total utility is left unchanged. An indifference curve is analogous to an equal-brightness contour (a so-called luminosity function), or to an equal-loudness contour. These psychophysical contours tell us how intensity can be substituted for frequency while brightness or loudness remains invariant. But an equivalence contour or an indifference curve does not by itself provide more than a nominal measure of the parameter of the function, e.g., brightness, loudness, or utility. (This problem, as it relates to utility, is discussed further below.)

The next step might have been to try to scale these parameters by the methods of direct appraisal. But the simple, direct approach of asking subjects to make forthright judgments of apparent magnitude seemed, and still seems to many, to be somehow impossible, or at least fruitless. Something more subtle, indirect, and "scientific" seemed called for by such an obviously elusive and difficult problem.

For the measurement of sensation, it was the physicist Fechner [13] who supplied the subtlety and the indirection. Plateau [22], it is true, proposed to measure sensation by more direct procedures—judgments of equal-appearing intervals—but Plateau did not follow through with the vigor and thoroughness of Fechner. The ingenuity of Fechner's attempt to derive scales of magnitude from measures of resolving power appealed to many, and probably still does. But, as we have seen, on prothetic continua, the Fechnerian scales do not accord with those constructed by the direct judgment of magnitudes and ratios, nor, for that matter, with those constructed from equal-appearing intervals.

For the measurement of utility, it was von Neumann and Morgenstern, anticipated by Ramsey [24], who supplied the subtlety and the indirection. They did not pursue precisely the Fechnerian approach, but their strategy resembles Fechner's in the general sense that, from judgments made in an experiment aimed only tangentially at the central issue, measures of a subjective magnitude are deduced with the aid of assumptions. It is perhaps too early to tell what the payoff of this approach will be for the empirical measurement of subjective value, because concrete efforts to interpret and experiment with N-M utility have barely gotten under way. My own pessimism about the prospect may have no sounder basis than an untutored intuition, but I rather suspect that the measurement of utility will not yield to assault from the rear.

However that may be, the N-M conception of utility will probably thrive as a formal discipline, for it has all the fascination of an elegant mathematical model. Its formal axioms have been modified and extended and argued about by many. Whatever may be the leverage that axiomatization can bring to bear on a stubborn empirical question, the advantage of the leverage should certainly accrue to the problem of utility, for some high talents are being exercised on the analytic aspects of the issue. Of course, there may be some truth in the allegation that, when a model maker faces a problem he cannot solve, he transforms it into one that he can solve, in which case the empirical aspect of the problem of measurement may conceivably get lost in the shuffle. But that remains to be seen.

Mathematicians have paid less attention to the problem of formal models applicable to the measurement of sensation than to models related to utility, but they have not neglected sensation entirely. Mention should be made of N. Wiener's early effort [46] to develop a formal system based on what he calls the "very beautiful theory of measurement" developed by Whitehead and Russell in *Principia Mathematica*. Wiener undertakes his task because, as he says, "things do not, in general, run around with their measures stamped on them like the capacity of a freight car: it requires a certain amount of investigation to discover what their measures are." With this observation, the empirical scientist would heartily agree. But what the man in the laboratory might find less easy to accept is one of Wiener's concluding statements to the effect that, "what most experimenters take for granted before they begin their experiments is infinitely more interesting than any results to which their experiments lead." The devotee of logic and mathematics is often impatient with the scientist's grubbing through the empirical tangle of natural phenomena. No less impatience is sometimes felt by the empiricist for what he regards as the empty elegance of the model maker's productions. The activities of both

are obviously essential to the scientific enterprise, but the clash of
their differing attitudes sometimes leads to vigorous pronouncements.

A RATIO SCALE OF UTILITY?

Let us return now to the question posed earlier: can utility be measured in utiles the way brightness is measured in brils or loudness is
measured in sones? The concept of utility envisaged by this question is the older concept, the subjective value of money as conceived by
those who developed the so-called law of diminishing marginal utility.
This law expresses the intuitively plausible notion that subjective value
is a negatively accelerated function of dollars: each additional dollar
added to a person's wealth represents less subjective value than the
one preceding it. The question is, what, if anything, can the recent
developments in psychophysics teach us about this problem of the
utility of money?

That the laws of psychophysics may have relevance for utility is
a reasonable conjecture, for it seems clear that utility, like brightness,
is the name for a response of a human organism to an external con-
figuration of the environment. In this sense, money is as much a
stimulus as is a light wave. Light gives rise to brightness and money
gives rise to utility only because both these stimuli interact with human
beings. The problem is to assess the product of these interactions.

One of the first difficulties that presents itself is the fact of human
variability. Not all people react in the same way to money, any more
than they all react in the same way to the intensity of a light. But
just as we need not renounce the measurement of brightness because
some persons are blind and some are photophobic, so we need not
give up on the measurement of utility merely because a recluse has
been found dead of malnutrition on a mattress stuffed with greenbacks.
If we are interested in standardizing a scale of brightness for a given
condition of viewing, we must forego the hope that our scale will represent the visual responses of all citizens. We can, however, aspire to
the less ambitious goal of erecting a scale that will describe the
typical responses of the median observer in a population of interest.
Having such a scale, we can then more effectively press the question
of individual differences and idiosyncrasies, if that problem proves
important. Knowing the function that obtains under one set of
circumstances, we can then explore the variations produced by other
conditions.

Let us consider then what the utility scale for the median subject must be like. First of all, does utility behave as a prothetic or as a metathetic continuum? We do not really know, of course, but there seems good reason to expect that it is prothetic. It has more the earmarks of a "quantitative" than a "qualitative" continuum.

If utility is a prothetic continuum, and if it behaves like the dozen or more other prothetic continua that have been explored, then the expectation is that utility is a power function of dollars. Furthermore, if it is true that marginal utility is a diminishing function of dollars, the exponent of the power function must be less than 1.0.

If these considerations are valid, we may replace the traditional logarithmic function of Bernoulli with a power function having a fractional exponent. "To this day," says Savage, "no other function [than the logarithmic] has been suggested as a better prototype for Everyman's utility function" [24]. What I am suggesting is that the power function, which characterizes subjective magnitude on numerous other prothetic continua, may be more congenial to Everyman than is the logarithmic function.

It is important to note that in asserting this possibility we are assuming that utility can be measured on better than an interval scale. The N-M version of utility, the measure of which is derived from risky choices, envisages interval measurement only, and the question naturally arises: on what grounds can we hope to do better? A possible answer to this question is suggested by the analogy we have drawn between utility and the perceptual continua, such as brightness and loudness. As Galanter and I have tried to show [40], on perceptual continua of the prothetic variety, it has repeatedly turned out that subjects are typically unable to partition the continuum into equal subjective intervals (Figs. 2 and 3). When methods calling for the production of equal-appearing intervals are employed to establish an interval scale on the continuum, we end up with a function that is nonlinear against subjective magnitude. Curiously enough, on these prothetic perceptual continua, the best way to erect an interval scale is to proceed directly to a ratio scale, which, of course, contains the interval scale. This is in some ways a fortunate state of affairs, for a ratio scale is more powerful and useful than an interval scale. The strategy suggested by these psychophysical developments is that the utility theorist might profitably forget about scaling utility up to a linear transformation and try directly for the larger prize of scaling it up to a similarity transformation.

But all this is mainly conjectural as far as utility itself is concerned. Thus far we have merely noted some suggestive analogies between subjective value and other subjective variables. Nevertheless, analogies are often useful—"indeed an indispensable and inevitable tool for scientific progress" [21]. Even if we could go no further at this time, it might still be profitable to take these analogies seriously and to explore what use could be made of a utility function that is a power function of dollars. It might at least be an aid to our understanding of attitudes about wealth. But the interesting question would still remain: how can we prove that utility is a power function, and how do we determine the exponent?

Assuming that we are prepared to discount the many *a priori* objections commonly raised against methods that ask for direct subjective appraisals, and that we are willing to try to adapt to the problem of utility some of the ratio-scaling procedures that have proved fruitful in psychophysics, where do we find ourselves? Perhaps the most obvious difficulty confronting us stems from the nature of the "stimulus" scale itself. We measure dollars on the ratio scale of numerosity, and it is hard to see how we could ask our subject for a numerical appraisal of his valuation of money without ourselves naming numbers of dollars. In this respect, utility and brightness present different problems. We can present for judgment a series of visual intensities with no numbers attached, but we cannot present magnitudes of wealth devoid of numerical indices. The danger, of course, is that the subject will merely judge numbers and not his own subjective reaction to the wealth for which the numbers stand. Whether this will prove a fatal defect in our experiment is, as I have already indicated, an experimental question and not a matter for armchair decision. With care and ingenuity in the setting of the problem, we may come off better than pessimism would prophesy.

As a matter of fact, encouraging grounds for optimism are already coming to hand. E. H. Galanter has described to me the preliminary outcome of an attempt to extend our ratio-scaling procedures to the measurement of subjective value. One of the procedures tried goes essentially like this. The experimenter says to a subject: "Suppose I were to tell you that I am going to give you $10. That would make you happy, would it not? All right, now think this over carefully. How much would I have to give you to make you twice as happy?"

Similar proposals involving different initial sums are made to other groups of subjects. For still other subjects, the question is inverted and they are asked to say how much it would take to make them half as happy.

The median estimates obtained thus far from a large group of college students support a crucial point. Regardless of the initial sum named, the median number of dollars required to double "happiness" is approximately a constant multiple of the initial sum. The median value of this multiple has ranged from about 3.5 to 5. It seems clear that the typical subject faced with this decision does not merely multiply the number of dollars by two. Furthermore, the sum required to produce half as much of this "monetary euphoria" is about 20 per cent of the initial sum announced. Thus the outcome for "halving" is fairly consistent with that for "doubling," and both are consistent with the basic principle observed in psychophysics, namely, that equal stimulus ratios produce equal subjective ratios. It follows that subjective value, as appraised under these conditions, approximates a power function of the number of dollars. Furthermore, the size of the exponent of the power function is in the vicinity of 0.4 or 0.5. If we take the exponent to be 0.5, and if we define the utility of $1 as equivalent to 1 utile, a segment of the utility function can be graphed as in Fig. 4. A curve of this general form apparently governs the subjective value of money viewed as a potential acquisition.

Regardless of the many possible shortcomings of an experiment of this sort, the outcome to date is encouragingly consistent with the

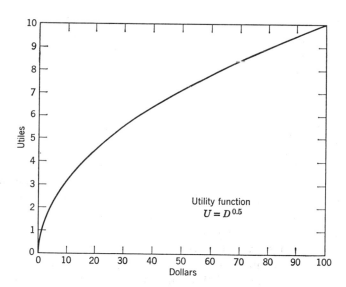

Fig. 4. Utility function relating subjective value in utiles to number of dollars.

power functions obtained in the scaling of more than a dozen other subjective continua. It is also reassuring that the fractional exponent is consistent with the law of diminishing marginal utility—the law that in the eyes of so many has seemed intuitively so obvious. It begins to appear that utility may, indeed, be a prothetic variable measurable on a ratio scale.

INDIFFERENCE CURVES

It is interesting to note that Thurstone considered the possibility that the utility function, which he called the "satisfaction curve," might be a power function of a particular degree, i.e., satisfaction might be proportional to the square root of the amount of a commodity [44]; see also [17]. This form of the utility curve he derived from the assumption that the slope of the curve is inversely proportional to the value of the satisfaction already attained. But Thurstone rejected this power function in favor of a logarithmic function, derived from the assumption that the slope of the curve is inversely proportional to the amount of the commodity in question. Thurstone acknowledged that the postulate leading to the power function was "psychologically preferable," but he felt that the logarithmic function was in better accord with the results of an experiment in which, for a single subject, he determined a set of "indifference curves" based on choices among combinations of various numbers of hats, shoes, and overcoats. The subject was asked questions of the sort, "Which would you prefer, 8 hats and 8 pair of shoes *or* 6 hats and 9 pair of shoes?"

Although Thurstone's experiment was not extensive enough to provide more than a rough indication of the form of the indifference curves, his undertaking raises an interesting question. If sufficient valid data on indifference relations could be obtained by such a procedure, what might they tell us about utility? As is usually true in these attempts to derive the utility function from "indirect" experiments, the answer depends on the kinds of assumptions we are prepared to make. But if we are willing to grant the kinds of assumptions Thurstone proposes, we can construct families of indifference curves based on the two laws: logarithmic function and power function.

Figure 5 shows three representative indifference curves based on the assumption that utility is proportional to the logarithm of the amount of the commodity. Two imaginary commodities A and B are considered. It is assumed that unit amount of A has the same utility as unit amount of B, and that along any one curve the sum of the

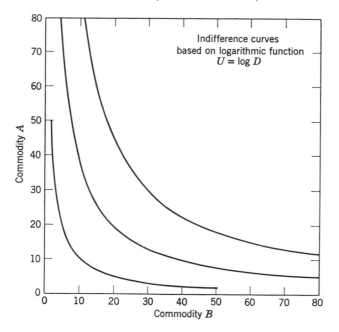

Fig. 5. Form of an indifference map derived from the assumption that utility grows as the logarithm of the amount of the commodity.

utilities is constant, i.e., $U(A) + U(B) = K$. The value of the parameter K is different for each curve.

Figure 6 shows a similar family of indifference curves based on the assumption that utility is proportional to a power function of the commodity and that the exponent is 0.5. We note that both sets of curves are concave upward as we would expect them to be, and as the economists usually plot them. The two sets of curves differ in detail, but it is a serious question whether data like those obtained by Thurstone could lead to a decision between them. From an inspection of Thurstone's results, I would venture to guess that, with a proper adjustment of the scale values, the curves based on the power function could be made to fit the data quite as well as the curves based on the logarithmic function. A crucial test via this approach would undoubtedly call for a more extensive set of empirical data.

It should also be noted that the curvatures of the indifference curves derived from the power function (Fig. 6) depend on the value of the exponent. Thus, if the exponent were 1.0, it would mean that utility

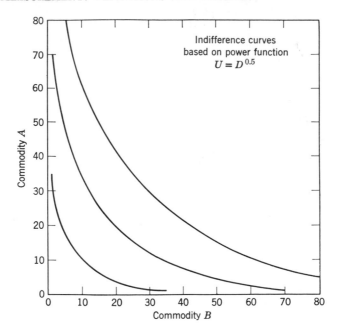

Fig. 6. Form of an indifference map derived from the assumption that utility grows as a power function of the amount of the commodity.

is a linear function of the amount of the commodity. In this case, the indifference curves would turn out to be straight lines. As the exponent becomes smaller, the curvature of the indifference curves increases. Since the curvature can be altered in this manner, it would seem somewhat unlikely that a valid set of indifference relations of the kind described by Thurstone would, in general, turn out to be inconsistent with the hypothesis that utility is a power function.

One more interesting question suggests itself. Is it more than a coincidence that Galanter's experiment, described above, gives an exponent of the same order of magnitude (0.5) as the one Thurstone considered and rejected? [8] It seems fair to say that, in their present state, these experimental results are not inconsistent with the hypothesis that the utility of the additional (marginal) dollar is inversely proportional to the value of the utility already achieved. This

[8] It is of historical interest that Daniel Bernoulli cited a letter by Gabriel Cramer in which Cramer used this same square-root law to illustrate how utility might be supposed to vary with amount of money. See translation in *Econometrica*, 1954, **22**, p. 34.

simple principle of relativity has a certain intuitive appeal, as Thurstone was well aware. Although we prove nothing empirical by postulating simple principles, it is not without interest that, if we were to start from the assumption that marginal utility is inversely proportional to utility, we would end up with a power function similar to the one Galanter has obtained. It would be a neat and happy outcome if this simple principle should continue to turn out to have empirical foundation.

MERITS OF THE METHODS

In the foregoing discussion we have considered three approaches to the problem of measuring utility. Two of the approaches involve tangential attacks on the issue; the other approach endeavors to obtain direct appraisals of subjective value. The indirect approaches rest on the assumption that utility can be deduced either from choices made under circumstances involving risk (N-M utility) or from choices that determine an indifference curve. The direct approach rests on the assumption that a person can assess the ratio between the subjective values, to him, of two given amounts of a commodity. It would, of course, be a delightful state of affairs if all three methods led to the same result, but, thus far, this genial concordance has yet to be firmly demonstrated. It may well be that we will have to recognize that there are different measures of utility, each applicable to a different problem or a different circumstance. Nevertheless, for the particular problem of the measurement of the subjective value of money, viewed as a potential acquisition, we might properly pose the question as to whether one approach may seem more germane than another. Perhaps this is not an issue that can be settled at this time, but I should like to note some considerations that may be relevant to it.

An argument in favor of the indirect methods is that they seem, in a sense, to put less of a burden on the subject in the experiment. All he has to do is make a choice between options, which is something most of us do daily. Correlated with this is the contention that, by limiting our concern to choice behavior, we anchor utility more firmly to a behavioristic basis. It is alleged that we thereby get away from the "subjectivism" of introspection.

A disadvantage of the indirect approaches is that they force us to make additional assumptions, some of which may be difficult or impossible to justify.

The direct approaches to the measurement of utility have the obvious advantage of being straightforward. The only assumption involved is that the subject can make the quantitative appraisals asked for. But in the opinion of some people, it is precisely this assumption that constitutes the chief disadvantage of the procedure. Objections to this assumption seem to take two principal forms.

One type of objection raises the question of the inherent difficulty of the judgment involved. Thus, some of my colleagues ask themselves whether they could say how much money would make them twice as happy as $10, and they find it would be difficult to give an answer. Since the answer is difficult, it is probably wrong. Therefore, the argument runs, we should look for an easier problem.

The other objection stems from the assumption that introspective evidence is not admissible in matters of this sort. We must found our measurements on objective behavior.

The best answer to these or any other objections would be the demonstrated power and effectiveness of the direct procedures—the scientific usefulness of the empirical results. Such usefulness can be demonstrated for some of the direct measurements made on perceptual continua, but it is much too early to appeal to this pragmatic criterion to justify the direct approach to utility. Therefore, until the test of scientific fertility can be applied, we can only argue the case for reasonableness. In this spirit, then, an answer to the foregoing objections might run as follows.

Admittedly, behavior is what we are interested in when we study utility. But there is behavior and behavior. It is behavior when a subject turns a dial to adjust the intensity of a light to meet a "subjective" criterion. And it is no less a matter of behavior when he names a sum of money that meets a "subjective" requirement. We can be just as operational and behavioristic when dealing with verbal responses as when studying overt muscular acts. The fact that the subject "thinks" before talking need be no more of an embarrassment than that he "thinks" before acting. What I am really suggesting here is that the semantic convention under which we use the terms "subjective" and "objective" does not necessarily imply a philosophical dualism, for these terms are merely the labels we attach to two classes of behavioral phenomena. As a matter of convenience, we make a rough distinction between these two classes of behavior, but they are both capable of operational definition [29].

Regarding the other question—the difficulty of making direct judgments of utility—this might be said. The fact that a judgment may be difficult is essentially irrelevant. The question is, can the judgment be made? In particular, can it be made by the members of the population in whose utility function we are interested? This is an empirical question, of course, and can be decided only by experiment—not by a particular scholar's deciding that he himself could not make the judgment. An occasional subject may refuse to answer when asked to judge utility, but, for the most part, people seem to attempt a serious answer when asked a serious question. The answers constitute the objective, behavioral data which we proceed to process as we would process a set of meter readings. Of course, if the answers showed no thread of consistency, we would quickly decide that they were useless, for there would then be no sense in talking about the responses of the typical subject. On the other hand, if the answers determine a utility function, at least to a reasonable order of approximation, we can then proceed to the real question of scientific interest: to what use, if any, can we put the determined function, and what role, if any, can it play in the furthering of insight and understanding?

REFERENCES

1. Behan, F. L., and R. A. Behan. Football numbers (continued). *Amer. Psychologist,* **9,** 1954, pp. 262–263.
2. Bruner, J. S., J. S. Goodman, and G. A. Austin. *A study of thinking.* New York: Wiley, 1956.
3. Burke, C. J. Additive scales and statistics. *Psychol. Rev.,* **60,** 1953, pp. 73–75.
4. Campbell, N. R. *Physics. The elements.* Cambridge: The University Press, 1920.
5. ———. *What is science?* 1921; reprinted New York: Dover Publications, 1952.
6. ———. *An account of the principles of measurement and calculation.* London: Longmans, Green, 1928.
7. ———. *Symposium: measurement and its importance for philosophy.* Aristotelian Society, Suppl. Vol. **17.** London: Harrison, 1938.
8. Coombs, C. H. Psychological scaling without a unit of measurement. *Psychol. Rev.,* **57,** 1950, pp. 145–158.
9. ———. *A theory of scaling.* Ann Arbor: University of Michigan Press, 1952.
10. ———, H. Raiffa, and R. M. Thrall. Some views on mathematical models and measurement theory. *Psychol. Rev.,* **61,** 1954, pp. 132–144.
11. Davidson, D., P. Suppes, and S. Siegel. *Decision making.* Stanford: Stanford University Press, 1957.
12. Edwards, W. The theory of decision making. *Psychol. Bull.,* **51,** 1954, pp. 380–417.
13. Fechner, G. T. *Elemente der Psychophysik.* Leipzig: Breitkopf & Hartel, 1907.
14. Final report. *Advanc. Sci.,* 1940, No. 2, pp. 331–349.

15. Garner, W. R., and W. J. McGill. The relation between information and variance analyses. *Psychometrika,* **21,** 1956, pp. 219–228.
16. Goodman, L. A., and W. H. Kruskal. Measures of association for cross classifications. *J. Amer. stat. Assn.,* **49,** 1954, pp. 732–764.
17. Gulliksen, H. Measurement of subjective values. *Psychometrika,* **21,** 1956, pp. 229–244.
18. Hardy, G. N. Theory of numbers. *Science,* **56,** 1922, pp. 402–405.
19. Lord, F. M. On the statistical treatment of football numbers. *Amer. Psychologist,* **8,** 1953, pp. 750–751.
20. Neumann, J. von, and O. Morgenstern. *Theory of games and economic behavior* (2nd ed.). Princeton: Princeton University Press, 1947.
21. Oppenheimer, R. Analogy in science. *Amer. Psychologist,* **11,** 1956, pp. 127–135.
22. Plateau, J. A. F. Sur la mesure des sensations physiques, et sur la loi qui lie l'intensité de ces sensations à l'intensité de la cause excitante. *Bull. Acad. roy. Belg.,* **33,** 1872, pp. 376–388.
23. Russell, B. *The principles of mathematics* (2nd ed.). New York: Norton, 1937.
24. Savage, L. J. *The foundations of statistics.* New York: Wiley, 1954.
25. Senders, Virginia L. A comment on Burke's additive scales and statistics. *Psychol. Rev.,* **60,** 1953, pp. 423–424.
26. Siegel, S. A method for obtaining an ordered metric scale. *Psychometrika,* **21,** 1956, pp. 207–216.
27. ———. *Nonparametric statistics.* New York: McGraw-Hill, 1956, p. 76.
28. Stevens, S. S. On the problem of scales for the measurement of psychological magnitudes. *J. unif. Sci.,* **9,** 1939, pp. 94–99.
29. ———. Psychology and the science of science. *Psychol. Bull.,* **36,** 1939, pp. 221–263. Reprinted in M. H. Marx (ed.), *Psychological theory, contemporary readings.* New York: Macmillan, 1951, pp. 21–54; P. P. Wiener (ed.), *Readings in philosophy of science.* New York: Scribner's, 1953, pp. 158–184.
30. ———. On the theory of scales and measurement. *Science,* **103,** 1946, pp. 667–680.
31. ———. Mathematics, measurement and psychophysics. In S. S. Stevens (ed.), *Handbook of experimental psychology.* New York: Wiley, 1951.
32. ———. Pitch discrimination, mels, and Kock's contention. *J. acoust. Soc. Amer.,* **26,** 1954, pp. 1075–1077.
33. ———. The measurement of loudness. *J. acoust. Soc. Amer.,* **27,** 1955, pp. 815–829.
34. ———. On the averaging of data. *Science,* **121,** 1955, pp. 113–116.
35. ———. Calculation of the loudness of complex noise. *J. acoust. Soc. Amer.,* **28,** 1956, pp. 807–832; *see also* Calculating loudness. *Noise Control.,* **3**(5), 1957, pp. 11–22.
36. ———. The direct estimation of sensory magnitudes—loudness. *Amer. J. Psychol.,* **69,** 1956, pp. 1–25.
37. ———. On the psychophysical law. *Psychol. Rev.,* **64,** 1957, pp. 153–181.
38. ———. Problems and methods of psychophysics. *Psychol. Bull.,* **54,** 1958, pp. 177–196.
39. ———, and H. Davis. *Hearing: its psychology and physiology.* New York: Wiley, 1938.

40. Stevens, S. S., and E. H. Galanter. Ratio scales and category scales for a dozen perceptual continua. *J. exp. Psychol.*, **54**, 1957, pp. 377–411.
41. Stevens, S. S., and J. Volkmann. The relation of pitch to frequency: a revised scale. *Amer. J. Psychol.*, **53**, 1940, pp. 329–353.
42. Stigler, G. J. The development of utility theory. *J. polit. Econ.*, **58**, 1950, pp. 307–327, 373–396.
43. Thrall, R. M., C. H. Coombs, and R. L. Davis (eds.). *Decision processes.* New York: Wiley, 1954.
44. Thurstone, L. L. The indifference function. *J. soc. Psychol.*, **2**, 1931, pp. 139–167.
45. Whitehead, A. N. *Science and the modern world.* New York: Macmillan, 1925.
46. Wiener, N. A new theory of measurement: a study in the logic of mathematics. *Proc. London math. Soc.*, Ser. 2, **19**, 1920, pp. 181–205.

3

MEASUREMENTS
AND MANAGERIAL DECISIONS

Paul Kircher

ASSOCIATE PROFESSOR OF BUSINESS ADMINISTRATION
UNIVERSITY OF CALIFORNIA, LOS ANGELES

In recent years there has been an increase in the attention given to all types of measurements as an aid to management.   In addition to emphasis on regular accounting reports, this interest has taken a variety of forms.
Analyses based on such data as the following are typical:

> Comparisons with standard costs
> Budget projections
> Labor need estimates
> Sales projections based on correlations
>   with personal disposable income
> Production schedules
> Inventory maxima and minima
> Reorder points
> Optimum reorder quantities
> Make or buy comparisons
> Financing alternatives
> Minimum cost distribution patterns
>   (transportation-linear programming), etc.

As part of an increasing interest in "management accounting," it also has become evident that managers must pay more attention to the changing value of the dollar measuring unit, and its effect on measurements, than had been felt necessary for published reports.

Measurement in financial accounting, largely the province of the CPA, encountered difficulties with its measurements, of course. But these difficulties have tended to be focused more on the nature of the entity to be measured, on the question of whether the balance sheet (static) or the income statement (dynamic) was more important, and on methods of making the measurement. The measuring unit, the dollar, is simply accepted as given by the economy.

Interest in management accounting also has brought increasing recognition of the large areas which are not measurable as yet, and which have to be handled by the "art of management." Personnel relations, consumer motivations, and other areas may employ statistical techniques, but, as a rule, these have not been translatable into accounting data.

As business management has become more and more interested in using scientific tools to aid in making decisions, it has become increasingly evident that present methods of measurement in the business field are frequently inadequate.

Yet when management turns to other fields for help, it finds that the fundamentals of measurement, as such, have not been clearly defined, even by scientists. Each discipline or science has developed its own techniques and methods, with few attempts at coordination with others. This is true in spite of the fact that it is difficult to evaluate the effectiveness of any system, of measurement or of any other logical activity, from criteria that are part of the system itself. If the system can be viewed from "outside," from a more fundamental point of view, it often is easier to correct mistakes and to obtain insights that lead to new and better methods.

As in all logical analyses, there are many aspects of business which rest on undefinable terms or unprovable propositions. In the past, these have been so numerous and so important that business has been characterized as an art. There have been few precepts of general significance—each problem the manager encountered was seen as being a brand-new one, at least in some respects. "Business is an experiment."

We can expect that much of this "undefinability" will continue. Nevertheless, there are many relationships which can be measured in business. In situations where methods such as linear programming have proved useful, businessmen are coming to recognize that decision making can be moved to a higher plane. In these situations, it can be seen that when certain objectives are clearly defined, and the factors of the situation are objectively measured, then decisions are almost automatic. Scheduling the operations becomes mechanical—it can be done on an electronic computer.

As a simple example, suppose the manager makes the decision that he will choose the course which earns the highest profit. Suppose he has three courses open to him (such as shipping routes). If he can measure the profitability (cost, assuming roughly equal quality of service) of each of the three routes, then the policy decision in effect makes the operating decision.

MODELS OF MANAGEMENT PROBLEMS
BASED ON MEASURABLE DATA

An interest in management science has led the author to try to find a way to classify the methods which are being used to solve business problems.

It appears that they can be grouped roughly into three categories:

Descriptive Models. Descriptive models attempt to portray the relationships that are seen to exist in a situation. This is the first major product of a business analysis, once desired goals have been set, a reason for making the measurement that has been made known, and measuring methods have been adopted and employed.

Predictive Models. Given a set of relationships (descriptive models), if one factor can be predicted, and the relationship holds, then the other factors are predicted. In business, this is a common practice in such activities as budgeting. If you know the gross margin percentage, and you can predict your sales revenue, then you know how much your cost of goods sold should be. From this you can estimate how much goods to buy or process.

Decision Models. A decision model is a set of predictive models, together with some optimizer—a means of choosing between them. A simple example is a price-setting model that considers only sales volume and variable costs. Another is a linear programming solution. In both cases, a descriptive model is needed: the set of given cost and quantity-to-be-supplied relationships. The predictive model gives the total cost for any solution that meets the supply requirements. Given the added requirements that the least cost (or greatest profit) be chosen, the decision model gives a definite answer as one or as a set of best solutions.

If we could prepare a set of budgets (predictive models) covering all possibilities, and if we wished to make the maximum profit, then the budget decision could be made automatically by examining the bottom line of the list of budgets to find the largest figure for profit. If we wished to optimize something else, the models would have to be set up to measure that "something else."

MODEL BUILDING

There is some debate as to how models should be used in the management decision process. Although linear programming, queueing theory, and other techniques have provided some solutions, the fact that so large a part of the management process is still unmeasurable makes many interested parties believe that model building has limited application to management. Major research efforts at the present are being made in the direction of attempting to build such models. At UCLA, for example, we are actively developing management gaming models for use on our computers. I am developing descriptive, predictive, and decision models concerning internal activity within a given firm.

A number of other groups are also active in this effort. The American Management Association recently announced a large-scale management gaming model which it is already using to train executives. Other similar activities are being reported such as those of the Institute of Management Science and The Operations Research Society.

Yet we are still a long way from being able to put policy making on a scientific basis. Policies are always set in an atmosphere of much uncertainty. Indeed, a major difference between the human brain and the so-called electronic computer brain is that the human being can operate so effectively with partial information. At present, a computer must have a complete program or it will stop or give inaccurate results.

A person learns faster (at present). Policy making can be improved, with experience, as certain situations tend to repeat themselves. But lessons can be learned only if the important factors in each situation are measured, so that they can be compared and correlated with the results of the decisions. Moreover, the better they can be identified and measured the more the decisions can be made automatic, thus freeing human beings to concentrate on areas where they are still most effective.

NEED FOR RESEARCH

If improvements are to be made in the management decision process, a major research effort must be directed toward the attempt to establish the basic structure of the business measurement process. By dividing the process into its important elements, each of these may be studied with more precision, and the relationships between them can be seen more clearly.

In a paper I presented to the 1955 national meeting of the Operations Research Society of America, the following elements were identified:

1. Determination of the objective of the business entity—the purpose which is to be served in a particular situation.

2. Determination of the types of factors which might serve to attain the objective.

3. Selection of the key aspects of the factors—the aspects which are to be measured.

4. Choice of:

(a) a measuring method;

(b) a measuring unit.

5. Application of the measuring unit to the object to be measured—the central action of measurement.

6. Analysis of the measurement—relating it to other measurements (other in time or in kind).

7. Evaluating the effectiveness of the measurement by determining the extent to which it assisted in the attainment of the objective.

Each of these needs to be investigated in some detail. Since it is impossible to describe all the various considerations within the scope of a single article, an attempt is made to indicate something of the direction and purpose of the research by relating each of the above elements to a few specific problems.

Examples will be given from:

(a) Some highly developed and effective systems, such as the measurement of length.

(b) Some highly developed but less effective systems, such as accounting.

(c) Some moderately developed systems, such as job evaluation.

(d) Some areas where systems hardly exist, as yet, such as selection and evaluation of executives.

The following discussion of the list of elements and the examples are drawn in part from my article on measurement which appeared in *Advanced Management,* October 1955.

DEFINING THE OBJECTIVE

The first and most obvious element or step in the measurement process is to define the objective. Obvious as it is, however, it is not always easy to do.

Executives have struggled with the problem of objectives ever since companies grew from the single proprietor stage. Now that social consequences are a major consideration, many executives spend a great deal of their time attempting to establish policies which exhibit business statesmanship which will lead to stability and continuation of earnings as well as to immediate gains.

Unless these problems are better defined, it will not be possible to develop the objectives in terms that will be susceptible of some sort of quantification. In other words, it is necessary to set the stage for measurement.

Without a clear understanding of the purposes which a to-be-hired executive is to serve, for example, it is difficult to establish standards by which to select him, or, later, to judge his performance. Since the evaluation is made, anyhow, considerable confusion and hardship result.

DETERMINATION OF RELEVANT FACTORS

The second step is to determine which factors may be employed to attain the objective.

In physical problems, this step is often clearly definable. When it is, the measurement process may become relatively easy, unless certain factors are physically inaccessible or unless methods have not been sufficiently developed to handle the particular type of problem. For example, if the purpose is to provide a means of travel across a river, at minimum cost, certain obvious alternatives are present—a bridge, a ferry, or a tunnel. (Of course, every such problem also presents an opportunity for the "genius" who can by-pass the problem, e.g., by finding a better route that does not go near the river, or by using helicopters.) Excepting the unusual solutions, the problem then becomes one of measuring the expected flow of traffic, the cost of construction and operation of the various alternatives, and expressing the costs and capacities in comparable terms.

With a problem such as the selection of an executive, the "factor" choice is considerably more difficult. In the first place, although the company organization chart may appear to offer a "slot" which is to be filled, it is not possible, with present knowledge, to describe the position in terms comparable to those which can be used to describe the quantity of traffic flow—the expected weights of the vehicles, etc.

Even if it were possible to define the job narrowly, at the executive level, the individual capabilities of the manager chosen will soon start reshaping the responsibilities and activities concerned.

Moreover, it is at least theoretically desirable that each vacancy should be the occasion for a re-examination of the company organization to see whether the position should be redefined, or perhaps even eliminated. Such considerations add a great deal to the difficulty of the measurement problem.

SELECTION OF KEY ASPECTS

Once it has been determined what the purpose is, and the objects to be measured, it is necessary to select those aspects which can, and should, be measured. These are the aspects which are themselves quantifiable, and which are related in some way to the quantifiable aspects of the purpose or objective of the entity involved.

An example can be drawn from accounting. Various types of assets and liabilities are measured in order to obtain information concerning the revenue and expense flows, and the financial position of the firm. These indicate the degree of attainment of the profit-making objectives of the business.

The illustration from accounting is especially interesting since accountants have deliberately chosen to restrict their activities to those measurements which they believe can be made within a certain standard of accuracy. This means that certain other items, vital to the well-being of the firm, are resolutely omitted. For example, the company's investments in advertising its products or in developing its executives, etc., are not considered to be assets, but are written off in the period of expenditure, as a rule. Good will has almost disappeared from company statements.

In certain types of job evaluation, it is possible to quantify some of the key aspects. For example, a stenographer should be able to take shorthand at so many words per minute and type at a given rate in order to perform the duties of a given job. Other important attributes, however, such as the ability to get along with others, are harder to quantify.

In choosing an executive the problem is much more difficult. There is little knowledge as to the particular abilities which are required for a manager to act successfully in a specific situation. Even where certain abilities have been ascertained as desirable, it is seldom that they can be expressed in terms which are quantifiable. They are seldom established on the basis of what the man can do; rather they are usually expressed in terms of what he *is*—e.g., sincere, capable, loyal, patient, trained, experienced, etc. These attributes are difficult to express quantitatively, and thus are difficult to relate to later performance, however measured.

CHOICE OF MEASURING METHOD AND UNIT

The act of choosing a measuring method and a measuring unit has been given considerable attention throughout history, but so far not much of the theoretical work is helpful to businessmen. Mathematics, "the Queen of the Sciences," is a logical process the object of which, in the words of Comte, is "the indirect measurement of magnitudes," and "it constantly proposes to determine certain magnitudes from others by means of the precise relations existing between them."

Most of theoretical mathematical work, however, has deliberately avoided the problems of application, especially to anything so crass as business problems. The essence of mathematics is deductive reasoning from explicitly stated assumptions. Only since World War II have many mathematicians discovered, much to the surprise of most of them, that business problems are difficult, challenging, and can be as intellectually interesting as the act of contemplating abstract "number."

In recent years, however, activity in the application field has increased tremendously. Three societies have been formed: The Institute of Management Sciences, The Operations Research Society of America, and the Society for Industrial and Applied Mathematics.

Perhaps the most advanced work in the field of measurement, of a type useful for choosing executives, has been done by the applied psychologists. In their attempts to measure such things as intelligence, men like Thurstone have had to develop scales where "zero" could not be fixed, nor could absolute intervals be specified. In several works Stevens has shown how various types of scales are possible, depending upon the type of manipulation which can be performed on the measurements—the nominal, ordinal, interval, and ratio scales. (See p. 25.)

Further developments have been hampered, however, by lack of clear-cut definitions of the relationship between the concepts we call "qualitative" and those we call "quantitative." Following the mathematicians, most writers appear to treat "quantity" as referring to an abstraction which somehow has almost a physical significance of its own.

It would appear to be more useful to establish firmly the concept that quantities are measurements of qualities. For example, the quality "length" occurs in various physical objects. By choosing some standard unit and determining the number of repetitions of the unit in the object, the length can be expressed as a quantity. Then, following Stevens, the manipulations of arithmetic—addition, etc.,—can be attempted to see what type of scale is involved.

In this process of measurement the problem for the observer is to identify certain characteristics in the object to be measured, characteristics which appear similar to those in the measuring unit, and which also have some identifiable relationship to the purpose of the measurement. These characteristics should be invariant, in the sense that they can be identified and seen to persist. Basically, of course, every object and every event in the universe is unique, and it is constantly changing through time. To find invariant characteristics, then, requires the human process of abstraction.

In measuring an executive, for example, the objective desired may be to organize a research program. It is necessary to determine which types of ability are required for this, then to find a means of measuring those types of ability in the alternative men available. Each type of ability must be defined in such a way that it can be seen as a distinct part of a complicated personality. It must also be comparable to a part of the complicated personalities of the other candidates.

We are far behind the physical sciences in our ability to accomplish this. So far behind, in fact, that many people consider any effort in this direction to be useless. However, it does appear to offer the best hope for eventual improvement over present intuitive methods, so research in this direction will probably continue.

The importance of invariance can be seen in the difficulties which arise when the measuring unit chosen has varying characteristics. The dollar, the measuring unit of accounting, is an example. Changes in purchasing power not only create difficulties of evaluation but also can lead to serious inequities. An appreciable part of the "income" taxed by our government in recent years is really the result of the diminished value of the dollar unit.

APPLICATION OF THE MEASURING UNIT

The simplest method of measurement is to identify the unit characteristics in the object to be measured, and then merely to count the recurrences. Almost equally simple are the cases where the unit can be directly compared, as in measurement of length or weight. More advanced measurements, such as in astronomy, require the construction of chains of relationships.

Most business measurements involve quantity of performance in given time periods since business is a dynamic process. The time factor introduces many complications. Another major factor in business measurements is the force of custom. Even when systems are demonstrably weak, the difficulties of retraining and re-educating the users of data, to say nothing of the problem of development of a better system, frequently operate to hinder improvements.

On the other hand, custom does offer some advantages. Most businessmen are familiar with the major elements of the accounting system, and so can interpret results even when these are not as precise as one might wish.

In newer fields, such as measurement of executive abilities, there are several systems in use. They exhibit few attributes in common. The result is that acceptance of the systems is correspondingly more difficult to achieve.

ANALYSIS OF THE MEASUREMENTS

The area of analysis of measurements in business has seen startling advances in recent years, and there is reason to hope that even greater improvements can be achieved. Primary interest has centered on attempts to relate various measurements into integrated systems that reflect the business operations. These attempts usually involve the construction of mathematical models of the operations.

Developments in linear programming, game theory, communication theory, etc., have shown that complicated situations can be resolved by the use of models if the relevant data can be obtained and if the relationships are of certain types. Whereas the use of some of these models requires advanced training in mathematics, others are simpler and yet very effective.

EVALUATING THE MEASUREMENT

In a speech to the Controllers Institute, M. L. Hurni, of General Electric's Management Consultation Services Division, gave a summary of the management problem which indicates how measurements are used and evaluated.

According to Hurni, the examination of an operation or of a situation within an operation, as a problem in logic, consists in doing fundamental research upon the operation itself.

It involves systematic examination of the environment in which the business exists, for such things as the possible structure, range, and probability of specific demands upon the business, the recurrence or lack of recurrence of particular aspects of the environment, and the drift in the environment from a given known position.

It includes systematic examination of the resources of the business, for the purpose of determining quantitatively the identifying characteristics of such resources. For example, characteristics of performance, or probable malfunctioning, and the balances, limitations, and restraints that may exist within the resources.

It includes the development and testing of models of action that give a description of the relation between the environment and the resources and which will define needs for performance and contribution, the information which must be communicated to make such performance or contribution possible, units of measure of the resultant performance, and the statement of possible risks that will result from a range of probable courses of action.

In short, the purpose of the problem in logic is not the taking of specific action but the attainment of more complete understanding so that increasingly purposeful action may be taken with greater assurance.

IMPROVEMENT OF MEASUREMENT PROCESS

The foregoing sections were primarily an attempt to show why measurement is of such significance to business. This section is a condensed presentation of an analysis of improvements which need to be made in the measuring process.

Purpose. It may appear obvious that a business measurement would have purpose. In fact, it seems that, in the general sense, every measurement must be purposeful. The purpose may be no more than curiosity, but at least measurement is an activity which must have a reason.

The importance of this rather obvious statement, given a broad definition of purpose, is that, if one is to make a formal measurement, one must accept responsibility for making some effort to define one's purpose.

As in many other types of activity, this step is too often taken for granted. The result is that someone else who wants to use the measurement may have to struggle to interpret the data gathered by the original investigation. It even happens that the researcher himself forgets and changes his viewpoint, so that he later makes use of data in a way that is difficult to justify.

General Structure—Concepts. Given a purpose, the next step is to improve the definitions of the concepts involved. These include concepts concerning the situation to be measured and those of the measuring process itself. (I personally favor concepts developed in such works as Bridgman's *The Logic of Modern Physics* and Churchman's *Theory of Experimental Inference.*)

Under Bridgman's "operational" definition, one cannot know what "length" means until one knows the operations that were performed in order to obtain the figure given as the length of an object.

This concept is very true in accounting. A generation ago, Canning concluded his classic *Economics of Accountancy* with the comment that "income" is the figure the accountant gets after he applies the procedures he adopts. Through the years these procedures have changed. Perhaps the most important of these changes has been a shift in emphasis from the balance sheet to the income statement. Originally the owner's equity was the item he watched:

$$\text{Assets} - \text{liabilities} = \text{owner's equity}$$

This was transformed into the typical balance sheet:

Assets	= *Liabilities*	+ *Owner's Equity*
(he owns, valued at cost of acquisition)	(he owes, at amount due)	(shares of stock plus retained earnings)

The progress of the business was judged by comparing the balance sheet today with that for a previous point in time. The change in the owner's equity was his income (after considering withdrawals or investments).

Now the emphasis is on the difference between two flows—the inward flow of resources (revenues) and the outward flow (expenses). The net is called "income." This "income" still equals the change in owner's equity between the two dates—the start and end of the income period— but the shift in emphasis has caused many subtle changes in the way partially completed transactions are measured.

Model Building.   Once the concepts are in hand, the next step is to relate them in a formal way that results in a model. Various aspects of this have been discussed earlier. It is evident that a great deal more needs to be done, even though it is probable that a major part of current research effort is going on in this area.

Scale and Choice of a Measuring Unit.   Every analysis of the problem of measurement has stressed this stage. The British Association for the Advancement of Science had a committee which worked on this phase for almost ten years without achieving agreement. An interesting work is that of Campbell, available in several references including the recent *The World of Mathematics*. This book contains material from Professor Stevens, whose work on scales is of considerable help in understanding this step of the problem.

Application.   A good deal of scientific literature on measurement is concerned with the problem of determining when it is possible to quantify. There seems to be general agreement that this can only be determined empirically.

The importance of measurement in many fields is so great that some writers, like Lord Kelvin, have implied that without it one cannot be considered scientific. This attitude seems somewhat overdrawn, since it would eliminate much of the classification work in fields like geology and botany. However, the implication that quantitative knowledge is of a higher order seems obvious.

It is not an easy task to determine when measurement is appropriately applied. As Professor Knight is said to have stated about some of his fellow economists: "If they can't measure, they measure anyhow."

Analysis.   Churchman's book on the *Theory of Experimental Inference* gives a survey of the problem of analysis. This phase of measurement has received some attention, as in books on statistics.

But there is not enough work like Churchman's, which gives a critical analysis.

There are many volumes of work on analysis of accounting records and financial statements. But it may be doubted whether a study of any of them would give much inspiration to researchers in other fields, such as a student who is attempting to improve his ability to analyze measurements in physics.

Evaluation. At the end of any process such as measurement the researcher should pause to determine whether his original purpose has been achieved.

Again, there are numerous works in special fields which help the user evaluate specific systems. In accounting, we have the whole CPA profession auditing the measurement process performed by others in the business field.

However, the standards developed by years of work of many able accountants still are not in a form likely to be of much help to a worker in another field. By the same token, it is still difficult to see how other measurement processes can be used to improve accounting.

INTEGRATION OF MODELS WITH "ART" OF MANAGEMENT—GRAND STRATEGY

Since so much of management depends on nonmeasurable information, the usefulness of models will always be limited if we cannot develop means of integrating them with the methods used to make decisions when both types of information—measurable and nonmeasurable—are pertinent.

The word "strategy" appeals as giving something of the flavor of this combination, though, of course, the word also has other meanings. This problem is one which has engaged many business thinkers.

The Harvard Graduate School of Business Administration has developed the case method in order to provide realistic material to train its students in making strategic decisions. The original concept was taken in part from the Law School. The originators of the case method hoped that if they gathered enough material, certain principles of business management would become evident. This original intent has not been fully fulfilled. In recent years, the school has tended to regard each case as a separate situation, and has de-emphasized the attempt to derive principles from them.

Nevertheless, it seems that this type of analysis will have to be made if the integration referred to above is ever to be formally acceptable.

THE NEED FOR COOPERATION

It would seem that there is little question but that administration is a major human activity. Intelligent men spend the better part of their lives engaged in management. Yet, for some reason, this form of activity has received less attention from scientists than have rocks, insect habits, the movements of stars, or a hundred other types of phenomena.

Two-hundred years ago, an English gentleman could echo Dr. Johnson's opinion that management of affairs was a harmless way to kill time. This attitude has died hard among scientists. Of course, a major reason is the fact that scientists who tried to study business too often have succumbed to the financial lures thrown their way as soon as they had some understanding in the field. At the same time, businessmen have not been anxious to encourage pure research in their field when they could see greater profits from using the same talents on applied research.

In spite of all this, the problems remain. Scientists no longer have the excuse that they cannot interest themselves in management because the problems are trivial. It has become evident that many such problems are exceedingly intricate. Mathematicians, psychologists, and others drawn to this field have found to their surprise that many business problems far exceeded their ability to define, measure, and analyze. Many of the papers presented at the AAAS meeting raised issues of measurement which have a direct bearing on management problems.

Measurement in business is handicapped by lack of knowledge in areas such as the following, discussed in several papers presented at the AAAS meeting.

1. Definitions.
2. Concepts.
3. Preparation of the state before measurement.
4. Effect on the system of the measuring method used.
5. Distributions of probabilities in situations which cannot be more closely analyzed, as in quantum mechanics.
6. The need to measure the "manifest" in order to determine the "latent."
7. Concept of an "operator."

EXAMPLE OF MANAGEMENT PROBLEMS

In order to illustrate, for the nonbusiness reader, the scope of measurement problems in business, perhaps a few references from current business literature would help:

Scheduling. A news report describes the way the Buick Motor Car Company will use an electronic computer to keep track of the variations possible on their production line. Consumers have options which include a variation of about 30 colors, dozens of accessories, etc., on several different model groups and body styles. The potential range of variations is in the hundreds of thousands. To keep the assembly line moving, the right combination must be scheduled to come together with almost split-second accuracy.

Consulting. A management consultant firm describes the services they offer. These involve appraisal of such areas as economic and industry trends, financing, market development, proper distribution, production effectiveness, equipment utilization, development of people and organization, etc.

Management Effectiveness. In the December 1956 issue of *Management Review*, the publication of the American Management Association, appears a typical article on the problems of measuring managerial effectiveness and converting the measurement into a suitable bonus plan. The author, Philip Gustafson, suggests that if a company puts 25 per cent of its profits into the bonus kitty, the first problem is to determine how much the top performers should get. He suggests that the top three might get 50 per cent of their salaries, the bottom three 10 per cent. Then the others can be rated in between, and their bonus calculated on an appropriate scale.

Another interesting item appeared in the *Administrative Science Quarterly* (Cornell University). Prewar and postwar figures show that the Soviet enterprises regularly produce from 70 to 90 per cent of their month's quota in the last 10 days of the month, and as low as 2 per cent in the first 10 days.

In addition to prestige, publicity, and advancement, a Soviet manager gets as much as double his salary for meeting his quotas. He gets no bonus at all for 99 per cent production, and loses his job if he fails too often.

Managers get a bonus of as much as 10 per cent for each 1 per cent production rise above the quota. But a ratchet principle raises subsequent quotas to the new level, so that the manager will try to meet the quota but not to exceed it.

About a third of the managers fail to meet the quota and eventually lose their jobs. In 1955, Bulganin complained that the executives of many enterprises change much too often. Recent decentralization in Russia, no doubt, has increased this problem.

Selling. Eugene J. Benge in *Sales Management,* June 15, 1956, reports on a study made to determine the 10 most significant attributes and the percentage by which the scores of the excellent salesmen exceeded those of poor salesmen. These were: self-confidence—75 per cent; planning ability—74 per cent; industriousness—60 per cent; persuasiveness—52 per cent; intelligence—48 per cent; technical knowledge—44 per cent; interest—44 per cent; ambition—38 per cent; health—30 per cent; and social development—26 per cent. But what is the validity or significance of these data?

Production. A paper by Elwood S. Buffa, Operation Research Report No. 45, *The Additivity of Universal Standard Data Elements,* is significant. The basic thesis of the paper is (after examination of the research literature) that the hypothesis of additivity has not been tested adequately to date, since most of the research reported has tested for correlation or interaction between elements rather than for additivity. In two studies where additivity was tested, the results disagree.

Purchasing. One way to eliminate guesswork in choosing suppliers is to establish a rating system, according to James O. Bengston, president of the Chicago Apparatus Co., laboratory equipment supplier. The method, originated by the General Electric Company, helps the customer to rate the somewhat intangible factors of quality and service, and to weigh them against the price factor. This is how it works:

Point values are assigned to each of the three factors; for example, price might be assigned 40 points, quality 30 points, and service 30 points.

Next, vendors are given a price rating, based on current quotations. The lowest price is given a full rating, in this case 40 points. Other vendors are graded to this scale; thus if vendor *B*'s prices are 10 per cent higher, his rating might be 10 per cent lower, or 36 points.

To rate quality, the buyer compares the number of acceptable lots with the total lots received. If vendor *A*'s merchandise has been acceptable 95 per cent of the time, his rating for quality would be 28.5 (95 per cent of the possible 30 points).

Service is the most difficult of the three factors to evaluate, and perhaps the most critical. To simplify the rating, some companies keep a record of the percentage of merchandise received within 10 days of the order. Others use a more complicated system, based on delivery promises and the performance of certain critical materials.

Once the ratings are compiled, the customer can rate his source as excellent, good, fair, or unacceptable by totaling the ratings of the three categories. The customer can also review each factor separately for possible trouble spots.

The above examples were chosen to show the range of problems encountered by businessmen. To these should be added those which are obvious measurement problems, such as the typical accounting and statistical reports, of which there are a great variety.

THE SCIENTIST'S ROLE IN MANAGEMENT

Somehow or other, decisions of the type described in the examples have to be made by administrators. Decisions like these are made every day in business and government. For example, budget decisions are a major factor in determining the rate of missile research, even after Sputnik. Because of the importance of business-type decisions in our type of economy, an improvement in the method of decision making might well have more real influence on human life than almost any other conceivable change, barring a fundamental religious revival or atomic annihilation.

As commercial and governmental transactions have increased in size, complexity, and the number of people affected, it has become essential that some simplifying techniques be developed so that human intelligence can still cope with the problems that arise. New systems of communication and data analysis, including the use of electronic computers, have shown promise for meeting the sheer mechanical part of the problem. New scientific analysis methods also show promise in meeting the conceptual needs.

Faced with the heightened emphasis on scientific work, we find ourselves on the horns of a dilemma. Many new research ventures and many highly technical production and distribution operations must be administered. Who will manage them? Scientists or "business managers"? Each group has been tried, and each has shown shortcomings because of a lack of ability in one or the other field.

Moreover, in making decisions, both of these groups will have to rely on the accuracy and appropriateness of measured data with which they deal. If our physical resources are not properly valued, and if the transactions which involve them cannot be measured in a meaningful way, then decisions about their use become unrealistic.

A scientist is rightfully reluctant to make pronouncements to other scientists unless he is sure of his ground. But where a scientist seeks strong proofs, the business manager, faced with the need for making immediate decisions, is willing to settle for rules of thumb.

It should be possible for scientists who have pioneered in the study of measurement problems to extend their work so as to make their findings useful to managers, even though the scientists have not completed their work. At the least, they might prevent some of the blunders that now occur.

All this is apart from a purely commercial motive. Our social and defense problems are becoming enormous. It is a matter of survival that we help managers who are engaged in practical applications of measurement.

It seems reasonable to hope that this book will be but one of many attempts to demonstrate the importance of an interdisciplinary attack on the problems of measurement. Also I hope that the material can be presented in a way which makes it useable by those who are seeking guidance for the development of better ways to handle worldly affairs.

4

WHY MEASURE?

C. West Churchman

PROFESSOR OF BUSINESS ADMINISTRATION
UNIVERSITY OF CALIFORNIA, BERKELEY

INTRODUCTION

"Measurement" is one of those terms which has attained a social prestige. Apparently—all other things being equal—it is better to measure than not to measure. Some people think that the social sciences do not—or cannot—measure; and one implication of the thought is "less power to them!"

Why should measuring have this preferential status? What is it that measuring accomplishes that nonmeasuring does not? These are the questions to be dealt with in this paper.

At the outset one can suggest a rather obvious answer to this question, namely, that measurement assigns numbers to objects. But this suggestion can scarcely be adequate to explain why measurement is to be preferred to nonmeasurement in some contexts. Why is number assignment a good idea? Whatever it is that number assignment accomplishes may give us a clue to the meaning of measurement. The contrast between quantitative and nonquantitative information seems to imply a contrast between "precise" and "vague" information. Precise information is information that enables one to distinguish objects and their properties to some arbitrarily assigned degree of refinement.

We are thus driven to a first formulation of the function of measurement which will suffice to define the problem area of this paper. There is no reason to be precise for precision's sake, of course. But the reason that precision is useful is that precise information can be used in a wide variety of problems. We know that we can measure the lengths of some objects very precisely. This means that, in the various situations where we want information about length, we can obtain the information we want. Sometimes we do not need to make a fine distinction between objects, and sometimes we do. But whatever our needs, length measurements can be found to satisfy them—within bounds, of course. Beyond the bounds there are still problems of length measurement which have not been solved—the very fine and the very far.

Suppose, then, we propose that the function of measurement is to develop a method for generating a class of information that will be useful in a wide variety of problems and situations. This proposal is very tentative. It needs defending in terms of the historical usage of the term "measurement" and the practice of measurement. It needs clarification, since "wide variety" may include time, place, persons, problem type, and many other properties of breadth and depth.

Instead of considering these important questions, I want to continue the theme with which I started. Suppose we acted as though we knew what the proposal meant to a sufficient extent to enable us to develop the problems entailed in such a functional definition.

We can begin by noting one rather striking consequence of the proposal. The objective of measurement can be accomplished in a number of ways, as this volume of papers clearly shows. The qualitative assignment of objects to classes and the assignment of numbers to objects are two means at the disposal of the measurer for generating broadly applicable information. But which means is better? The striking consequence of the proposal is that measurement is a decision making activity, and, as such, is to be evaluated by decision making criteria.

In this sense, i.e., measurement taken as a decision making activity designed to accomplish an objective, we have as yet no theory of measurement. We do not know why we do what we do. We do not even know why we measure at all. It is costly to obtain measurements. Is the effort worth the cost?

I have no intention of developing a functional theory of measurement here. Instead, I want to reconsider some of the well-known aspects of measurement in the light of the tentative proposal given above. In each case, I want to ask what alternative decisions the measurer has, and to what extent he has guides which enable him to select the best alternative. The topics selected for discussion do not necessarily represent the best way of organizing measurement activities; I have selected them because they have each received considerable attention in the literature on measurement. In each case, it will be found that the measurer is caught between at least two desirable aims, and the more he attempts to emphasize one aim, the more he must sacrifice another—which is the typical problem setting of the decision maker.

The topics to be considered are: (1) the selection of a *language;* (2) *specification* of the items and their properties; (3) *standardization* of the information to permit adjustment to various times and places; and (4) *accuracy* and *control* of the measurement process.

Any "scheme" of measurement does violence both to reality and to the functional meaning since there are many methods of accomplishing a goal. I do not intend to imply, therefore, that these topics must occupy the attention of the measurer in this order. But it is safe to assume that every measurer must decide:

1. In what language he will express his results (*language*).
2. To what objects and in what environments his results will apply (*specification*).
3. How his results can be used (*standardization*).
4. How one can evaluate the use of the results (*accuracy* and *control*).

There is a distortion which I will have to introduce in order to discuss these topics. The method of deciding how to handle any one of the problems does eventually involve consideration of all the rest. But the main point here is to show that a true decision problem does occur in the case of each of the four topics, rather than to suggest how the decision problem is to be solved.

LANGUAGE

The measurer must develop a language which adequately communicates to another person what the user must do to utilize the information contained in the measurement. The emphasis here is on the language of communication.

One aim of the language of measurement is to communicate to as many potential users as possible since this will increase the scope of utilization. Another aim is to enable the user to employ the information when there is need for fine distinctions since this also will increase the scope of utilization. These two aims are apparently in conflict—

the more common the language the more difficult it is to use the language for portraying fine distinctions.

One way out of a dilemma is to escape through the horns. This I think has been the solution proposed by advocates of "fundamental" measurements. Suppose there are some operations which can be described in unequivocal language so that virtually every intelligent person will understand what is meant, or can be trained to understand. Suppose, too, we can find a process by which other operations can be understood in terms of these more elementary ones, and that these operations permit greater and greater refinement. If this were so, then we could accomplish *both* a wide scope of communication and a in which the process of going from the "simple" language and "simple" operation might be the comparison of straight rods: by successive steps we go from the "simple" language of comparison to the more complicated language of measuring the distances between the planets. Another example of a "simple" operation is the preference comparison of commodities: we may try to go from the "simple" language of preferences to the more complicated language of utilities.

In recent years there has been considerable study of the various ways in which the process of going from the "simple" language and "simple" operations can take place. These studies have resulted in formalizations of measurement language which are undoubtedly important in the development of the theory of measurement. For example, the symbol "$<$" can be made to denote an operation of comparison of two objects (e.g., "shorter than," or "is preferred to"). Sometimes the comparisons obey some simple rules like transitivity ($a < b$ and $b < c$ implies $a < c$), which enable us to introduce into the language the concept of ordering. But we can only introduce the concept if the comparisons obey the rules; i.e., we cannot enrich the language unless certain rules are upheld. The measurer is faced with a decision making problem when the rules fail. He may look about for another comparison operation with which he is satisfied and for which the rules hold, or he may abandon the rule itself and look for other rules to enrich the language. In any case, it seems to be confusing to say, for example, that "transitivity" fails over the class of preference comparisons. Such statements hide the fact that the measurer may always select another meaning for "preference" (there are clearly very many possible meanings) rather than let the rule fail *if* this seems economically advisable.

The language of measurement may be enriched in many ways. In each case the measurer has to decide whether the formalization is advisable. An enrichment of the language often makes the measurements more useful as items of information. But additional rules must be satisfied, often at the expense of a great deal of research time. For examples of some of the kinds of measurement languages one may construct, see Stevens' paper, p. 25. Stevens is not concerned, of course, with comparisons of the values of the language schemes he discusses.

The process of developing a measurement language which I have been discussing has the following character. A formal system is constructed which includes terms, and relations between the terms. Some of the terms and at least one of the relations are taken to be "primitive" in the formal sense: the terms and relations are not explicitly defined. These terms and relations are also taken to be semantically primitive: the things and the comparisons which they denote are supposed to be simple to understand or to perform. This method of constructing the language of measurement is neither the only one nor necessarily the best one available to the measurer. A language without semantic primitives has many obvious advantages, besides more realistically reflecting the actual operations of measurement (where nothing is simple to understand or to perform). But the techniques of developing such a language have not yet been explored. Further discussion of this point would take the present discussion too far from its central purpose.

Finally, the amount of complexity that one should permit in a measurement language is also a problem of considerable importance. The more complicated a language, no matter how it is developed, the fewer the number of people who will understand it. In some cases, this restriction on communications seems clearly desirable. In other cases, e.g., in inspection work, one tries to develop a language that will be widely understood although it may not be very precise.

In sum, the language of measurement does entail a decision problem. The more precise a language the less broadly is it understood. To put it otherwise—if one wanted to be cute about it—the clearer a language the more confusing it is to most people. Precise languages narrow the class of users but increase the degree of refinement that any user can attain. The proper balance between breadth and depth is the linguistic decision problem of measurement.

SPECIFICATION

The problem of the specification of measurement is the problem of deciding what objects are being described and under what circumstances. This is simply the problem of deciding on the scope of application of the measurements in terms of time, place, and individuated items. This is not a decision about how the application is to be made, which will be considered under another head.

A conflict of aims is clear in this instance as well. It would be very fine if we could develop information that could be used in connection with all our problems, i.e., on all things at all times and places. But the more general information becomes the more expensive it becomes to acquire, or, else, the more useless it becomes in any specific context.

Perhaps one illustration will suffice to clarify the issues. In the theory of detonation, we would like to measure the sensitivity of various compounds. It would be a nice thing if we could measure how sensitive a piece of mercury fulminate is wherever the piece may be, no matter what its size, and no matter what is happening to it. But we do not do this at all. The term "sensitive" applies only to compounds which have a specific kind of shape and which exist in a specific class of environments. We restrict the term to these items and environments because we feel it would be entirely too costly to try to extend the scope beyond them, relative to the gains made from the more extensive information. Generalizing: each measurer is involved in the economic problems of balancing the "costs" of extending the application of measurement and the "returns."

STANDARDIZATION

We turn now to the aspect of measurement that enables us to utilize information in a wide variety of contexts. In searching for a suitable title under which this topic could be discussed, I could find no better one than "standards." Standards of measurement are designed to provide a basis for adjusting experience in widely different contexts. Although the term is usually used in a narrower sense than the one adopted here, the purpose of standards so exactly corresponds to the notion of "wide applicability" that the extension of meaning seems legitimate.

It is strange that in philosophical discussions of measurement, the problem of standards is often neglected. This may be because it is often assumed that the problem is trivial, or not nearly as important as setting up an adequate language. Yet even a casual inspection of the process of measurement shows how very intricate and delicate is the operation of standardizing measurement readings.

The necessity for standards of measurement is based, in part, on an almost obvious observation that not all human experience takes place at the same time or in the same circumstance. Even if there were but one mind in all the world, such a castaway would need to compare the experience of one moment and place with that of another moment and place. He would have to communicate with his own past. The devices that men have used to make these comparisons are many indeed. One of the most direct methods consists of reconstructing each experience into an experience of a given moment and a given time, i.e., the present experience is "adjusted" into the experience that would have taken place under some standard set of conditions. This is not the only way in which experiences of various moments can be communicated, but it is a very powerful device for communication. Robinson Crusoe cannot bring along his hut as he searches for a flagstone for his hearth. But he does need to compare an experience on the beach with a past experience in his hut. He does this (say) by the use of a piece of string. He argues that if the string length fits the flagstone, the flagstone will fit the hearth. What he is really saying is that each experience—of the hearth and the flagstone—can be adjusted to a comparison with the string under "standard" conditions.

The general purpose of standards can now be made clear. One wants to be able to assert that x has property y under conditions z at time t in such a manner that the information contained in the assertion can be used in a wide number of other conditions and times to enable many different kinds of people to make decisions. The assertion that company x had a net income of y dollars in the U.S.A. during 1919 means nothing at all unless there is some way in which this property can be compared with a net income in 1956, say, or in England. Hence, the need for a "standard" dollar. Even the standard dollar does not accomplish the desired result of transmitting meaningful information if the circumstances in which the company operated (e.g., postwar economy) were different from the circumstances of today (cold-war economy). We require richer standardization to enable us to make meaningful comparisons of such a company's activities.

The decision problem of standards arises because of two rather obvious needs. First of all, one wants to find a method of measurement such that a minimum amount of adjustment is required when times, places, and people change. This desire for simplification is so strong that many thinkers have believed that certain simple sensations have this very desirable property: reports about such sensations can be understood intelligibly by a wide number of people in a wide variety of circumstances. A witness of an accident can report which car was going faster, a laboratory technician can report the color of litmus paper, a stock clerk can report the number of items in a bin; in each case the report is supposed to be reliable, no matter how the surrounding conditions vary.

The other need that standards are supposed to supply is precision. This is the need to differentiate aspects of the world we live in. The planning of a large meeting only demands a rough notion of the size of the crowd, say, between 2000 and 3000, in order to select a meeting hall economically; but the planning of a dinner meeting requires much greater precision. The decisions about instrument readings, highly refined products, bridges, and the like, all demand extreme precision.

It requires little reflection to see that the aim of minimizing the effort to adjust data usually conflicts with the aim of precision. In effect, the "cost" of adjusting data rises as more precision is attained, just as the cost of the absence of precision goes up as we attempt to find "simpler" data. Experience has shown that it is possible to be naive with respect to precision in an attempt to be simple in procedures. All of the supposedly "simple" instances mentioned above—a report of a witness, of a laboratory technician, of a stock clerk—are not simple at all if the decision on which they are based has any importance. There are countless instances in which such reports have been shown to be faulty, and these instances have pointed to the need for "checking" the accuracy of the data. Such checks amount to setting up standards to which the data can be adjusted. For example, what is meant by saying that one car was seen to be speeding more rapidly than another? As a first approximation: the witness who saw this was "reliable." What does "reliable" mean? As a second approximation: had any other normal person been at the scene, he would have made the same report. What does "normal person" mean? As a third approximation: a person with an intelligence quotient in a certain range, with emotional factors below a certain level of intensity, with vision in a certain range, etc.

This "normal" is the standard of measurement for a "witness" report. It may be noted that defense attorneys often argue that the witness's report is *not* adjustable to this standard, e.g., that the witness is excitable, or known to exaggerate, etc. Usually, when the witness is shown to have a property significantly different from the standard, his report is rejected. In this case, we can say that the "adjustment" has been a rejection. This terminology will enable us to emphasize the economic gains that occur when "unreliable" reports can be adjusted to reliable ones, rather than rejected. If we knew, for example, that a witness was normal on all counts except an emotional instability of a certain type, then we might be able to adjust his report to the report that would have occurred if a completely normal person had been at the scene of the accident. We could do this if we could establish a law relating visual reports in various circumstances to the degree of a specific emotional disturbance. This kind of thing Bessel accomplished in his study of observer reaction times. It is not necessary to discard the readings of a "slow" observer if we can find a method of adjusting his readings, e.g., by adding a constant to each one.

Thus, we see three "levels" of standardization of data. The first tries to restrict itself to data reports that are virtually certain to remain invariant with time and place so that zero adjustment is required. This level minimizes the cost of adjustment, but the data themselves have little precision and, consequently, little value where refined distinctions are needed. The second level consists of rejecting data not collected under standard conditions. The method of adjustment is simple, but the waste of information may be considerable. The third level consists of adjusting data to standards by means of "laws" that enable one to say: *if* report R_1 was made at time t_1 in circumstance z_1 by a person having properties w_{11}, w_{12}, etc., then report R_0 would have been made at time t_0 in circumstance z_0 by a person having properties w_{01}, w_{02}, etc. The "standards" are specified in terms of circumstance, observer, and observer actions.

It seems natural enough to ask why reports should be adjusted to a standard report. If laws exist that enable one to adjust in the manner stated above, why not adjust directly from one circumstance to the problem context without going through the medium of a standard?

The reason for standardized data is easy enough to give. Without standards, one would have to report all the relevant information about the time, place, persons, etc., in addition to the data report itself. Otherwise, no one would know what values to assign to the variables in the laws that enable one to use the report in other circumstances. But once a standard has been given, then all data reports can be adjusted to the standard, and all that is needed is the data report itself. Thus, the standard conditions constitute a data-processing device that simplifies the amount of reporting required. But the construction of an optimal standard is a very complicated problem, as anyone knows who has followed the literature on the selection of a standard of length. Indeed, the whole problem of standards has received a great deal of attention by various professional societies. But as far as I know, the philosophers of measurement, i.e., those interested in tying together the whole structure and function of measurement, have tended to ignore this work.

ACCURACY AND CONTROL

There are two other aspects of measurement—each fully as important as those just discussed. These are concerned with the accuracy of the measurements and with the control of the measuring process.

Accuracy is itself a measurement—the measurement of the degree to which a given measurement may deviate from the truth. No procedure can claim the name of measurement unless it includes methods of estimating accuracy.

"Deviation from the truth" must be defined in terms of the uses to which the measurement is put. This remark has the awkward consequence that accuracy is a highly relative term, the meaning of which depends on the individual decision maker. But measurements are pieces of information applicable in a wide variety of contexts and problems. This means that it must be possible to find accuracy measurements which are applicable in a wide variety of contexts and problems. It must be admitted that, at present, we tend to adopt a rather naive solution to the problem of measuring accuracy by using one over-all figure such as the probable error or standard deviation of the mean. For example, in statistical literature, accuracy is sometimes defined in terms of a "confidence interval." In so far as this computed interval has any meaning, it tells us that a certain range of numbers constructed out of observations has a specific probability of including the "true" measurement. Each set of observations is the basis for forming a net to "catch" the truth, and the confidence interval tells us the probability of a successful catch. But it is almost always difficult to determine how the information supposedly contained in a confidence interval can be used; i.e., what difference would it make if the confidence interval were twice as large, or half as large? Most statisticians seem to prefer to negotiate this tricky question by urging the decision maker to set his own size of confidence interval. Since most decision makers honestly do not see the purpose of the interval in the first place, the interval is set "arbitrarily," i.e., pointlessly.

Now the problem of accuracy is to develop measures that enable the measurement user to evaluate the information contained in the measurements. It seems clear that to date we have overemphasized one aim and underemphasized another. We have tried to develop general measures of accuracy at the cost of their meaningfulness in specific contexts. The decision problem of accuracy, therefore, has not been adequately solved, except possibly for some industrial processes where there is repetition of data and cost functions can be obtained.

Control is the long-run aspect of accuracy. It provides the guarantee that measurements can be used in a wide variety of contexts. In other words, a control system for measurement provides optimal information about the legitimate use of measurements under varying circumstances. The economics of control are extremely difficult to work out. It is certainly not economical to check measurements at every feasible instant, nor is it economical to use measurements without any check. What the proper amount of control should be and what its structure should be are in general unsolved problems.

It may be noted that control is, in effect, the test of a good standard. If adjustments can satisfactorily be made to a standard in accordance with the criteria of control, then the standards have been sufficiently specified. If not, then either the laws of adjustment must be changed or, else, additional specifications must be added to the standard.

SCIENCE AND DECISION MAKING

Enough has been said to establish the point that measurement involves highly complicated—and as yet unsolved—decision problems. It is important, I think, to point out that I realize that many people feel that decision making models cannot be applied to scientific work. They arrive at the feeling in various ways. Some feel that formal decision models applied to scientific decisions would stifle the creative powers of the scientist. Others feel that the "costs" and "returns" of the scientific input and output are intangibles. These feelings may be right, but at least we owe it to ourselves as scientists to determine whether they are right, and this means a frank statement of our decision problems, which is what I have started to do in this paper. My argument is not with people who feel this way.

But others may feel that science is immortal, and what is not solved today will be solved sometime. Existing decision making models implicitly or explicitly assume a penalty for delays. Perhaps to an immortal mind no such penalty is relevant. Thus, we can investigate some aspects of our measurements now, and let the next generation solve some more. People with this attitude are serious opponents of the endeavor of this paper. However, they cannot be right. Science may be immortal—and I hope it is—but this does not imply a zero penalty for delay. It is ridiculous (I feel) to think that science is a gradual accretion of bits of knowledge. Instead, we ought to think that, as time goes on, scientists will feel that the distance between what they know and what they could know is greater and greater. Hence, the penalties for wrong steps become magnified, not diminished, the longer the life of the institution. Therefore, the decision making problems of science are terribly important ones, and decision making models that penalize for delay, i.e., for overemphasis or underemphasis of some kind of activity, can be appropriately applied to science today.

SUMMARY

The decision making problems of any of the aspects of measurement are enormously difficult, and even an approximation to their solution still escapes us. Everything that has been said here about measurements is applicable to a broader class called "information" and "data." A rather significant portion of our resources is devoted to generating and processing data. However, it is apparent that no one knows how the data should be expressed (the decision problem of data *language* is unsolved), what data are needed (the decision problem of data *specification* is unsolved), how the data are to be used in various contexts (the decision problem of *standardization* is unsolved), and how the data are to be evaluated (the decision problem of *accuracy* and *control* is unsolved).

II

SOME THEORIES OF MEASUREMENT

5

MENSURATION
AND OTHER MATHEMATICAL
CONNECTIONS OF
OBSERVABLE MATERIAL

Karl Menger

PROFESSOR OF MATHEMATICS
ILLINOIS INSTITUTE OF TECHNOLOGY

Mensuration may be regarded as an application of numbers to reality. The purpose of this paper is to describe formal aspects of mensuration that are shared by the application of other mathematical ideas (especially of functions and operators) to other phases of reality. In some ways it may be a weakness of that analogy—in other ways, its strength —that the various parallel mathematical connections of observable entities have altogether diverse origins. Some pages will, therefore, be devoted to descriptions of the genesis of mensuration and its analogues.

HELMHOLTZ'S THEORY

As far as physical objects are concerned, the oldest approach to the subject, and probably still the best, is the theory of Helmholtz.[1] It is

---

[1] Helmholtz's paper [1] seems to have been overlooked by many English writers. No reference to it is found in either Russell's *Principles of Mathematics* or Campbell's *Physics: The Elements*, or Whitehead and Russell's *Principia*, or in the extensive bibliography in E. V. Huntington, "A Complete Set of Postulates for the Theory of Absolute Continuous Magnitude," *Trans. Amer. Math. Soc. 3*, 1902, p. 264.

based on the assumption that there be given a class $\mathcal{C}$ of elements (such as thin rods or objects that can be put on a balance) any two of which can be compared with one another, and combined into one element.

Examples of procedures leading to the *comparison* of two elements include placing two rods next to one another, and putting two objects simultaneously on opposite scales of a balance with equal arms. Two rods are said to be *equivalent* if the procedure reveals that they coincide on both ends; two weights, if the balance is in equilibrium.

Equivalence, which will be denoted by $\equiv$, is assumed to be *symmetric*. Indeed, if the said balance is in equilibrium, it remains in this condition after the weights are interchanged. More delicate is the assumption that equivalence based on physical procedures is *transitive*; that is to say, that $A \equiv B$ and $B \equiv C$ imply $A \equiv C$.

Examples of combining two elements of $\mathcal{C}$ include placing two weights on one and the same scale of a balance, and fusing two rods, using one as the straight extension of the other.

Combination, which will be denoted by $+$, is assumed to be:

(a) *In Harmony with Equivalence.* $A \equiv B$ implies $A + C \equiv B + C$.
(b) *Commutative.* $A + B \equiv B + A$.
(c) *Associative.* $A + (B + C) \equiv (A + B) + C$,

for any elements A, B, C belonging to the basic class $\mathcal{C}$.

If each of three elements A_1, A_2, A_3 is equivalent to one and the same element A, and $B \equiv A_1 + A_2 + A_3$, then one writes

$$B \equiv 3A \text{ and, of course, also } B \equiv 3A_1, \ B \equiv 3A_2, \ B \equiv 3A_3.$$

In this sense, a yard is said to be 3 feet and, in fact, three times any sample of a foot. More generally, for any two positive integers m and n,

$$\text{if } \quad A \equiv A_1 \equiv A_2 \equiv \cdots \equiv A_m \quad \text{and} \quad B \equiv B_1 \equiv B_2 \equiv \cdots \equiv B_n$$

$$\text{and} \quad A_1 + A_2 + \cdots + A_m \equiv B_1 + B_2 + \cdots + B_n,$$

then one writes:

$$mA \equiv nB, \quad A \equiv (n/m)B, \quad \text{and} \quad B \equiv (m/n)A.$$

As Pythagoras discovered, there are no integers m and n thus connecting a side S and a diagonal T of one and the same square. However, the relation between S and T (which may be expressed in the formula $T = \sqrt{2}\,S$) can be described by means of inequalities such as

$$S < T < 2S, \quad \tfrac{5}{4}S < T < \tfrac{3}{2}S, \quad \tfrac{11}{8}S < T < \tfrac{23}{16}S, \quad \cdots$$

Here, the $<$ relation can be expressed in terms of $\equiv$ and $+$, provided certain further assumptions about combining are admitted. Dodging (for the sake of simplicity and because of their problematic relevance for physical mensuration) questions of continuity, one finds the following further postulates sufficient:

(d) *Difference Postulate.* If $A \not\equiv B$, then there exists an element D such that $A + D \equiv B$ and/or $B + D \equiv A$.

(e) *Postulate of the Absence of Nil.* $A + B \not\equiv A$ for any two elements A and B.

(f) *Bisection Postulate.* For any element A, there is an element A' such that $A \equiv 2A'$ or $A' \equiv \frac{1}{2}A$.

(g) *Archimedes' Postulate.* For any two elements A and B, there exists a positive integer m and an element C such that $mA \equiv B + C$.

Indeed, these assumptions justify the following definition:

$A < B$ if and only if there exists an element D such that $A + D \equiv B$.

In many a class $\mathbb{C}$, there are procedures permitting the direct establishment of the relation $A < B$. Examples include the tipping of the balance toward the weight B and coincidence of the rods A and B at one end while the other end of B projects. The justification of the preceding definition lies in the fact that, by virtue of postulates (a)–(e), the $<$ relations can be proved to be:

1. *In Harmony with Equivalence.* $A \equiv A', B \equiv B'$, and $A < B$ imply $A' < B'$.

2. *Transitive.* $A < B$ and $B < C$ (or $B = C$) imply $A < C$.

Indeed, $A + D_1 \equiv B$ and $B + D_2 \equiv C$ imply

$$A + (D_1 + D_2) \equiv (A + D_1) + D_2 \equiv B + D_2 \equiv C \text{ and, hence, } A < C.$$

3. *Asymmetric.* $A < B$ implies $B \not< A$.

Indeed, $A + D_1 \equiv B$ and $B + D_2 \equiv A$ would imply $A + (D_1 + D_2) \equiv A$, in contradiction to postulate (e). For similar reasons, $A < B$ and $A \equiv B$ are incompatible. Hence:

4. *Trichotomy Law.* Any two elements A and B of $\mathbb{C}$ satisfy exactly one of the relations

$$A < B \text{ or } A \equiv B \text{ or } B < A \text{ (also written } A > B).$$

According to Archimedes' postulate, $A < B$ implies the existence of a largest positive integer k_0 such that $k_0A < B$, namely, the least integer such that $B < (k_0 + 1)A$. Similarly, Postulate (g), applied to $\frac{1}{2}A$, yields an integer k_1 such that

$$\frac{k_1}{2}A < B < \frac{k_1 + 1}{2} A$$

and, more generally, for any positive integer n, an integer k_n such that

$$\frac{k_n}{2^n} A < B < \frac{k_n + 1}{2^n} A.$$

Hence, for any two elements A and B of $\mathcal{C}$, there is a chain of inequalities of the type of those connecting S and $T = \sqrt{2}\,S$. This completes, for practical purposes, the definition of relations between two elements of the class $\mathcal{C}$.

A few remarks about the last four postulates may be added. In (d), it would be possible to replace "and/or" by the exclusive "or," as brought out by the Trichotomy Law. The name of Postulate (e) is motivated by the fact that (e) rules out the existence of a nil-element N such that $A + N \equiv A$. Neither, consequently, can there exist two elements related to one another as are 2 and -2. Their sum would be nil and leave a third element unaffected when combined with it, just as $5 + (-2 + 2) = 5$, which would contradict (e). The class of all positive integers satisfies six of the seven postulates—all except (f). An example of a system satisfying all postulates except (g) is the class of all ordered pairs of real numbers

(x, y) such that either $x > 0$ or $x = 0$ and $y > 0$.

It satisfies Postulates (a)–(f) if

$$(x, y) + (x', y') \equiv (x + x', y + y').$$

One finds $(x, y) < (x^*, y^*)$ if and only if $(x^*, y^*) \equiv (x, y) + (u, v)$, where either $u > 0$ or $u = 0$ and $v > 0$; that is to say,

$(x, y) < (x^*, y^*)$ if and only if $x < x^*$ or $x = x^*$ and $y < y^*$.

Postulate (g), however (which, incidentally, was known long before Archimedes), is not satisfied by this class, which is one of Veronese's non-Archimedean systems. Indeed, for each positive integer m and each element (u, v), where $u \geq 0$, it is readily seen that

$$m(0, 1) \not\equiv (1, 0) + (u, v), \text{ that is, } (0, m) \not\equiv (1 + u, v).$$

A class $\mathcal{C}$ satisfying Postulates (a)–(g) will be called a *positive ratio class*. In it, one may select an element, E_1, and then associate with each element A of $\mathbb{C}$ the ratio A/E_1. Clearly, in this way one associates the number 1 with E_1 and with each equivalent element. The process just described is referred to as *mensuration;* E_1 is called the chosen *unit;* A/E_1, the *measure* of A.

Two remarks must be added. Without reference to specific principles of comparison and combination, one cannot for two objects A and B answer the question: Is $A = 3B$? The question is incomplete. Even if A is a wooden yardstick and B a metal rod, 1 ft long, the question has a clearly affirmative answer only if it is understood that the principle of comparison is length. If the comparison is based on weight, then A $= 3B$ may well be false, and $A = \frac{1}{6}B$ true.

It should further be noted that the positive numbers not only connect the elements of any ratio class pairwise but also themselves constitute a positive ratio class, provided two numbers are called equivalent if and only if they are equal, and two numbers are combined by ordinary addition. Indeed, the positive numbers in this way satisfy Postulates (a)– (g). If the number 1 is selected as a unit, then each number is its own measure.

But while numbers are elements of a ratio class, objects belonging to other ratio classes, such as heavy bodies or rods, are neither numbers nor in a reasonable way reducible to numbers. (Pythagoras, the only philosopher who ever dreamed of such a reduction, was not more successful with his arithmetical monism than his predecessor Thales had been in reducing reality to water.) What can be reduced to numbers are certain relations between certain observable objects, namely, between elements of one and the same ratio class.

FORMAL PROPERTIES OF RATIOS

If this paper were primarily concerned with mensuration as such, numerous points in the foregoing presentation would have to be elaborated on.

In many a class, more than one procedure is needed to establish equivalence. If there are two, then there should be pairs of elements to which both procedures are applicable, and each such pair that is equivalent according to either procedure should be equivalent according to the other.

It obviously is impossible to put one and the same weight, A, simultaneously on opposite scales of a balance. Hence the procedures of direct comparison may yield an equality that is nonreflexive (i.e., does not satisfy A equals A). Nor is equality by direct comparison necessarily transitive. If two rods, A and C, are attached to opposite sides of a table, a movable rod B may well be equal to both of them without A and C being directly comparable. Equality by direct comparison is extended *by definition* to an equivalence relation that is transitive, symmetric, and reflexive.

The transitivity assumption is beset by even graver difficulties—"in the large" and "in the small." In the large, consider long chains of colored light in which consecutive members are equal in brightness, e.g., a chain beginning with red and changing via orange and yellow to green; and another chain beginning with the same red and changing via purple and blue to green. Only elaborate experiments may prove that any two such chains terminate in green lights that are equal (or even close) in brightness. In the small, consider a chain consisting of only three objects in which the first and the third (slightly) differ even though both have subliminal differences from the second.

Two rods A = aa' and B = bb' may be combined into one rod in four ways, depending upon whether a or a' is attached to b or b'. There is not, in general, for two objects A and B belonging to a class ℭ a unique object A + B. A unique combination can be defined only for the classes of mutually equivalent objects belonging to a class ℭ—a possibility based on the harmony of combination with equivalence.

But since this paper is devoted to formal aspects of mensuration, I will not elaborate on the genesis of ratios but rather enumerate some simple consequences of their definition.

I. *Multiplicative Transitivity.* If A = pB and B = qC for three elements A, B, and C and for two positive numbers p and q, then A = $(p \cdot q)$C.

II. *Reciprocal Asymmetry.* If A = pB, then B = $(1/p)$A.

III. *Unitary Reflexivity.* A = 1A.

IV. *Contravariance by Division.* If A = pB and B' = rB, then A = (p/r)B'.

Clearly, III and IV are consequences of I and II. Property IV is referred to as contravariance because, if B is replaced by B', the ratio of A to B changes in a way that is reciprocal to the connection of B' with B. Transitivity and asymmetry are illustrated by the implications:

$$yd = 3 \text{ ft and ft} = 12 \text{ in. imply yd} = 36 \text{ in.}$$

$$lb = 16 \text{ oz implies oz} = \tfrac{1}{16} \text{ lb.}$$

3 ft, $\tfrac{1}{16}$ lb, and, more generally, any number followed by the designation of an object, are sometimes called *denominate* numbers; in contrast, 3 and $\tfrac{1}{16}$ are referred to as *pure* numbers. Only the latter are

objects of arithmetic. In order to make results of mensuration amenable to the direct application of arithmetic, it is therefore advisable to restate them in terms of pure numbers. Instead of

$$1 \text{ yd} = 3 \text{ ft}, \quad A = 3B \quad \text{or} \quad A = (n/m)B \quad \text{or} \quad A = pB,$$

one may also write

$$\text{yd/ft} = 3, \quad A/B = 3, \quad A/B = n/m, \quad A/B = p, \quad \text{respectively.}$$

A/B is read: A in B. The last formulations are analogous to saying

a certain distance in miles is 920,

rather than

that distance is 920 miles.

The preceding formulations of Properties I–IV of ratios are in terms of denominate numbers. In terms of pure numbers, they may be restated as follows: For any elements A, B, C, and B′ and any positive numbers p, q, and r:

I′. If $A/B = p$ and $B/C = q$, then $A/C = p \cdot q$.
II′. If $A/B = p$, then $B/A = 1/p$.
III′. $A/A = 1$.
IV′. If $A/B = p$ and $B'/B = r$, then $A/B' = p/r$.

Clearly, these facts may be further restated without any reference to the symbols p, q, and r:

I″. $A/C = (A/B) \cdot (B/C)$;
II″. $B/A = 1/(A/B)$;
IV″. $A/B' = (A/B)/(B'/B)$,
for any elements A, B, C, and B′.

It should be clearly understood that the formula

$$(\text{yd/ft}) \cdot (\text{ft/in}) = \text{yd/in}$$

is an equality of two numbers: $3 \cdot 12$ and 36, even though each of the three numbers involved is described as the characteristic of a relation between two objects, namely, their ratio. Moreover, $\text{ft/in} = 12$ just as $\text{year/month} = 12$, wherefore

$$\text{ft/in} = \text{year/month} = \text{lb/oz} - 4.$$

Similarly,

$$\text{ft/in} + \text{lb/oz} + 32 = \text{min/sec.}$$

OPPOSITE CLASSES AND FULL RATIO CLASSES

For many a positive ratio class $\mathcal{C}$, there exists another positive ratio class $\mathcal{C}^-$ whose elements are in a certain opposition to those of $\mathcal{C}$, somewhat as liabilities are opposed to assets, or repellent forces to attractions. The opposite to objects weighing down a scale of a balance are balloons which, when attached to a scale, lift it up. Two lifts, like two weights, can be compared with one another on a balance and combined into one lift. The class of all lifts, therefore, is a positive ratio class.

Two opposite positive ratio classes $\mathcal{C}$ and $\mathcal{C}^-$ can be included in one class $\mathcal{C}^*$ any two elements of which can be compared and combined provided that it is possible to combine each element of $\mathcal{C}$ with each element of $\mathcal{C}^-$, the result, with one exception, belonging to either of the classes $\mathcal{C}$ or $\mathcal{C}^-$. For instance, any balloon may be attached to any heavy object, the combination having, in general, either a weight or a lift. Exceptional is the case where the combination of a heavy object and a balloon, placed on the same scale, produce equilibrium on a balance whose other scale is empty. The class of all those combinations that are weightless as well as liftless will be called the nil class, $\mathcal{N}$. It turns out that any two elements of $\mathcal{N}$ are equivalent; i.e., two elements of $\mathcal{N}$, placed on opposite scales, keep a balance in equilibrium. Combined (that is, on the same scale), they yield an element of $\mathcal{N}$.

Any two elements of the class $\mathcal{C}^*$ (consisting of the elements of $\mathcal{C}$, $\mathcal{C}^-$, and $\mathcal{N}$) can be compared and combined. Postulates (a), (b), (c), and (f) are satisfied, but (d) and (e) require modifications.

(d*) For any two elements A and B, there is an element D such that $A + D \equiv B$, and an element D' such that $B + D' \equiv A$.

(e*) For any element A,

$$A + N \equiv A \text{ if (and only if) N belongs to } \mathcal{N}.$$

The combination $D + D'$ of the elements mentioned in (d*) clearly is a nil element. Two elements whose combinations belong to $\mathcal{N}$ are called *opposite*. Applied to any element A and any nil element N, Postulate (d*) yields the existence of an element A' such that $A + A' \equiv N$, i.e., of an element opposite to A. As is readily seen, two elements that are opposite to one and the same element are equivalent, and the combination of an opposite of A and an opposite of B is opposite to the combination of A and B.

In this way the classes of mutually equivalent objects in $\mathcal{C}$ and $\mathcal{C}^-$ fit into $\mathcal{C}^*$ just as two opposite rays fit into a straight line. However, while in each of the classes $\mathcal{C}$ and $\mathcal{C}^-$ a $<$ relation can be introduced, the two relations cannot be combined into one transitive relation in $\mathbb{C}^*$ that would be in harmony with addition. For just as A < 3A in $\mathbb{C}$, the opposites in $\mathbb{C}^-$ satisfy A' < 3A'. Only if the relation in one of the two classes, say in $\mathbb{C}^-$, is reversed, and any nil element is said to be <A and >A', do the two relations blend in $\mathbb{C}^*$. With regard to the class $\mathbb{C}^*$, Archimedes' postulate must be restricted to elements A and B with a positive ratio, i.e., to elements that are both in $\mathbb{C}$ or both in $\mathbb{C}^-$. In particular, the element A in (g) must not be a nil element, since each multiple of an element of $\mathfrak{N}$ belongs to $\mathfrak{N}$.

The development of mathematical symbols that cope with the relations in a full ratio class $\mathbb{C}^*$ presented difficulties that defied the powers of antiquity. In particular, to the great disadvantage of their arithmetic, the ancient Greeks lacked symbols for 0 and −1 to describe the ratio of any nil element to any non-nil element, and of any non-nil element to an opposite, respectively. The former lacuna in their symbolism affected their entire arithmetical notation and barred them from the development of positional numerals. Importing the cipher 0 from India, Renaissance mathematicians not only introduced the simple numerals that the Western world has used ever since, but extended the ratio concept to the class $\mathbb{C}^*$ excluding only ratios—of nil elements as well as non-nil elements—to nil elements. A full ratio class $\mathbb{C}^*$ exhibits the formal Properties I–IV with the only exception that in II the element A (and, consequently, in IV the element B') must be non-nil. Nor can a nil element (excluded from Archimedes' law) serve as a unit. Hence II' is replaced by:

$$\text{If } A/B = p \neq 0, \text{ then } B/A = 1/p.$$

GRADUATION, AN ADDITIVE ANALOGUE TO MENSURATION

An important analogue to positive ratio classes is described in the following definition: A class $\mathfrak{G}$ is said to be *oriented* if a number, denoted by A − B, called the *transition* from B to A—briefly, A from B—is associated with any ordered pair (A, B) of elements according to the following conditions:

I'. *Additive Transitivity.* A − B = k and B − C = l imply A − C = k + l.

II'. *Negative Asymmetry.* A − B = k implies B − A = −k.

III'. *Null Reflexivity.* A − A = 0.

IV'. *Contravariance by Subtraction.* A − B = k and B' − B = m imply A − B' = k − m.

Clearly, these postulates for transitions are the additive analogues of the multiplicative properties of ratios in positive ratio classes. Consequently, a positive ratio class can be oriented (i.e., made an oriented class) by setting

$$A - B = log \ (A/B) \qquad \text{for any two elements A and B,}$$

where the logarithm is to an arbitrary base, but to the same base for all pairs.

In an altogether different way, a positive ratio class in which a unit E_1 has been chosen can be oriented by defining

$$A - B = A/E_1 - B/E_1 \qquad \text{for any two elements A and B;}$$

that is to say, by equating $A - B$ to the difference of the measures of A and B. More generally, any class in which a number fC is associated with each element C can be oriented by setting

$$A - B = fA - fB \qquad \text{for any two elements A and B.}$$

On the other hand, the following example of an oriented class $\mathcal{L}$ is not based on the assumption of any such f being defined on $\mathcal{L}$. The elements of $\mathcal{L}$ are the points on a directed physical line—something like a straight-edge without end on either side—in which unordered pairs of points or spots are treated just as are thin rods in Helmholtz's theory. That is to say, congruent pairs of points are regarded as equivalent; a combination of pairs (A, B) and (C, D) is a pair (A, E) such that B is between A and E while (B, E) is congruent to (C, D). One chooses a unit distance (thus making the unordered pairs a positively measured class) and, for any ordered pair (A, B), defines $A - B$ as the distance or the negative distance between A and B according as, on the directed line $\mathcal{L}$, B is to the right or to the left of A. Finally, one sets $A - A = 0$ for any point A. Then $\mathcal{L}$ satisfies the postulates for an oriented class.

The formal properties of transitions may be restated without any reference to the symbols k, l, m, namely, as follows:

I''. $(A - B) + (B - C) = A - C$.
II''. $A - B = -(B - A)$.
IV''. $A - B' = (A - B) - (B' - B)$.

Less common than the corresponding formulation for ratios are denominate formulations of the laws for transitions, where $A = k + B$ is read: A is k above B.

I. $A = k + B$ and $B = l + C$ imply $A = k + l + C$.
II. $A = k + B$ implies $B = -k + A$.

In analogy to measuring the elements of a positive ratio class, one may (as it is often called) *graduate* an oriented class $\mathcal{G}$ by selecting an element 0_o, called the *origin*, and associating with each element A the transition $A - 0_o$—a number called the *degree* of A.   The degree of the origin 0_o is the same number 0 that characterizes the ratio of nil elements to non-nil elements in a full ratio class.   Conceptually, however, 0_o has nothing whatever to do with the nil class.   Even in graduating a full ratio class, there is no reason for choosing a nil element as the origin. For instance, in graduating the full ratio class of weights and lifts, one may find it convenient to choose a non-nil element as origin.   In computing the average weight in pounds for a large sample of the male population, one chooses, say, 160 as origin and thereby avoids large terms in the sum to be computed.

In a positive ratio class, it is not even possible to exhibit a nil element that might serve as origin.   In the directed line $\mathcal{L}$, the full ratio class of the transitions from one point to another has an altogether gliding character.   No point in $\mathcal{L}$ is predestined to be identified with the nil transition (from any point to itself) in preference to any other point. The choice of such an origin is quite arbitrary.   Physical scientists seem to be less aware of the difference between nil in mensuration and zero in graduation than are psychologists.[2]

FLUENTS AND FUNCTIONS

The observables and mathematical connectives to be discussed in the following sections are more complex than physical objects (rods, weights, etc.) and numbers, and cannot be taken for granted without a careful analysis.   Reviving a term that was introduced and extensively used by Newton but that later fell into almost complete oblivion, I will call those observables *fluents*.   Descartes had introduced specific fluents, namely coordinates, into the geometry of the physical space, and Galileo had investigated time, the distance traveled by a moving body, and its speed. But Newton was the first to study fluents on a large scale and to make general statements about fluents which, however, he introduced in a somewhat vague description: *"Fluentes vocabo quantitates has, quas considero tamquam gradatim & indefinitè crescentes."*   For that matter, the traditional literature in applied mathematics lacks explicit definitions even of specific fluents such as those studied in mechanics.   In the cen-

[2] Economists base the graduation of values on assumptions about relations $\equiv$ and $<$, rather than about $\equiv$ and $+$.   While comparison is harder in the realm of values and intensities than it is in the realms of rods and weights, combination of values and intensities presents almost insuperable difficulties.

turies after Newton, the nature of fluents has been obscured by confounding them with numerical variables, that is, symbols such as the letters x and c in assertions about many numbers, e.g., in the statements

$$(x + 1)^2 = x^2 + 2x + 1 \qquad \text{for any number x;}$$

$$c^2 - 1 = (c + 1) \cdot (c - 1) \qquad \text{for any number c.}$$

Time, distance traveled, speed, etc., were called "variable quantities," "variable numbers," and even simply "variables," although those fluents are entirely different from variables such as x and c in the preceding examples. The confusion has been enhanced by using the same letter x (in italic type) for numerical variables as well as for fluents. In this paper, the difference between them is expressed visibly by designating fluents (and functions such as *log*) in italics and using letters in roman type as number variables. (Only in quoting the traditional way of writing, I retain the customary indiscriminate use of italic x.)

The obscurity of the traditional references to fluents is strikingly illustrated by the fact that those references are often not even recognized as such. For instance, Tarski [2] complains that in some books the symbol x is said

. . . to denote certain numbers or quantities, not "constant numbers" however (which are denoted by · · · '0', '1', · · ·) but so-called "variable numbers" or rather "variable quantities." Statements of this kind have their source in a gross misunderstanding. The "variable number" x could not have any specified property, for instance, it could be neither positive nor negative nor zero; or rather the properties of such a number would change from case to case; that is to say, the number would sometimes be positive, sometimes negative, and sometimes equal to zero. But entities of such a kind we do not find in our world at all; their existence would contradict the fundamental laws of thought. The classification of the symbols into constants [such as '0', '1', · · ·] and variables, therefore, does not have any analogue in the form of a similar classification of the numbers.

These remarks about numbers and symbols for numbers are, of course, incontestable. The words "variable quantities," however, as quoted by Tarski in the literature, hardly refer to numbers and symbols for numbers. They usually refer to fluents such as speed and acceleration; the values of fluents indeed do change from case to case and, indeed, are sometimes positive and sometimes nonpositive.

A few examples will illustrate the definitions of fluents by which I have proposed to fill the old gap in the literature [3, 4]. By t (the time in seconds) I mean the class of all pairs (T, tT) for any act T of reading a clock calibrated in seconds, where tT denotes the result of this act, that is, the number read on the clock. Similarly, p (the gas pressure in atmospheres) is the class of all pairs (P, pP) for any act P of reading a pressure meter calibrated in atmospheres, where pP denotes the number read as the result of the act P. [It will be noted that, in this paper, a letter in italic type followed by a capital in roman type denotes *a value of a fluent*—its value for an act, a sample or the like. In many books such a value would be denoted by t(T) or p(P). But no one writes *log* (5) fearing that *log* 5 might be mistaken for the product of the logarithm and 5; and I am confident that no reader will attempt to multiply the time t by an act T of clock reading.]

As far as their general pattern is concerned, the aforementioned definitions of t and p resemble the widely accepted definition of the logarithmic function or the function *log* as the class of all pairs (x, *log* x) for any number x > 0, including, for instance, the pairs (5, *log* 5) and (1, 0). Of course, this definition of *log* is comprehensible only to one who knows the meaning of *log* x for any x > 0—that *log* x is the exponent to which the base (e or 10, according to agreement) must be raised in order to yield x. The definition of *log* does not aim at teaching anyone how to compute, say, *log* 5 or any other value of the function *log*. What it describes is the function in its entirety, in contradistinction to its numerical values. Similarly, in order to understand the preceding definitions of t and p, one must know how to read clocks and pressure meters. The definition does not aim at teaching anyone how to recognize clocks or how to avoid parallaxes in reading meters. The definitions introduce time and pressure in their entirety. And these entireties (as well as the function *log*) are of great importance since, as will become apparent in the following section, it is in terms of them that some of the most important scientific and mathematical laws attain their simplest expression.

Without mentioning further examples of fluents, let us proceed to the general definition: A fluent u is a class of pairs (A, uA) for any element A of a class of extramathematical entities $\mathcal{C}$ (called the *domain* of u), where uA is a number, called the *value* of u for A. The assumption that with each element A of $\mathcal{C}$ there corresponds exactly one number or value, uA, can also be expressed by saying that the class of all pairs denoted by u does not include two pairs (A, a) and (A', a') such that A and A' are identical while a $\neq$ a'.

The domains of t and p, as defined above, consist of acts of observation. Such fluents might be called *subjective*. Various observers may well arrive at discrepant values if they simultaneously read the same pressure meter. Science, therefore, also operates with what might be called *objective* pressure in atmospheres—a fluent p^* whose domain consists of instantaneous gas samples. p^* might be defined as the class of all pairs (G, p^*G) for any such sample G. The value p^*G is computed by averaging the numbers read simultaneously by various observers or by utilizing what Bridgman calls paper-and-pencil-operations. People's height in inches is another objective fluent: the class h or h/in of all pairs (M, hM) for any member M of a certain group of people, where hM denotes M's height in inches. (Some statisticians refer to fluents such as h/in or w/lb as *variates* and call their domains *populations*.) If e is any measured or graduated class, then the class of all pairs (C, mC) for any C belonging to e, where mC is the measure or degree of C, is a fluent.

If all values of a fluent are equal, the fluent is said to be *constant;* e.g., the speed of a parked car is constant (of value 0) and so is the gravitational acceleration at, say, the North Pole.

If the class a in the definition of a fluent is allowed to include elements of any kind, I will call the resulting class of pairs a *functor*. Thus the logarithmic function is a functor. Its domain is the class of all positive numbers. Its value for any number x > 0 is *log* x. Indeed, each function is a functor—a functor whose domain is a class of numbers. From what has been said about fluents in general, it follows that a function does not include two pairs of numbers (b, a) and (b', a') such that b = b' and a ≠ a'. This so-called one-valuedness of functions is a feature of the utmost importance in scientific and practical applications of the concept.[3]

A functor whose domain is a class of functions is traditionally called a *functional*. Examples are the classes of all pairs

$$(f, \int_0^1 f) \quad \text{and} \quad (f, \int_0^1 \sqrt{1 + (\mathbf{D}f)^2})$$

for any continuously differentiable function f with the domain [0, 1]. Traditionally, the values for f of these functionals are written

$$\int_0^1 f(x)\, dx \quad \text{and} \quad \int_0^1 \sqrt{1 + (f'(x))^2}\, dx,$$

respectively. They are equal to the area under the curve which is the graph of f in a Cartesian plane, and to the length of that curve.

When presenting the new theory of fluents, at this point one frequently hears three objections

1. Some mathematicians say: "If subjective time t is the class of all pairs (T, tT) for any act T of clock reading, and objective pressure p^*

---

[3] Only very special multivalued functions play a role in the theory of complex functions. For a definition of those functions as classes of pairs of complex numbers, see [5].

is the class of all pairs (P, p*P) for any instantaneous gas sample P—and this is what physicists have always meant by time and pressure—then t and p* are nothing but functions defined on the classes of clock readings and of gas samples, respectively. More generally, each fluent u, when introduced as a class of pairs (A, uA) for any element A of a class $\mathcal{Q}$, is simply what everyone calls a function on $\mathcal{Q}$. What then is new in this theory?"

The contention that t and p*, as here defined, are just what physicists have always meant by time and pressure is most reassuring since it is the very purpose of the theory of fluents to make precise the meaning of time, pressure, etc., and to develop exact schemes for the application of mathematics to those terms. From the literature it appears, however, that few scientists have ever bothered expressing that meaning articulately, and that those who did have called time a class of numbers and not a class of pairs (τ, $t\tau$). Their views were supported by mathematicians who referred to time as a variable, just as they referred to the letter x in x $+$ 1 $=$ 1 $+$ x. Moreover, although physicists refer to time and pressure as "variable quantities" and even as "variables," they never (except when thinking of their relations to other fluents, see 2 below) call them "functions." Scientists definitely reserve the latter term for the logarithmic function, for the trigonometric functions as tabulated in the sine and cosine tables, for the classes of pairs of numbers supplied by computing machines as solutions of differential equations, and the like. If t, p*, and any fluent u fall under the mathematicians' function concept, then the latter is blatantly at variance with the almost universal scientific usage; therefore I prefer to call the wider, comprehensive concept *functor*. It is important to realize that, between fluents and what most scientists call functions, there are conceptual as well as operative differences. The domain of fluents is extramathematical, that of functions is mathematical. Moreover, functions, as will become apparent in the next section, connect fluents just as numbers connect physical objects, and they are the only functors with this connective power. Whereas numbers and functions describe relations between objects and between fluents, one cannot, à la Pythagoras, reduce either physical objects to numbers or scientific fluents to functions. The function *log* is to the pressure p, roughly speaking, what the number 3 is to a yardstick. Reality should be clearly distinguished from mathematical ideas. The mere fact, that what on the object-number-level is a truism must be said (and even defended) on the fluent-function-level, is another symptom of the existing confusion about these matters, which vindicates the new theory.

2. Some physicists say: "Distance traveled by a falling object certainly is a function; e.g., it is a function of the time and a function of the speed. In fact, all fluents are functions."

But this remark is comparable to saying: "A certain man is a number; e.g., he is 55 years old and weighs 170 lb. All people are numbers."

3. Some statisticians say: "In the theory of probability, Kolmogorov, Neyman, Doob, Halmos, and others introduce random variables as functions namely, as functions on so-called fundamental probability sets. The concept of fluents is simply an extension of that idea to scientific variables, renamed fluents."

Examples of probability sets and random variables will clarify the relations between the latter and scientific fluents. Consider the class of the six possible outcomes of throwing a die $(1, 2, \cdots, 6)$ or the pair of possible outcomes of tossing a coin (H, T). Suppose one somehow associates with each of the (six or two) outcomes a non-negative number, called the *probability* of the outcome, in such a way that the (six or two) associated numbers have the sum 1. The sextuple or pair of outcomes in conjunction with that probability is called a *fundamental probability set*—briefly, f.p.s. Three examples follow.

F.P.S.1. (Model of an unbiased die.) One associates the probability $\frac{1}{6}$ with each outcome.

F.P.S.2. (Model of a die that is in a certain way biased in favor of 5 and 6.) One associates the probability $\frac{1}{8}$ with each of the outcomes 1, 2, 3, 4; and the probability $\frac{1}{4}$ with 5 and 6.

F.P.S.3. One associates any non-negative number, c, with H, and $1 - c$ with T; for instance, $\frac{1}{2}$ and $\frac{1}{2}$ in the model of an unbiased coin.

By a random variable, Kolmogorov means any functor whose domain is a f.p.s. Two random variables are regarded as equal if and only if the functors are equal and the probabilities on their domains are equal.

Example 1. The function assuming for each element of F.P.S.1 (that is, for each of the numbers $1, 2, \cdots 6$) that very number: the value 1 for 1; 2 for 2; $\cdots$ 6 for 6.

Example 2. The function assuming the value 3 for each even number belonging to F.P.S.1, and the value 0 for each odd number in that set.

Example 3. The same function as in Example 2 defined, however, on F.P.S.2.

Example 4. The function on F.P.S.2 assuming for each of the numbers 1, 2, 3, 4 the value $\frac{1}{8}$, and for 5 and 6 the value $\frac{1}{4}$, that is, the probability function of F.P.S.2. In fact, any probability function on any (finite) f.p.s. is a random variable in the sense of Kolmogorov.

Example 5. Any functor defined on F.P.S.3, that is, a functor assuming any value (say, 5) for H, and any value (say, -3) for T.

None of these so-called random variables is a scientific fluent—either a subjective or an objective fluent. Their domains do not consist of acts of observation, gas samples, members of a population or the like, nor is their value for an element of the domain determined either by observing that element or by meter reading or the like.

Conversely, the scientific fluents t, p^*, and the height h in a population are not random variables in the sense of Kolmogorov. There is no reasonable way of associating a probability with an act of observation or a gas sample or a member of a population.

A scientific fluent becomes what (in contrast to Kolmogorov's *probabilistic random variables*) might be called a *statistical random variable* [6] if a probability function is somehow defined on the class of its values; i.e., if the *range* of the fluent (rather than, as in the theories of Kolmogorov, Neyman, Doob, and Halmos, its *domain*) is a f.p.s. The class d of all pairs (D, dD) for any act D of throwing a die, where dD is the result of the act, becomes a statistical random variable if its range is, for instance, F.P.S.1; i.e., if the probability $\frac{1}{6}$ is associated with each outcome. Another example of a scientific fluent that becomes a statistical random variable is the class d_o of all pairs (D, d_oD) for any act D of throwing a particular die for which the class of possible outcomes is F.P.S.2. (The choice of this particular f.p.s. may be motivated by the relative frequencies of the outcomes in past experiences with that die.)

After this digression into three objections, it must be added (to complete the discussion of fluents and functions) that the confusion between them has been enhanced by a curious lacuna in the mathematical treatment of functions. The fathers of mathematical analysis created (or took over from their predecessors) the symbols *log*, *cos*, *arctan*, etc., for some important functions. They even introduced symbols (distortions of the letter r) for roots, but no comparable symbols for powers, even though powers are still more important than roots. Worst of all, the founders of analysis failed to introduce a symbol for a function of paramount importance—the identity function associating with any number that same number—in other words, for the class of all pairs (x, x) for any number x. This shortcoming in the symbolism of classical analysis is comparable in gravity with one precedent only—the lack of a symbol for zero in the arithmetic of antiquity.

Traditionally, the identity function is referred to as "the function x"—a procedure entailing rigmarole of the type "the function x assumes the value x for any number x." Moreover, for the sake of uniformity, even the operations with functions that do possess symbols have been adjusted to the unfortunate treatment of the identity and power functions; and, grotesquely, the functions *log* and *cos* are referred to as "the functions *log x* and *cos x*" in analogy to "the functions x and x^2." How keenly some mathematicians feel the difficulty, and how hard they struggle to overcome it, is shown by the following passage (and others) in a recently published book [7]:

> The function whose domain is the set of all real numbers and which has the value x^2 for x should have a briefer description. A particular way out of this particular situation is to agree that x is the identity function . . . in which case x^2 might reasonably be called the squaring function. The classical device is to use x^2 both for the function and for its value for x. A less confusing approach is to designate the squaring function by $x \to x^2$. This sort of notation is suggestive and is now coming into common use. It is not universal and the statement $(x \to x^2)(t) = t^2$ would require explanation. Finally it should be remarked that, although the arrow notation will undoubtedly be adopted as standard, the λ-conversion of A. Church has technical advantages. The square function might be written as $\lambda x: x^2$. No parentheses are necessary to prevent ambiguity.

In their attempts to fill the century-old gap, mathematicians thus try almost everything—everything except the simple idea of introducing a symbol for the identity function and establishing uniformity by adjusting operations with the power functions to the treatment of *log* and *cos*, instead of the other way around.

As early as 1944, I decided to rescue the identity function from its anonymity.[4] I use the letter j to denote the class of all pairs (x, x) for any number x. The value of j for 1 is 1—in a formula, $j1 = 1$ just as $log\ 1 = 0$. More generally, $jx = x$ for any x.

Accordingly,	is the class of all pairs
j^2	(x, x^2) for any x;
j^{-1}	(x, x^{-1}) or $\left(x, \dfrac{1}{x}\right)$ for any x $\neq$ 0;
$j^{\frac{1}{2}}$	(x, $x^{\frac{1}{2}}$) or (x, $\sqrt{x}$) for any x $\geq$ 0.

For instance,

$$j^2 3 = 3^2\ [=9];$$

$$j^{-1}(-3) = (-3)^{-1} = \frac{1}{-3}\left[= -\frac{1}{3}\right];$$

$$j^{\frac{1}{2}}9 = 9^{\frac{1}{2}} = \sqrt{9}\ [=3].$$

[4] See the author's "Algebra of Analysis," [8], and the 1955 edition of *Calculus. A Modern Approach* [3]. In earlier editions of *Calculus*, the identity function was denoted by *I*. Some mathematicians as well as nonmathematicians have recommended to me the symbol *id* for the identity function—a symbol that has various advantages but does not lend itself to the description of power functions as conveniently as does j in the symbols j^2, j^{-1}, etc.

In this way it is easy to deal with functions in their entirety, for instance, with sums and products of functions, such as

$$log + j \quad \text{and} \quad j^2 \cdot cos \quad \text{or} \quad log \cdot tan.$$

In symbolizing products, I never omit the dot (except in symbols such as $3j$ or πj^2 designating products whose first factors are scalar and are indicated by numerals), since mere juxtaposition will denote substitution, just as it does in the traditional symbol $log\ tan\ x$ for the function $log\ tan$, that is, the class of all pairs (x, $log\ tan$ x) in contrast to the class of all pairs (x, log x $\cdot tan$ x).   For instance, $cos\ j^2$ and $j^2\ cos$ are the results of substituting j^2 into cos, and cos into j^2, respectively, cos^2 being an alternative symbol for the latter.   For any function f, the result of substituting $16j$ into f is the class $f(16j)$ of all pairs (x, $f(16x)$) for any x.

The constant functions 0 and 1—the italicized numerals distinguish the constant functions from their values, the numbers 0 and 1—do not affect any function in addition and multiplication, respectively:

$$0 + f = f = f + 0 \quad \text{and} \quad 1 \cdot f = f = f \cdot 1 \quad \text{for any function } f.$$

Similarly, the identity function is neutral with regard to substitution:

$$jf = f = fj \quad \text{for any function } f.$$

This is a most important property of the function j which classical formulas cannot even express as long as the identity is referred to as "the function x."   Indeed, no one would understand the meaning of

$$x(f(x)) = f(x) = f(x(x)) \quad \text{for any function } f(x).$$

Actually, however, most traditional books simply omit this and some other important statements about substitution, the functional operation par excellence.   More generally, the lack of a symbol for the identity function has contributed to the channeling of analysis in additive-multiplicative studies at the expense of substitutive investigations, just as the lack of a symbol for zero had badly confined Greek arithmetic.

With regard to opposite elements, one can say

$$-f + f = f + -f \subseteq 0;$$
$$\frac{1}{f} \cdot f = f \cdot \frac{1}{f} \subseteq 1;$$
$$f^*f \subseteq j, \quad ff^* \subseteq j,$$

where $\subseteq$ means "is a *restriction* of," and f^* is called the *inverse* of f. For instance, $(j^3)^* = j^{\frac{1}{3}}$.

The domain of $-f$ coincides with that of f. The domain of $1/f$ is a part of that of f; the two coincide if f does not assume the value 0. The domain of f^* is a part of the range of f; the two coincide if f is monotonic (i.e., increasing or decreasing).

FUNCTIONAL CONNECTION, A SUBSTITUTIVE ANALOGUE OF MENSURATION

Historically, connections of fluents by functions were first established in geometry—in physical geometry dealing with material cubes, circles, etc.[5] For instance, the side in feet of a cube is the third root of the volume in cubic feet of that cube—in symbols,

$$sQ = \sqrt[3]{vQ} \quad \text{for any cube Q,}$$

and, similarly,

$$aC = \pi(rC)^2 \quad \text{for any circle C.}$$

Traditionally, these statements are expressed, without any reference to cubes and circles, in formulas connecting fluents and not numbers:

$$s = \sqrt[3]{v} \quad \text{and} \quad a = \pi r^2.$$

The first connects

s, the class of all pairs (Q, sQ) for any cube Q

with

v, the class of all pairs (Q, vQ) for any cube Q.

The connecting function is the cubic root, $\sqrt[3]{\ }$. Similarly, a is connected with r by πj^2, the function assuming for any x the value πx^2.

In the domain of instantaneous gas samples at one and the same temperature, say at 100°, Boyle found that the volume v^* (in a proper unit) is connected with the pressure p^* by

$$v^*G = \frac{1}{p^*G} \text{ for any sample G at } 100° \text{—briefly, } v^* = \frac{1}{p^*}.$$

The brief form is the one adopted by physicists, who (like geometers) invariably dispense with references to the elements of the domains of fluents. Mathematicians, on the other hand, lacking symbols for power functions, write $x^{-1} = 1/x$ and, accordingly, express the connection of the secant with the cosine function by writing

[5] In contrast, postulational geometry, initiated by Euclid, is the system of conclusions that can be drawn from assumptions about points, lines, etc., without analyzing the nature of those objects. The assumptions reflect, in idealized form, observations made on corresponding physical objects.

$$sec \text{ x} = \frac{1}{cos \text{ x}}, \text{ and not simply } sec = \frac{1}{cos}.$$

The latter, of course, is the natural counterpart of

$$j^{-1} = \frac{1}{j} \quad \text{and} \quad v^* = \frac{1}{p^*}.$$

Galileo's laws concerning falling objects connect fluents with unequal domains: t, the class of all pairs (T, tT) for any act T of reading a timer that is calibrated in seconds and was set going when a certain object was dropped; and s, the class of all pairs (S, sS) for any act S of reading the mark opposite the falling object on a vertical scale, calibrated in feet. The traditional formula, $s = 16t^2$, expresses that

$$sS = 16(tT)^2 \text{ for any two simultaneous acts T and S.}$$

The connection of speed with time, $v = 32t$, is also based on values for simultaneous acts.[6]

The results of substituting fluents into functions, for instance, $\sqrt[3]{v}$, s^3, $16t^2$, might be called *denominate functions* just as ⅓ yd, 3 ft, and 16 oz are called denominate numbers. Arithmetic deals with "pure," and not with denominate numbers, and analysis deals with "pure," and not denominate functions—with the cubic root, $\sqrt[3]{\ }$ or $j^{⅓}$, with j^3 and $16j^2$, and not with the cubic root of volume or the like.

Just as yd/ft = 3 is an alternative way of writing 1 yd = 3 ft,

I will write	as an alter- native for	or for	in the domain of
$v /\!/ s = j^3$	$v = j^3 s$	$v = s^3$	} cubes
$s /\!/ v = j^{⅓}$	$s = j^{⅓}v$	$s = \sqrt[3]{v}$	
$a /\!/ r = \pi j^2$	$a = \pi j^2 r$	$a = \pi r^2$	circles
$s /\!/ t = 16j^2$	$s = 16j^2 t$	$s = 16t^2$	} falling
$v /\!/ t = 32j$	$v = 32jt$	$v = 32t.$	} bodies

(Of course, $jt = t$, just as $jf = f$ for any function f.) It will be noted that, for cubes,

(1) $v /\!/ s = j^3$ and $s /\!/ v = j^{⅓}$,   where $j^3 j^{⅓} = j$ (substitution!),

just as

---

[6] This is the second passage in this paper that demonstrates the necessity of references to the domains of fluents and to their (in general extramathematical) elements. The first passage was the distinction between statistical and probabilistic random variables on p. 113.

$$yd/ft = 3 \quad \text{and} \quad ft/yd = \tfrac{1}{3}, \qquad \text{where } 3 \cdot \tfrac{1}{3} = 1 \text{ (multiplication!)};$$

and that for falling objects

$$(2) \quad s \,//\, t = 16j^2, \quad t \,//\, v = \tfrac{1}{32}j, \quad s \,//\, v = \tfrac{1}{64}j^2,$$

$$\text{where } \tfrac{1}{64}j^2 = 16j^2(\tfrac{1}{32}j) \text{ (substitution!)},$$

just as

$$yd/ft = 3, \quad ft/in = 12, \quad yd/in = 36,$$

$$\text{where } 36 = 3 \cdot 12 \text{ (multiplication!)}.$$

If a fluent is functionally connected with another fluent, the latter is often called *independent*, the former, *dependent*. It should, of course, be added *in the connection under consideration*, since, for instance, s is independent in the connection $v = s^3$, and dependent in the connection $s = \sqrt[3]{v}$.

If many fluents are connected with one and the same fluent, then that common independent fluent plays a role comparable to that of the unit in mensuration and of the origin in graduation. In many fields, the time lends itself to this role. The connecting functions, the *histories* of the fluents, correspond to the measures and degrees of objects.

In defining functional connections of fluents in general, a difficulty arises. Let u and v be any two fluents with the domains $\mathcal{C}$ and $\mathcal{B}$, respectively; i.e.,

u is the class of all pairs (A, uA) for any A belonging to $\mathcal{C}$;

v is the class of all pairs (B, vB) for any B belonging to $\mathcal{B}$.

How can the function j^2 or, in fact, any function f connect u with v? Obviously, some numbers uA must be the values assumed by j^2 or f for some numbers vB. But (unless both u and v are constant fluents, say, of values 25 and 5, respectively) certainly not *all* numbers uA are the squares of *all* numbers vB. *Which* values of u, then, are the values of j^2 or of f assumed for *which* values of v? In general, one cannot say that f connects the values of u and v for the *same* element of the domains; $\mathcal{C}$ and $\mathcal{B}$ need not have any element in common (example: the domains of Galileo's s and t). Nor can one in general say that f connects the values of u and v for *simultaneous* elements of their domains; the concept of simultaneity may be inapplicable to the elements of $\mathcal{C}$ and $\mathcal{B}$ (example: $\mathcal{C} = \mathcal{B} = $ class of all cubes). Without further data, the questions: Is $u = v^2$? and Is $u = fv$? are incomplete and unanswerable just as is the question in the realm of objects: Is A = 3B?

In order to make the questions complete, principles of comparing the objects and of pairing the domains must be given. The pairing of $\mathfrak{a}$ and $\mathfrak{B}$ (the domains of u and v) can be achieved as follows. Let $\mathfrak{B} \times \mathfrak{a}$ denote the class of all ordered pairs (B, A) such that A belongs to $\mathfrak{a}$, and B to $\mathfrak{B}$. Let Π be a subclass of $\mathfrak{B} \times \mathfrak{a}$, that is, a class of such pairs (B, A). I will say that u is connected with v by j^2 or f relative to Π, and I will write

$$u = v^2 \text{ (rel. } \Pi) \qquad \text{and} \qquad u = fv \text{ (rel. } \Pi)$$

if and only if, for any pair (B, A) belonging to Π, the ordered pair of numbers (vB, uA) belongs to j^2 or to f, respectively; in other words, if

$$uA = (vB)^2 \quad \text{or} \quad uA = f(vB) \qquad \text{for each pair } (B, A) \text{ belonging to } \Pi.$$

In terms of pure rather than denominate functions, the condition can be expressed by writing

$$u \,/\!/\, v = j^2 \text{ (rel. } \Pi) \qquad \text{or} \qquad u \,/\!/\, v = f \text{ (rel. } \Pi).$$

If one writes $a = s^2$ or $v^* = fp^*$ in the domains of squares Q and of gas samples G, respectively, then one tacitly presupposes that these formulas will be understood relative to the class I of identical elements of the respective domains, i.e., the class of all pairs (Q, Q) and that of all (G, G). In the second case, f can be identified with j^{-1}. Similarly, the formula $sec = 1/cos$ is meant relative to the class of all pairs (x, x) of equal numbers, i.e., relative to the function j. The physical law $s = 16t^2$ is based tacitly on the choice of Galileo's class Γ of all pairs (T, S) of *simultaneous* acts of reading timers and meters.

Whereas in physics and mathematics practically all functional connections of functors are based on pairings of their domains by either identity or simultaneity, biologists and sociologists use a great variety of principles; they realize that in each correlation study they have to describe the principle of pairing that they adopt. Let $\mathfrak{M}$ denote the male population of the U. S., and h the height in inches on the domain $\mathfrak{M}$. In various studies, sociologists consider various subclasses of $\mathfrak{M} \times \mathfrak{M}$; for instance, the class Π' of all pairs (M, M'), where M' is the father of M, or the class Π'' of all pairs (M, M''), where M'' is the twin brother of M (if M has a twin brother). Accordingly, they study the class of all pairs of numbers (hM, hM') or the class of all pairs (hM, hM'').

It is important to realize that the class of pairs relative to which two functors are functionally connected may lack the one-to-one character that the classes I, Γ, and Π'' happen to possess. The aforementioned class Π' includes pairs whose second members are the same whereas the first members are not. So does the class j^2 of all pairs (y, x) such that x = y^2, relative to which the fluent j^3 is the ⅔th power of the fluent j^4; in a formula,

$$j^3 = j^{3/2}j^4 \text{ (rel. } j^2).$$

Indeed, for each pair (y, x) belonging to j^2 (that is, such that x = y^2), the pair $(j^4y, j^3x) = (y^4, x^3) = (y^4, y^6)$ belongs to the function $j^{3/2}$. Incidentally, relative to j, the fluent j^3 is not a function of the fluent j^4 at all. If there were a function g such that $j^3 = gj^4$ (rel. j), then, for each pair (y, x) belonging to j (that is, such that x = y), the pair $(j^4y, j^3x) = (y^4, x^3) = (y^4, y^3)$ would belong to g. But there is no function to which, e.g., both $(2^4, 2^3)$ and $((-2)^4, (-2)^3)$ belong, since these pairs have equal first, and unequal second, members.

Functors may also be connected relative to classes including pairs with equal first, and unequal second, members such as the class II of all pairs (y, x) where x^2 = y. For instance,

$$j^{24} = j^4j^3 \text{ (rel. II)},$$

whereas j^{24} is the 8th power of j^3 (rel. j).

It is in applying functions to science and geometry that the paramount importance of their one-valuedness becomes obvious. Mathematicians defining a function as the association of one *or more* numbers with each element of a class of numbers [9] (i.e., as a class of pairs of numbers without restrictions) imply that every fluent is a function of every other fluent (relative to every pairing of their domains) and thus divest the function concept of any significance.

Generalizing Implication (2), one obtains the following analogue to the first formal property of ratios:

I. *Substitutive Transitivity.* If $u = fv$ (rel. II) and $v = gw$ (rel. P), then $u = fgw$ (rel. IIP).

Here, P is a subclass of $\mathcal{C} \times \mathcal{B}$, where $\mathcal{C}$ is the domain of w; and IIP is the class of all pairs (C, A) such that A belongs to $\mathcal{A}$ and C belongs to $\mathcal{C}$, and that there exists an element B of $\mathcal{B}$ for which (B, A) belongs to II and (C, B) belongs to P. The denominate fluent fgw may be taken either as $f(gw)$ (the result of substituting the fluent gw into f) or as $(fg)w$ (the result of substituting w into fg). The two substitutions have the same result.

In order to generalize Implication (1), let II* denote the class of all pairs (A, B) such that (B, A) belongs to II. Then one obtains:

II. *Inversive Asymmetry.* If $u = fv$ (rel. II), then $v = f^*u$ (rel. II*), f^* being the inverse function of f.

This law is an analogue of the reciprocal asymmetry in full ratio classes (see p. 105) rather than in positive ratio classes.

III. *Identical Reflexivity.* $u = u$ (rel. I).

IV. *Contravariance by Inversion.* If $u = fv$ (rel. II) and $v' = hv$ (rel. Σ) then $u = fh*v'$ (rel. $\Pi\Sigma$*).

In pure rather than denominate form, the preceding laws read:

I'. If $u // v = f$ (rel. II) and $v // w = g$ (rel. P), then $u // w = fg$ (rel. ΠP).

II'. If $u // v = f$ (rel. II), then $v // u = f*$ (rel. II*).

III'. $u // u = j$ (rel. I).

IV'. If $u // v = f$ (rel. II) and $v' // v = h$ (rel. Σ), then $u // v' = fh*$ (rel. $\Pi\Sigma$*).

Clearly, these laws may be restated without reference to the symbols f, g, and h.

I''. $u // w$ (rel. ΠP) $= (u // v)$ (rel. II)$(v // w)$ (rel. P) (substitution!).

II''. $v // u$ (rel. II*) $= [u // v$ (rel. II)]*.

The formulas from Law I' on equate pure functions. If, in the domain of squares, l and p are the side and the perimeter (in the same unit), then $p^2 // l = 16j^2$, just as for falling objects $s // t = 16j^2$. Consequently, one may write in analogy to the formulas at the end of the section on p. 103:

$$s // t = p^2 // l = \tfrac{1}{2}p^2 // l + 8j^2 = \tfrac{1}{2}(s // t + p^2 // l).$$

Of particular interest are the effects of changes of the units in which fluents are measured on the functions connecting the fluents. Suppose, for instance, that, relative to a certain pairing of the domains,

$$h/\text{in} = f(w/\text{oz}).$$

It follows that $12h/\text{ft} = f(16w/\text{lb})$, or

$$h/\text{ft} = \tfrac{1}{12}f(16w/\text{lb}).$$

Thus, in pure form,

$$(h/\text{in}) // (w/\text{oz}) = f \text{ implies } (h/\text{ft}) // (w/\text{lb}) = \tfrac{1}{12}f(16j).$$

Generalizations are left to the reader.

OPERATOR ACTION, AN ANALOGUE OF MENSURATION

Knowing the meaning of the number *log* x for any positive number x, one can define the function *log* as the class of all pairs (x, *log* x) for any x > 0. Similarly, knowing the meaning of the function $\mathbf{D}f$ (the derivative of f) for any differentiable function f, one can define the operator $\mathbf{D}$ as the class of all pairs $(f, \mathbf{D}f)$ for any differentiable function f. The class includes, for instance, the pairs (sin, cos) and $(j^3, 3j^2)$, since $\mathbf{D}\ sin = cos$ and $\mathbf{D}j^3 = 3j^2$. Traditionally, this is expressed by saying that the functions $cos\ x$ and $3x^2$ are the derivatives of the functions $sin\ x$ and x^3. It is fortunate that no one calls their derivatives $cos\ y$ and $3y^2$. Yet an analogous procedure is customary with regard to other operators, in particular, to the Laplace transform $\mathbf{L}$. (It will be noted that all operators are herein denoted by letters in bold face.) Indeed, the fact that [10],

$$\mathbf{L}j^3 = 3j^{-4} \quad \text{and} \quad \mathbf{L}\ sin = \frac{1}{j^2 + 1}$$

is traditionally expressed by saying that the Laplace transforms of the functions t^3 and $sin\ t$ are the functions $3s^{-4}$ and $1/(s^2 + 1)$. Some of the difficulties in the symbolism of the operator calculus are artificially created by the lack of a symbol for the identity function. In fact, it is in the operator theory that the traditional anonymity of that function has some of its most obnoxious consequences.

Generalizing $\mathbf{D}$ and $\mathbf{L}$, one may define an *operator* as the class of pairs of functions resulting from the association of a function with each function belonging to a certain class, called the *domain* of the operator.

Operators are acted upon by operators just as functions can be substituted into functions. For instance, j^3 may be substituted into log, and one finds

$$log\ j^3 = 3\ log, \text{ that is, } log\ \mathrm{x}^3 = 3\ log\ \mathrm{x} \text{ for any } \mathrm{x} > 0.$$

It follows that

$$log\ (j^3)^3 = 3\ log\ j^3 = 3 \cdot 3\ log = 9\ log.$$

Similarly, $\mathbf{D}$ may be acted upon by $\mathbf{L}$, and one finds

(3) $\mathbf{LD} = j \cdot \mathbf{L}$, that is, $\mathbf{LD}f = j \cdot \mathbf{L}f$ for any differentiable function f

in dom $\mathbf{L}$ such that $f0 = 0$.

It follows that

(4) $\mathbf{LD}^2 = j \cdot \mathbf{LD} = j^2 \cdot \mathbf{L}$ for any twice differentiable function f such

that $f0 = \mathbf{D}f0 = 0$.

More generally, functions lend themselves to the substitution of fluents. Similarly, operators act upon what I will call *developments*. A development results from the association of a function with each element of a class (called the *domain* of the development). If the domain consists of functions, the development is an operator. From the enormous variety of scientific developments, I will here select three examples.

Example 1. Consider the class of all motions of a single particle. Each motion gives rise to fluents such as the position s and the velocity v. For each motion one may associate with the fluent s its history $\mathbf{S}s$, that is, the function $s \parallel t$ connecting s with the time t. The resulting development $\mathbf{S}$ is the class of all pairs

$$(s, \mathbf{S}s) = (s, s \parallel t) \text{ for any fluent } s \text{ (position during a motion).}$$

Similarly, a development $\mathbf{V}$ may be defined as the class of all pairs

$$(v, \mathbf{V}v) = (v, v \parallel t) \text{ for any fluent } v \text{ (velocity during a motion).}$$

According to classical mechanics, relative to the pairing by identity, $\mathbf{V}$ is connected with $\mathbf{S}$ by the operator $\mathbf{D}$:

$$\mathbf{V} = \mathbf{DS}, \text{ that is, } \mathbf{V}v = \mathbf{DS}s \text{ for any pair } (s, v) \text{ pertaining to the same motion.}$$

Instead, one can say $v \parallel t = \mathbf{D}(s \parallel t)$, or, in denominate form,

$$\text{if } s = ft, \text{ then } v = \mathbf{D}ft.$$

Under certain dynamical conditions, classical mechanics predicts the function f. If an elastic force acts on the particle, then, under certain initial conditions, the predicted function is sin; that is to say, $s \parallel t = sin$ or $s = sin\, t$, wherefore, in view of $\mathbf{D}\, sin = cos$,

$$v \parallel t = cos \qquad \text{or} \qquad v = cos\, t.$$

$\mathbf{DS}$, the derivative of the development $\mathbf{S}$, is what might be called a denominate operator. $\mathbf{V} = \mathbf{DS}$ may be written in "pure" form: $\mathbf{V} /\!/\!/ \mathbf{S} = \mathbf{D}$. If $\mathbf{A}$ is the acceleration development, then $\mathbf{A} /\!/\!/ \mathbf{V} = \mathbf{D}$. In analogy to the transitivity laws:

I. $\mathbf{A} = \mathbf{DV}$ and $\mathbf{V} = \mathbf{DS}$ imply $\mathbf{A} = \mathbf{DDS} = \mathbf{D}^2\mathbf{S}$.
I'. $\mathbf{A} /\!/\!/ \mathbf{V} = \mathbf{D}$ and $\mathbf{V} /\!/\!/ \mathbf{S} = \mathbf{D}$ imply $\mathbf{A} /\!/\!/ \mathbf{S} = \mathbf{DD} = \mathbf{D}^2$.

Example 2. Consider an oscillatory mechanical or electric system, determined by three numbers a, b, c, characteristic of mass, resistance, and elasticity or their electrical counterparts. For the sake of simplicity, all that follows is based on the assumption that the system is at rest when the observation begins. For each process, the applied (mechanical or electromotive) force p is a fluent whose value for any act of observation is a number. If with each such fluent p its history $\mathbf{P}p = p \parallel t$ is associated, the result is a development $\mathbf{P}$. Each input p elicits from the system a response q, and there is a development $\mathbf{Q}$, the class of all pairs $(q, q \parallel t)$. The development $\mathbf{P}$ can be shown to be connected with $\mathbf{Q}$ by the operator $a\mathbf{D}^2 + b\mathbf{D} + c$. Equating the Laplace transforms of $\mathbf{P}$ and $(a\mathbf{D}^2 + b\mathbf{D} + c)\mathbf{Q}$, and using (3) and (4), one readily finds

$$\frac{1}{aj^2 + bj + c} \cdot \mathbf{LP} = \mathbf{LQ} \qquad \text{or} \qquad \mathbf{Q} = \mathbf{L}^{-1}\left(\frac{1}{aj^2 + bj + c} \cdot \mathbf{L}\right)\mathbf{P}.$$

In "pure" form:

$$\mathbf{P} /\!/\!/ \mathbf{Q} = a\mathbf{D}^2 + b\mathbf{D} + c \text{ implies } \mathbf{Q} /\!/\!/ \mathbf{P} = \mathbf{L}^{-1}\left(\frac{1}{aj^2 + bj + c} \cdot \mathbf{L}\right).$$

Example 3. In the quantum-mechanical treatment of a single particle moving along a straight line, the observables q (coordinate) and p (momentum), contrary to what one often reads, are not operators. They are essentially the same fluents as s and v (position and velocity) in the classical treatment of the problem, as described in Example 1: two classes of pairs (act, result). For instance, q is the class of pairs (Q, qQ) for any act Q of observing the position.[7] Under certain dynamical conditions, quantum mechanics associates, in each state S of the particle, a function with q and another function with p, such that the integrals from $-\infty$ to ∞ of the functions are 1. Hence the functions may be interpreted as probability densities and thereby make the fluents p and q statistical random variables (see p. 113). Actually—but this is a technicality—the functions, traditionally denoted by ψs and ϕs, which, on the basis of the dynamical assumptions, by paper-and-pencil operations, are associated with q and p are complex-valued, and the said probability densities are the squares of their absolute values:

$$|\psi s|^2 = \psi s \cdot \psi s^* \qquad \text{and} \qquad |\phi s|^2 = \phi s \cdot \phi s^*.$$

The quantum-mechanically expected value of q in the state S is the (real) number

$$\bar{q}S = \int_{-\infty}^{\infty} (j \cdot |\psi s|^2) = \int_{-\infty}^{\infty} (j \cdot \psi s \cdot \psi s^*) \text{ for any state S.}$$

The class of all pairs $(S, \bar{q}S)$ is a fluent. More generally, for any function f, the expected value of the fluent fq in the state S is

$$\overline{fq}S = \int_{-\infty}^{\infty} (f \cdot |\psi s|^2) \qquad \text{for any state S.}$$

Other fluents define the quantum-mechanically expected values of other observable fluents, e.g.,

$$\bar{p}S = \int_{-\infty}^{\infty} \left(\frac{h}{2\pi i} D\psi s \cdot \psi s \right). \quad \text{But also } \bar{p}S = \int_{-\infty}^{\infty} (j \cdot |\phi s|^2).$$

It follows that an important operator **F** (essentially the Fourier transform, a complex analogue of the Laplace transform) connects ϕs with ψs:

$$\phi s = \mathbf{F}\psi s, \text{ for any state S; briefly } \phi = \mathbf{F}\psi.$$

Here, the development ϕ is the class of all pairs $(S, \phi s)$. In analogy to the asymmetry laws:

II. $\phi = \mathbf{F}\psi$ implies $\psi = \mathbf{F}^*\phi$, where the operator $\mathbf{F}^*$ is the inverse to $\mathbf{F}$.

In order to compare the quantum-mechanical predictions (i.e., the expected values of the fluents) with their observed values, one must somehow coordinate acts of observing position and momentum with the states of the particle. Here it must suffice to say that *simultaneous* acts Q and P are associated with one and the *same* state S in comparing qQ with $\bar{q}S$, and pP with $\bar{p}S$; and that the *same* act Q is used in comparing qQ with $\bar{q}S$, and fqQ with $\overline{fq}S$. So far, quantum mechanics, just as classical me-

---

[7] This treatment of the observables is in line with a remark made in the course of the *Symposium on Measurement* by Prof. Philipp Frank to the effect that the ultimate observations are meter readings in quantum mechanics as well as in classical mechanics.

chanics, has paired the domains of observable fluents by simultaneity and identity only.[8]

With regard to the values qQ and pP for simultaneous acts Q and P, quantum mechanics stipulates that the greater the likelihood of either being close to its expected value, the smaller is the corresponding likelihood for the other. For instance, if qQ is likely to be close to $\bar{q}S$, then it is not likely that pP is close to pS. Yet pS is the expected value of p in the state S, wherefore the likelihood of pP being close to any definite number $\neq pS$ is even smaller.

MULTIPLE MENSURATION AND ITS ANALOGUES

The discussion of the formal aspects of mensuration would be incomplete without at least a brief mention of analogues dealing with mixtures, spatial displacements, and the like, represented by ordered systems of numbers. In each case, a class $\mathcal{C}$ is present whose elements can be compared and combined. Postulates (a), (b), (c), (d*), (e*), and (f) are satisfied. There are certain subclasses—"rays"—each of which satisfies Archimedes' postulate (g). They come in pairs of opposite rays. Each pair, in conjunction with a nil class, constitutes a full ratio class or "line." The nil classes of all those lines coincide. In the usual way, one can define the dimension as the number of independent lines in $\mathcal{C}$. Binary mixtures and displacements in the plane constitute two-dimensional classes, where each element A has a "binary ratio" to any ordered pair of independent elements (B_1, B_2). The binary ratio is an ordered pair of numbers (p_1, p_2). This connection may be expressed:

in denominate form: $A = p_1 B_1 + p_2 B_2$;
or in pure form: $A/(B_1, B_2) = (p_1, p_2)$.

In their pure form, binary ratios are equated to elements of a pure Cartesian vector plane, whose points are defined as ordered pairs of numbers and are added componentwise.

The analogue to the transitivity laws in pure form reads as follows:

I. If $A/(B_1, B_2) = (p_1, p_2)$, $B_1/(C_1, C_2) = (q_{11}, q_{12})$, and $B_2/(C_1, C_2) = (q_{21}, q_{22})$, then $A/(C_1, C_2) = (p_1 q_{11} + p_2 q_{21}, p_1 q_{12} + p_2 q_{22})$.

By the use of matrices, the analogy to mensuration can easily be extended to connections of objects with n-tuples of objects.

In the realm of fluents, the analogues of multiple mensuration are connections of a fluent with several other fluents by functions of several places, such as the sum and the product (in contrast to which functions

---

[8] If time were quantized, other pairings would become equally natural, e.g., the pairing of acts in consecutive instants and the pairing of the corresponding values of the observables.

such as *log* and j^2 are called one-place functions). For instance, in the domain of instantaneous gas samples, the temperature t is a function of the pressure p and the volume v; i.e.,

$$t\mathrm{G} = F(p\mathrm{G}, v\mathrm{G}) \text{ for any gas sample G, briefly, } t = F(p, v).$$

As the former formula shows, the coordination of the domains (relative to which F connects t with p and v) is the identity. For ideal gases, measured in proper units, Boyle identified F with the product function P, whose value for any pair (x, y) is $P(\mathrm{x}, \mathrm{y}) = \mathrm{x} \cdot \mathrm{y}$. Hence $t = P(p, v)$ $= p \cdot v$. Instead of in terms of "denominate" two-place functions, the law may be expressed in the pure form

$$t \mathbin{/\!/} (p, v) = P \text{ (relative to coordination by identity)},$$

where the connection of t with the pair (p, v) is equated to the two-place function P. The analogues of the transitivity laws read:

I. If $u = F(v_1, v_2)$, $v_1 = G_1(w_1, w_2)$, and $v_2 = G_2(w_1, w_2)$, then $u = F(G_1, G_2)(w_1, w_2) = F(G_1(w_1, w_2), G_2(w_1, w_2))$.

I'. If $u \mathbin{/\!/} (v_1, v_2) = F$, $v_1 \mathbin{/\!/} (w_1, w_2) = G_1$, and $v_2 \mathbin{/\!/} (w_1, w_2) = G_2$, then $u \mathbin{/\!/} (w_1, w_2) = F(G_1, G_2)$.

I''. $u \mathbin{/\!/} (w_1, w_2) = u \mathbin{/\!/} (v_1, v_2)(v_1 \mathbin{/\!/} (w_1, w_2), v_2 \mathbin{/\!/} (w_1, w_2))$ (substitution!).

Here, for the sake of simplicity, the references to the coordination of the domains have been omitted.

$F(G_1, G_2)$ is the two-place function which, for any (x, y) assumes the value $F(G_1(\mathrm{x}, \mathrm{y}), G_2(\mathrm{x}, \mathrm{y}))$. Thus the realm of functors that may be connected by two-place functions includes, in particular, two-place functions with the identity pairing of their domains. It also includes one-place functions with the identity pairing. For instance, $P(j^2, j^3) = j^5$.

Little use has so far been made of two-place-operators associating a function with any ordered pair of functions.

CONCLUSION

It thus appears that mensuration is the first step on a long road. The general problem is to interrelate physical (extramathematical) observables by mathematical (extraphysical) connectives. Originally, the very definitions of those mathematical concepts (number, function, operator) were inspired by relations observed within various phases of the external world (objects, fluents, developments). Subsequently, the mathematical concepts became objects of extensive mathematical theories (number theory, analysis, operator theory)for their own sake.

A hierarchy of mathematical concepts evolves, which has herein been reflected in typographical distinctions: references to numbers are printed in roman type; functions are denoted in italics; operators, in bold face letters. Functions are certain classes of pairs of numbers; operators are certain classes of pairs of functions; functions of several places fit into the picture. Without stretching the imagination, one can venture three predictions:

1. Deeper insight into the scientific and sociological universe will reveal relations (showing traces of the formal aspects of mensuration) whose description will require still higher connectives in that hierarchy.

2. Those higher connectives will be of sufficient intrinsic interest to prompt the development of mathematical theories of higher order.

3. The very hierarchy of those concepts will become the topic of mathematical theories of a new type.

So far, at each stage, the connectives have been applicable to themselves, too: numbers have ratios to other numbers just as objects have to some other objects; functions are functions of other functions just as fluents are of some other fluents; operators are operators on other operators just as developments are on certain other developments.

The application of mathematical connectives to scientific material has given rise to mongrel concepts: denominate numbers such as 3 ft; denominate functions such as the logarithm of the pressure; denominate operators such as the Laplace transform of a force history. As to which are preferable—traditional formulas including denominate connectives or equalities of "pure" connectives to which the results of pure mathematics are automatically applicable—this is a matter of taste. But the issues should not be confused by lacunas in the mathematical symbolism such as the lack of a numeral for zero or a symbol for the identity function.

Nor should it be ignored that numbers, functions, and operators possess connective powers which other objects, fluents, and developments lack. One can count 3 ft, but one cannot determine the footage of 3. There is a logarithm of the pressure, but there is no pressure of the logarithm. A force history has a Laplace transform, but a Laplace transform has no force history. This is why numbers, functions, and operators occur in all branches of science as well as in mathematics, whereas yards, pressure, and force histories play central roles in certain branches of science but are altogether absent from other scientific investigations as well as from pure mathematics. It seems to me that a clear separation of the mathematical connectives from the scientific objects that they connect—as it were, a distinction between mind and matter—would clarify those numerous methods of applied mathematics that are analogues and generalizations of mensuration.

REFERENCES

1. H. V. Helmholtz, "Zählen und Messen erkenntnis—theoretisch betrachtet," in *Philosophische Aufsätze Eduard Zeller gewidmet,* Leipzig, 1887. Reprinted in *Gesammelte Abhandlungen,* Vol. 3, 1895, pp. 356–391.
2. A. Tarski, *Introduction to Logic,* New York, Oxford University Press, 1941, p. 4.
3. Karl Menger, *Calculus. A Modern Approach,* Boston, Ginn & Company, 1955, Chapter VII. (The first presentation of the definition and theory of "variables as studied in science" is included in Chapter VII, Illinois Institute of Technology edition, Chicago, 1952).
4. ———, "The Idea of Variable and Function," *Proc. Natl. Acad. Sci.,* **39,** 1953, pp. 956–961. "On Variables in Mathematics and in Natural Science," *Br. J. Phil. Sci.,* **5,** 1954, pp. 134–142.
5. ———, "A Simple Definition of Analytic Functions and General Multi-Functions," *Proc. Natl. Acad. Sci.,* **40,** 1954, pp. 819–821.
6. ———, "Random Variables and the General Theory of Variables," *Proc. Third Berkeley Symposium on Math. Stat. and Prob.,* **2,** 1954, pp. 215–231.
7. J. L. Kelley, *General Topology,* New York, D. Van Nostrand Co., 1955.
8. Karl Menger, "Algebra of Analysis," *Notre Dame Math. Lect.,* **3,** 1944.
9. A. A. Albert, *College Algebra,* New York, McGraw-Hill Book Co., 1946, p. 180ff.
10. See [2], 1955, p. 271ff. and p. 322.

6

MEASUREMENT, EMPIRICAL MEANINGFULNESS, AND THREE-VALUED LOGIC[1]

Patrick Suppes

ASSOCIATE PROFESSOR OF PHILOSOPHY
STANFORD UNIVERSITY

INTRODUCTION

The predominant current opinion appears to be that it is scarcely possible to set up criteria of empirical meaningfulness for individual statements. What is required, it is said, is an analysis of theories taken as a whole. There is even some skepticism regarding this, and it has been romantically suggested that the entire fabric of experience and language must be considered and taken into account in any construction of general categories of meaning or analyticity. What I have to say makes no contribution to the attempt to find a general criterion of meaning applicable to arbitrary statements. Rather I am concerned to exemplify a general method that will yield specific positive criteria for specific branches of science.

A brief analysis of two simple examples will indicate the sort of thing I have in mind. Consider the statement:

[1] This research was supported in part by the Group Psychology Branch of the Office of Naval Research. I am indebted to G. Kreisel for several helpful comments on an earlier draft of this article. [*Editorial Note:* This paper was separately invited and was not delivered at the Symposium on Measurement.]

(i)   *The mass of the sun is greater than* 10^6.

If a physicist were asked if (i) is true or false, he would most likely reply that it depends on what unit of mass is implicitly understood in uttering (i). On the other hand, if we were to ask him about the truth of the sentence:

(ii)   *The mass of the sun is at least ten times greater than that of the earth,*

he would, without any reservation about units of measurement, state that (ii) is true, and perhaps even add that its truth is known to every schoolboy. Now my main point is that we may insist that our systematic language of physics (or of any other empirical science) has no hidden references to units of measurement. The numerals occurring in the language are understood to be designating "pure" numbers. An excellent example of a physical treatise written without reference to units is provided by the first two books of Newton's *Principia*. (Units are introduced in the consideration of data in Book III, and occasionally in examples in the earlier books.) Newton avoids any commitment to units of measurement by speaking of one quantity being proportional to another or standing in a certain ratio to it. Thus he formulates his famous second law of motion:

The change of motion is proportional to the motive force impressed; and is made in the direction of the right line in which that force is impressed. (Cajori edition, p. 13.)

Systematic reasons for adopting Newton's viewpoint as the fundamental one are given in later sections. My only concern at the moment is to establish that adoption of this viewpoint does not represent a gross violation of the use of physical concepts and language by physicists. It seems obvious that, in *using* a unitless language, we would not find occasion to use (i), for there would be no conceivable way of establishing its truth or falsity, either by empirical observation or logical argument. In contrast, (ii) would be acceptable. Yet it is difficult to see how to develop a simple and natural syntactical or semantical criterion within, say, a formal language for expressing the results of measurements of mass, which would rule out sentences like (i) and admit sentences like (ii). The central purpose of this paper is to explore some of the possibilities for classifying as meaningless well-formed sentences like (i), or, more exactly, the analogues of (i) in a formalized language. Formalization of a certain portion of the unitless language of physicists is not absolutely necessary for expressing the ideas I want to put forth, but it is essential to a clear working out of details. Moreover, the exact formal construction seems to pose some interesting problems which could scarcely be stated for a natural language. In the final section, the possibility is explored of interpreting this formalized language in terms of a three-valued logic of truth, falsity, and meaninglessness.

INVARIANCE AND MEANINGFULNESS

In connection with any measured property of an object, or set of objects, it may be asked how unique is the number assigned to measure the property. For example, the mass of a pebble may be measured in grams or pounds. The number assigned to measure mass is unique once a unit has been chosen. A more technical way of putting this is that the measurement of mass is unique up to a similarity transformation.[2] The measurement of temperature in °C or °F has different characteristics. Here an origin as well as a unit is arbitrarily chosen: technically speaking, the measurement of temperature is unique up to a linear transformation.[3] Other formally different kinds of measurement are exemplified by (1) the measurement of probability, which is absolutely unique (unique up to the identity transformation), and (2) the ordinal measurement of such physical properties as hardness of minerals, or such psychological properties as intelligence and racial prejudice. Ordinal measurements are commonly said to be unique up to a monotone-increasing transformation.[4]

Use of these different kinds of transformations is basic to the main idea of this paper. An empirical hypothesis, or any statement in fact, which uses numerical quantities is empirically meaningful only if its truth value is invariant under the appropriate transformations of the numerical quantities involved. As an example, suppose a psychologist has an ordinal measure of I.Q., and he thinks that scores $S(a)$ on a cer-

---

[2] A real-valued function ϕ is a similarity transformation if there is a positive number α such that for every real number x

$$\phi(x) = \alpha x.$$

In transforming from pounds to grams, for instance, the multiplicative factor α is 453.6.

[3] A real-valued function ϕ is a linear transformation if there are numbers α and β with $\alpha > 0$ such that for every number x

$$\phi(x) = \alpha x + \beta.$$

In transforming from Centrigrade to Fahrenheit degrees of temperature, for instance, $\alpha = \frac{9}{5}$ and $\beta = 32$.

[4] A real-valued function ϕ is a monotone increasing transformation if, for any two numbers x and y, if $x < y$, then $\phi(x) < \phi(y)$. Such transformations are also called *order-preserving*.

tain new test T have ordinal significance in ranking the intellectual ability of people. Suppose further that he is able to obtain the ages $A(a)$ of his subjects. The question then is: Should he regard the following hypothesis as empirically meaningful?

Hypothesis 1. *For any subjects a and b if $S(a)/A(a) < S(b)/A(b)$, then* I.Q. $(a) <$ I.Q. (b).

From the standpoint of the invariance characterization of empirical meaning, the answer is negative. To see this, let I.Q. $(a) \geq$ I.Q. (b), let $A(a) = 7$, $A(b) = 12$, $S(a) = 3$, $S(b) = 7$. Make no transformations on the I.Q. data, and make no transformations on the age data. But let ϕ be a monotone-increasing transformation which carries 3 into 6 and 7 into itself. Then we have

$$\tfrac{3}{7} < \tfrac{7}{12},$$

but

$$\tfrac{6}{7} \geq \tfrac{7}{12},$$

and the truth value of Hypothesis 1 is not invariant under ϕ.

The empirically significant thing about the transformation characteristic of a quantity is that it expresses in precise form how unique is the structural isomorphism between the empirical operations used to obtain a given measurement and the corresponding arithmetical operations or relations. If, for example, the empirical operation is simply that of ordering a set of objects according to some characteristic, then the corresponding arithmetical relation is that of less than (or greater than), and any two functions which map the objects into numbers in a manner preserving the empirical ordering are adequate. More exactly, a function f is adequate if, and only if, for any two objects a and b in the set, a stands in the given empirical relation to b if and only if

$$f(a) < f(b).^5$$

It is then easy to show that, if f_1 and f_2 are adequate in this sense, then they are related by a monotone-increasing transformation. Only those arithmetical operations and relations which are invariant under monotone-increasing transformations have any empirical significance in this situation.

The key notion referred to in the last sentence is that of invariance. In order to make the notion of invariance or the related notion of meaningfulness completely precise, we can do one of two things: set up an

---

[5] For simplicity we shall consider here only the arithmetical relation $<$. There is no other reason for excluding $>$.

exact set-theoretical framework for our discussion (e.g., for classical mechanics, see [1]), or formalize a language adequate to express empirical hypotheses and facts involving numerical quantities. Here we shall formalize a simple language for expressing the results of mass measurements. It should be clear that the method of approach is applicable to any other kind of measurement, or combinations thereof.

EMPIRICAL MEANINGFULNESS IN THE LANGUAGE L_M

To avoid many familiar details, we shall use as a basis the formal language of Tarski's monograph [2] enriched by individual variables 'a', 'b', 'c', $\cdots$, 'a_1', 'b_1', 'c_1', $\cdots$, the individual constants: $o_1, \cdots, o_{10}$, which designate ten, not necessarily distinct, physical objects, and the mass term 'm', where '$m(a)$' designates a real number, the mass of a. The values of the individual variables are physical objects. The numerical variables are 'x', 'y', 'z', $\cdots$, 'x_1', 'y_1', 'z_1', $\cdots$. Tarski's numerical constants are: 1, 0, -1. We shall include, for purposes of examples, numerical constants for the positive and negative integers less than 100 in absolute value. The operation signs are those for addition and multiplication. We also include the standard sign for exponentiation with the fixed base 2. A *term* is any arithmetically meaningful expression built up from this notation in the usual manner. (We omit an exact definition.) Thus the following are terms: $m(a)$, $5 \cdot m(a) + 3$, $2 + 1$, $x + 3$, 2^x. Our two relation symbols are the usual sign of equality and the greater than sign. An *atomic formula* is then an expression of the form

$$(\alpha - \beta), \qquad (\alpha > \beta)$$

where α and β are terms with the restriction in the case of $(\alpha > \beta)$ that α and β are both numerical terms, that is, neither α nor β is an individual variable or constant. When no confusion will result, parentheses are omitted. *Formulas* are constructed from atomic formulas by means of sentential connectives and quantifiers. The symbol '$-$' is used for negation; the ampersand '&' for conjunction; the symbol '$\lor$' for disjunction (to be read 'or'); the arrow '$\rightarrow$' for implication (to be read 'if . . . then . . .'); the double arrow '$\leftrightarrow$' for equivalence (to be read 'if and only if'); the reverse '$\exists$' is the existential quantifier; and the upside down '$\forall$' the universal quantifier. Thus the following are formulas: $(\exists x)(m(a) = x)$, $(\exists x)(\exists y)(x > y)$, $0 > x \rightarrow m(b) > x$. We also use the standard symbol '$\neq$' for negating an equality. A formula is a *sentence* if it contains no free variables, that is, every occurrence of a variable is bound by some quantifier.

Sentences are true or false, but unlike the situation in the language of Tarski's monograph [2], the truth or falsity of many sentences in the language L_M constructed here depends on empirical observation and contingent fact. For example, the truth of the sentence:

$$(1) \qquad (\exists a)(\forall b)(b \neq a \rightarrow m(a) > 5 \cdot m(b))$$

is a matter of physics, not arithmetic.

Pursuing now in more detail the remarks in the first section, the intuitive basis for our classification of certain formulas of L_M as empirically meaningless may be brought out by considering the simple sentence:

$$(2) \qquad m(o_1) = 4.$$

It must first be emphasized that in the language L_M, the numeral '4' occurring in Sentence 2 designates a "pure" number. There is no convention, explicit or implicit, that '4' stands for '4 g', '4 lb', or the like. It is to be clearly understood that no unit of mass is assumed in the primitive notation of L_M. With this understanding in mind, it is obvious that no experiment with apparatus for determining the masses of physical objects could determine the truth or falsity of Sentence 2. It is equally obvious that no mathematical argument can settle this question. On the other hand, it is clear that sentences like:

$$(3) \qquad m(o_1) > m(o_2)$$

or

$$(4) \qquad m(o_3) = 5 \cdot m(o_4)$$

which are concerned with numerical relations between the masses of certain objects can be determined as true or false on the basis of experiment without prior determination of a unit of mass.

It seems to me that the use of "pure" numerals in L_M is more fundamental than the use of what we may term "unitized numerals". The justification of this view is that the determination of units and an appreciation of their empirical significance comes *after*, not before, the investigation of questions of invariance and meaningfulness. The distinction between Sentence 2 and the other three Sentences 1, 3, and 4 is that the latter sentences remain true (or false) under any specification of units. In other words, the truth value of these sentences is independent of the arbitrary choice of a unit. Paraphrasing Weyl, we may say:[6] *only the numerical masses of bodies relative to one another have an objective meaning.*

---

[6] Weyl's original statement is with respect to Galileo's principle of relativity, "Only the motions of bodies (point-masses) relative to one another have an objective meaning." (See [3].)

My claim regarding fundamentals may be supported by an axiomatic, operational analysis of any actual experimental procedure for measuring mass. Most such procedures may be analyzed in terms of three formal notions: the set A of physical objects, a binary operation Q of comparison, and a binary operation * of combination. The formal task is to show that under the intended empirical interpretation the triple $\mathfrak{A} = \langle A, Q, * \rangle$ has such properties that it may be proved that there exists a real-valued function $\mathbf{m}$ defined on A such that for any a and b in A

(i) aQb if and only if $\mathbf{m}(a) \leq \mathbf{m}(b)$,

(ii) $\mathbf{m}(a * b) = \mathbf{m}(a) + \mathbf{m}(b)$.

The empirically arbitrary character of the choice of a unit is established by showing that the functional composition of any similarity transformation ϕ with the function $\mathbf{m}$ yields a function $\phi \circ \mathbf{m}$ which also satisfies (i) and (ii), where $\circ$ is the operation of functional composition.[7]

We may think of such an operational analysis as supporting the choice of L_M, where the term 'm' of L_M designates a numerical representing function satisfying (i) and (ii). Roughly speaking, because this representing function is only unique up to a similarity transformation, we then expect any sentence to be empirically meaningful in L_M if and only if its truth value is the same when 'm' is replaced by any expression which designates multiplication of the representing function by a positive number. However, there are certain difficulties with deciding exactly how to make this intuitive definition of empirical meaningfulness precise. For example, if the definition applies to any sentences, then we have the somewhat paradoxical result that Sentence 2 and its negation are both empirically meaningless, but their disjunction:

(5) $m(o_1) = 4 \lor m(o_1) \neq 4$

is meaningful, since it is always true.

To facilitate our attempts to meet this problem, we first need to introduce the semantical notion of a *model* of L_M. For simplicity in defining the notion of model, and without any loss of generality, we shall from this point on consider L_M as not having any individual constants that designate physical objects.

On this basis, a model $\mathfrak{M}$ of L_M is an ordered triple $\langle \mathfrak{S}, A, \mathbf{m} \rangle$, where

---

[7] An axiomatic analysis in terms of these ideas may be found in [4]. However, the analysis given in [4] may be criticized on several empirical counts; for example, the set A must be infinite.

(i) $\mathfrak{S}$ is the usual system of real numbers under the operations of addition, multiplication, and exponentiation with the base 2, and the relation less than with the appropriate numbers corresponding to their numerical designations in L_M; [8]

(ii) A is a finite, nonempty set;

(iii) $\mathbf{m}$ is a function on A which takes positive real numbers as values. The intended interpretation of A is as a set of physical objects whose masses are being determined; the function $\mathbf{m}$ is meant to be a possible numerical function used to represent experimental results. We assume the semantical notion of *satisfaction* and suppose it to be understood under what conditions a sentence of L_M is said to be *satisfied* in a model $\mathfrak{M}$. Roughly speaking, a sentence S of L_M is satisfied in $\mathfrak{M} = \langle \mathfrak{S}, A, \mathbf{m} \rangle$ if S is true when the purely arithmetical symbols of S are given the usual interpretation in terms of $\mathfrak{S}$, when the individual variables occurring in S range over the set A, and when the symbol 'm', if it occurs in S, is taken to designate the function $\mathbf{m}$.

We say that a sentence of L_M is *arithmetically true* if it is satisfied in every model of L_M. And we deal with the arithmetical truth of formulas with free variables by considering the truth of their *closures*. By the closure of a formula we mean the sentence resulting from the formula by adding sufficient universal quantifiers to bind all free variables in the formula. Thus '$(\forall a)(m(a) > 0)$' is the closure of '$m(a) > 0$', and is also the closure of itself.

Using these notions, we may define meaningfulness by means of the following pair of definitions.

Definition 1. *An atomic formula S of L_M is empirically meaningful if and only if the closure of the formula*

$$\alpha > 0 \rightarrow (S \leftrightarrow S(\alpha))$$

is arithmetically true for every numerical term α, where $S(\alpha)$ results from S by replacing any occurrence of 'm' in S by the term α, followed by the multiplication sign, followed by 'm'. [9] If, for example,

$$S = \text{'} m(a) > m(b) \text{'}$$

$$\alpha = \text{'} (2 + 1) \text{'},$$

[8] Technical details about $\mathfrak{S}$ are omitted. Characterization of models of the purely arithmetical part of L_M are familiar from the literature.

[9] In this definition and subsequently we follow, without explicit discussion, certain use-mention conventions. It would be diversionary to go into these conventions, and it seems unlikely any serious confusion will result from not being completely explicit on this rather minor point.

then
$$S(\alpha) = \text{`}(2 + 1) \cdot m(a) > (2 + 1) \cdot m(b)\text{'}.$$

Definition 2. *A formula S of L_M is empirically meaningful in sense A if and only if each atomic formula occurring in S is itself empirically meaningful in the sense of Definition 1.*

It is clear on the basis of Definitions 1 and 2 that Sentence 5 is not empirically meaningful in sense A.

On the other hand, there is a certain logical difficulty, within ordinary two-valued logic, besetting the set of true formulas which are meaningful in sense A. Following Tarski [5], a set of formulas is a *deductive system* if and only if the set is closed under the relation of logical consequence, that is, a formula which is a logical consequence of any subset of formulas in the given set must also be in the set. Clearly it is most desirable to have the set of meaningful true formulas about any phenomenon be a deductive system, but we have for the present case the following negative result.

Theorem 1. *The set of formulas of L_M which are meaningful in sense A and whose closures are true is not a deductive system.*

Proof: The true sentence:
$$(\forall x)(x > 2 \rightarrow x > 1)$$

is meaningful in sense A, but the following logical consequence of it is not:
$$m(o_1) > 2 \rightarrow m(o_1) > 1,$$

for the two atomic sentences '$m(o_1) > 2$' and '$m(o_1) > 1$' are both meaningless in the sense of Definition 1.

To be sure, there are some grounds for maintaining that formulas that are empirically meaningless may play an essential deductive role in empirical science, but *prima facie* it is certainly desirable to eliminate them if possible.

A second objection to Definition 1 is that, by considering numerical terms α rather than similarity transformations, we have in effect restricted ourselves to a denumerable number of similarity transformations because the number of such terms in L_M is denumerable. The intuitive idea of invariance with respect to *all* similarity transformations may be caught by a definition of meaningfulness which uses the concept of two models of L_M being related by a similarity transformation. (The operation $\circ$ referred to in the definition is that of functional composition.)

Definition 3. *Let* $\mathfrak{M}_1 = \langle \mathfrak{S}, A_1, \mathbf{m}_1 \rangle$ *and* $\mathfrak{M}_2 = \langle \mathfrak{S}, A_2, \mathbf{m}_2 \rangle$ *be two models of* L_M. *Then* $\mathfrak{M}_1$ *and* $\mathfrak{M}_2$ *are related by a similarity transformation if and only if*:

(i) $A_1 = A_2$.

(ii) *There is a similarity transformation* ϕ *such that*

$$\phi \circ \mathbf{m}_1 = \mathbf{m}_2.$$

Using these notions, we may replace Definitions 1 and 2 by the following:

Definition 4. *A formula S of* L_M *is empirically meaningful in sense B if and only if S is satisfied in a model* $\mathfrak{M}$ *of* L_M *when and only when it is satisfied in every model of* L_M *related to* $\mathfrak{M}$ *by a similarity transformation.*

Unfortunately, we have for meaningfulness in sense B a result analogous to Theorem 1.

Theorem 2. *Let* $\mathfrak{M}$ *be a model of* L_M. *Then the set of all formulas which are meaningful in sense B and which are satisfied in* $\mathfrak{M}$ *is not a deductive system.*

Proof: Consider the two sentences:

(1) $\qquad\qquad (\forall a)(\forall b)(a = b \rightarrow (m(a) = 2 \rightarrow m(b) = 2))$

(2) $\qquad\qquad (\forall a)(\forall b)(a = b).$

It is easy to verify that Sentences 1 and 2 are satisfied in any model whose set A has exactly one element, and are meaningful in sense B, yet they have as a logical consequence the sentence:

(3) $\qquad\qquad (\forall a)(\forall b)(m(a) = 2 \rightarrow m(b) = 2)$

which is not meaningful in sense B. That this is so may be seen by considering a model with at least two objects with different masses. Let $A = \{o_1, o_2\}$, and let $\mathfrak{M}_1 = \langle \mathfrak{S}, A, \mathbf{m}_1 \rangle$ be such that $\mathbf{m}_1(o_1) = 2$ and $\mathbf{m}_2(o_2) = 3$, and let $\mathfrak{M}_2 = \langle \mathfrak{S}, A, \mathbf{m}_2 \rangle$ be related to $\mathfrak{M}_1$ by the similarity transformation $\phi(x) = 2x$. Thus $\mathbf{m}_2(o_1) = 4$ and $\mathbf{m}_2(o_2) = 6$. It is then easily checked that Sentence 3 is satisfied in $\mathfrak{M}_2$ but not in $\mathfrak{M}_1$.

The negative result of these two theorems indicates the difficulties of eliminating the appearance of empirically meaningless statements in valid arguments with meaningful premises. We return to this point in the next section in connection with consideration of a three-valued logic.

On the other hand, we do have the positive result for both senses of meaningfulness that the set of meaningful formulas is a Boolean algebra; more exactly, the set of such formulas under the appropriate equivalence relation is such an algebra. Here we carry out the construction only for sense B. We consider the theory of Boolean algebras as based on six primitive notions: the nonempty set B of elements; the operation $+$ of addition which corresponds to the sentential connective 'or'; the operation $\cdot$ of multiplication which corresponds to the connective 'and'; the operation $\bar{x}$ of complementation which corresponds to negation; the zero element 0, which corresponds to the set of logically invalid formulas; and the unit element 1, which corresponds to the set of logically valid formulas. We omit stating familiar postulates on these notions which a Boolean algebra must satisfy.

Let E be the set of formulas which are empirically meaningful in sense B. We define the equivalence class of a formula S in E as follows: $[S]$ *is the set of all formulas S' in E which are satisfied in exactly the same models $\mathfrak{M}$ of L_M as S is.* Let $\mathbf{E}$ be the set of all such equivalence classes; obviously $\mathbf{E}$ is a partition of E. The zero element $\mathbf{0}$ is the set of formulas in E which are satisfied in no model of L_M; the unit element $\mathbf{1}$ is the set of formulas in E which are satisfied in all models of L_M. If S and T are in E, then $[S] + [T]$ is the set of all formulas in E which are satisfied in the models of L_M in which either S or T is satisfied. If S and T are in E, then $[S] \cdot [T]$ is the set of all formulas in E which are satisfied in those models in which both S and T are satisfied. Finally if S is in $\mathbf{E}$, then $[\bar{S}]$ is the set of formulas which are satisfied in a model if and only if S is not satisfied in the model. On the basis of these definitions, it is straightforward but tedious to prove the following:

Theorem 3. *The system* $\langle \mathbf{E}, +, \cdot, -, \mathbf{0}, \mathbf{1} \rangle$ *is a Boolean algebra.* (The proof is omitted.)

I interpret this theorem as showing that the set of meaningful formulas in sense B of L_M has a logical structure identical with that of classical logic. In connection with other systems of measurement for which the set of transformations referred to in the analogue of Definition 3 is not a group, this classical Boolean structure does not necessarily result.

Exponentiation was introduced into L_M deliberately to illustrate the sensitivity of the decidability of meaningfulness to the strength of L_M. The problem of decidability for the arithmetical language of Tarski's monograph mentioned earlier is open when his language is augmented by notation for exponentiation to a fixed base. It seems unlikely that the decidability of meaningfulness in L_M can be solved without solving this more general problem. If L_M is weakened by deleting exponentiation to the base 2, then it easily follows from Tarski's well-known result that meaningfulness is decidable. On the other hand, if L_M is strengthened to include sufficient elementary number theory to yield undecidability of whether, for instance, a given term designates zero, then meaningfulness is not decidable, for the meaningfulness of formulas of the form $m(a) = t$, where t is a numerical term, would not be decidable.

A THREE-VALUED LOGIC FOR L_M

Since sentences like '$(\forall a)(m(a) > 2)$' of L_M cannot be determined as true or false on the basis either of logical argument or of empirical observation, it is natural to ask what are the consequences of assigning them the truth value *meaningless*, which we designate by 'μ', and reserving the values *truth* and *falsity* for meaningful sentences, which we designate by 'T' and 'F' respectively. The first thing to be noticed is that meaningfulness in sense B does not lead to a truth-functional logic in these three values. This may be seen by considering two examples. The component sentences of the sentence:

$$(\exists a)(m(a) = 1) \vee -(\exists a)(m(a) = 1)$$

have the value μ but the whole sentence is meaningful in sense B and has the value T. On the other hand, the component sentences of:

$$(\exists a)(m(a) = 1) \vee (\exists b)(m(b) = 2)$$

have the value μ and so does the whole sentence. Thus these two examples taken together show that disjunction is not truth-functional for a three-value logic of meaningfulness in sense B.

The state of affairs for meaningfulness in sense A is much better: it does lead to a truth-functional logic in the three values T, F, and μ. The appropriate truth tables are easily found by using the simple observation that a formula has the value μ if any well-formed part of it has that value. Thus as the tables for negation and conjunction we have:

S	$-S$		&	T	F	μ
T	F		T	T	F	μ
F	T		F	F	F	μ
μ	μ		μ	μ	μ	μ

Tables for the sentential connectives of disjunction, implication, and equivalence follow at once from the standard definitions of these connectives in terms of negation and conjunction. On the other hand, it is obvious that this three-valued logic is not functionally complete with respect to negation and conjunction. For example, we cannot define in terms of these two connectives a unary connective which assigns the value μ to formulas having the value T.

Besetting meaningfulness in sense A is the negative result of Theorem 1. This difficulty we shall meet head on by proposing a revision of the definition of the semantical notion of logical consequence. However, before turning to this definition, it will be advantageous to give a model-theoretic definition of meaningfulness which combines the virtues of sense A and sense B.

Definition 5. *A formula S of L_M is empirically meaningful in sense C if and only if every atomic formula occurring in S is meaningful in sense B.*

It is easily verified that the truth tables just given are satisfied when the value μ signifies meaninglessness in sense C. Moreover, the exact analogue of the Boolean structure theorem for sense B (Theorem 3) can be proved for sense C.

To meet the difficulty of having formulas which are meaningless in sense C be logical consequences of formulas which are meaningful in sense C, a revision of the standard definition of *logical consequence* is proposed. For this purpose we need to widen the notion of a model to that of a *possible realization* of L_M. A model of L_M requires that the arithmetical symbols be interpreted in terms of the usual system of real numbers, but no such restriction is imposed on a possible realization. For example, any domain of individuals and any two binary operations on this domain provide a possible realization of the operation symbols of addition and multiplication. Details of the exact definition of a possible realization are familiar from the literature and will not be given here. This notion is used to define that of logical consequence, namely, a formula S of L_M is a *logical consequence* of a set A of formulas of L_M if S is satisfied in every possible realization in which all formulas in A are satisfied. We may then define:

Definition 6. *Let S be a formula and A a set of formulas of L_M. Then S is a meaningful logical consequence of A if and only if S is a logical consequence of A and S is meaningful in sense C whenever every formula in A is meaningful in sense C.*

The central problem in connection with this definition is to give rules of inference for which it may be established that, if A is a set of formulas meaningful in sense C, then S is a meaningful logical consequence of A

if and only if S is derivable from A by use of the rules of inference.[10] For this purpose, we may consider any one of several systems of natural deduction. The eight essential rules are: rule for introducing premises; rule for tautological implications; rule of conditional proof (the deduction theorem); rule of universal specification (or instantiation); rule of universal generalization; rule of existential specification; rule of existential generalization; and rule governing identities.[11] To these eight rules we add the *general restriction* that every line of a derivation must be a formula meaningful in sense C. This means, for instance, that in deriving a formula by universal specification from another formula we must check that the result of the specification is meaningful. This restriction entails that the modified rules of inference are finitary in character only if there is a decision procedure for meaningfulness in sense C. Remarks on this problem were made at the end of the previous section. Because we have modified the rules of inference only by restricting them to meaningful formulas, it follows easily from results in the literature on the soundness of standard rules of inference that:

Theorem 4. *Let A be a set of formulas meaningful in sense C. If a formula S is derivable from A by use of the rules of inference subject to the general restriction just stated, then S is a meaningful logical consequence of A.*

Of considerable more difficulty is the converse question of completeness, namely, does being a meaningful logical consequence of a set of meaningful formulas imply derivability by the restricted rules? The following considerations suggest that the answer may be affirmative to this question. Let $L_M{}^*$ be a second language which differs from L_M in the following single respect: the one-place function symbol 'm' is replaced by the two-place function symbol 'r', where both argument places are filled by individual variables or constants. The intuitive interpretation of the formula '$r(a, b) = x$' is that the numerical ratio of the mass of a to the mass of b is the real number x, that is,

$$r(a, b) = m(a)/m(b).$$

Clearly every formula in $L_M{}^*$ is meaningful with respect to our intuitive criterion of invariance. (The practical objection to $L_M{}^*$ is that

---

[10] Although two kinds of variables are used in L_M, we may easily modify L_M to become a theory with standard formalization in first-order predicate logic and thus consider only modification of standard rules of inference for first-order predicate logic.

[11] By various devices this list can be reduced, but that is not important for our present purposes. Exposition of systems of natural deduction which essentially use these eight rules is to be found in [6], [7], and [8].

such a ratio language is tedious to work with and does not conform to ordinary practice in theoretical physics.) No restrictions on the rules of inference are required for L_M* and, consequently, the usual completeness result holds. The suggestion is to use translatability of meaningful formulas of L_M into L_M* to prove completeness of inferences from meaningful formulas of L_M. The possible pitfall of this line of reasoning is that translatability requires certain arithmetical operations which are preserved in every model but not necessarily in every possible realization of L_M.

Certain aspects of this construction of a three-valued logic for L_M seem worthy of remark. In the first place, the construction has assumed throughout use of a two-valued logic in the informal metalanguage of L_M. In particular, ordinary two-valued logic is used in deciding if a given sentence of L_M is satisfied in a given model of L_M. On the other hand, the relation between sets of empirical data on mass measurements and models of L_M is one–many. The empirical content of the data is expressed not by a particular model but by an appropriate equivalence class of models. Consequently, sentences of L_M which are not invariant in truth value (in the two-valued sense) over these equivalence classes do not have any clear empirical meaning even though they have a perfectly definite meaning relative to any one model. Thus it seems to me that to call a formula like '$m(a) = 5$' empirically meaningless is no abuse of ordinary ideas of meaningfulness, and in this particular situation accords well with our physical intuitions. If this is granted, the important conclusion to be drawn is that, for the language L_M, the three-valued logic constructed is intuitively more natural than the ordinary two-valued one.

REFERENCES

1. McKinsey, J. C. C., and Patrick Suppes, "On the Notion of Invariance in Classical Mechanics," *British J. Philosophy of Science*, **V**, 1955, pp. 290–302.
2. Tarski, A., *A Decision Method for Elementary Algebra and Geometry*, 2nd ed., Berkeley, University of California Press, 1951.
3. Weyl, H. *Space-Time-Matter*, 4th ed., London, Methuen, 1922, p. 152.
4. Suppes, Patrick, "A Set of Independent Axioms for Extensive Quantities," *Portugaliae Mathematica*, **10**, 1951, pp. 163–172.
5. Tarski, A., "Über einige fundamentale Begriffe der Metamathematik," *Comp. rend. soc. sci. et lettres Varsovie*, **23**, 1930, cl. iii, pp. 22–29. Reprinted in A. Tarski, *Logic, Semantics, Metamathematics*, Oxford, Oxford University Press, 1956.
6. Copi, I., *Symbolic Logic*, New York, Macmillan Co., 1954.
7. Quine, W. V., *Methods of Logic*, New York, Henry Holt & Co., 1950.
8. Suppes, Patrick, *Introduction to Logic*, New York, D. Van Nostrand Co., 1957.

7

A PROBABILISTIC THEORY
OF UTILITY AND ITS RELATIONSHIP
TO FECHNERIAN SCALING

R. Duncan Luce

PROFESSOR, DEPARTMENT OF PSYCHOLOGY,
UNIVERSITY OF PENNSYLVANIA

INTRODUCTION [1,2,3]

A measurement problem that pervades much, if not all, of social science in this: Given an individual's choices in a series of paired comparisons, where the stimuli vary along some dimension which is of concern to him, how to devise a relatively unique measure of their

[1] The last five sections of this article differ in but trivial ways from Sections A1.2 through A1.6 of Appendix 1 of *Games and Decisions* [4]. I have received Professor Raiffa's permission to reprint them here. The draft of my talk for the Measurement Symposium of the 1956 AAAS Christmas meetings, plus extensive critical comments by Professor Raiffa, served as a basis for the final draft of Appendix 1. When I prepared this paper a few months later, I did not see a sufficiently fresh approach to the material to warrant restating it.

[2] Many conversations and letters underlie the present version of this paper. I am particularly indebted to Professors P. F. Lazarsfeld and H. Raiffa, who devoted many hours to discussing earlier drafts of it, and to Professor John S. Chipman who, although he has never seen this paper in any of its drafts, much influenced it. He, in his capacity as associate editor of *Econometrica,* pointed out difficulties in the original technical exposition of the theory, which has since been revised and published [2].

[3] The preparation of this paper was done at Columbia University, and it was

subjective value, or worth, to him; or to infer a latent scale of values from the set of manifest data of the individual's pairwise choices. Although it is easy to point to the problem and to see that, in all likelihood, it is of widespread scientific interest, it is far from easy to see how to resolve it.   In each of the behavioral disciplines, there is a more or less long history of work on the problem in one form or another, and, as one would expect, there are just about as many approaches and vocabularies as there are sciences.   I mention this well-known fact because I shall be drawing upon portions of two of these approaches, that of psychology and of economics, without being able to afford the space to give an adequate history of either; and because any such amalgamation of ideas must also entail a mingling of terms which, at times, provides us with an abundance of riches.   I must ask you to bear with my arbitrary terminological choices.

The general approach that I shall take to this problem is to define the scale of value implicitly by a set of axioms which assert some of its properties.   These are, of course, properties that seem more intuitively acceptable or more basic than an explicit description of the scale might seem.   The mathematical argument, which is too lengthy to present here, allows one to transform the implicit definition into an explicit form.   The selection of the axioms is naturally a very subtle matter; we shall see this only too clearly later.   One tends to depart but little from tradition in these choices, and the traditions I shall cling to can be found in psychology and in a part of economics that borders closely on both psychology and statistics.

THE PSYCHOLOGICAL TRADITION

Suppose that a and b are two alternatives confronting a subject who must select between them according to some relevant dimension.   In psychophysics, it might be loudness; in a sociological study, attitude toward race; in much recent decision making work, it has been preference between alternatives.   I shall use the latter interpretation.   It is a widely accepted assumption of psychology, which for the most part has been idealized out of the corresponding economic models, that, generally, the probability is different from 0 or 1 of a particular person preferring a to b at a given instant, i.e., it is assumed that people do not generally exhibit perfect preference discrimination.   I say that this is an assumption of psychology because no way that I know of

supported in part by a grant from the National Science Foundation for the study of "the Mathematics of Imperfect Discrimination."

has been devised to verify or refute it. Furthermore, no way has yet been found to estimate such probabilities without either assuming that each subject in some population has the same probability of preferring a to b or assuming that independent samples can be obtained from a single subject by offering him the same choice at several different and carefully spaced times. As neither of these assumptions seems uniformly valid—indeed, in many cases both seem erroneous—the task of empirical estimation is very delicate; however, I do not want to enter into that issue here. I shall simply suppose that such probabilities exist.

One tradition of scaling in psychology, which, in large measure, stems from psychophysical studies of the last century and which is associated with the name of Fechner, can be stated roughly as follows: One searches for a numerical scale having the property that the probability of preferring one alternative to another, provided the probability is neither 0 nor 1, depends only upon the difference of the alternatives' scale values and not upon their separate values. Thus, if u denotes the scale and $P(a, b)$ the probability that a is preferred to b, then if $P(a, b) \neq 0, 1, P(a, b)$ shall be a function only of $u(a) - u(b)$. Because one can assume that stimuli from any one psychophysical dimension form a continuum, it turns out that this condition specifies a psychophysical scale uniquely, except for its zero and unit; but it does not do so when the alternatives are discrete, as in a preference experiment. Then there are many inherently different scales compatible with the Fechnerian condition. To have a reasonably unique scale, it appears that both the probabilities P must satisfy some restrictive conditions and a set of alternatives must possess some "mathematical structure." I do not want to explain what I mean by this, except to point out that one abstracts a psychophysical continuum by the real number system which has a very rich mathematical structure. A finite set of "unconnected" stimuli does not. There also seems to be an exchange relation between the conditions on P and the structure on the alternatives: The more structure possessed by the set of alternatives, the less stringent need be the conditions on P; and the less structure on the set, the stronger must be the conditions on P for a relatively unique scale to exist. In the psychophysical case, the conditions needed on P are relatively weak. On the other hand, in most social psychological scaling, only a finite number of alternatives are assumed, such as a set of political candidates, and little or no mathematical structure can be assumed. Thus, to have a single acceptable scale, quite strong assumptions must be made about the probabilities of preference. These include the familiar, but nonetheless controversial and largely untested, assumptions that certain variables are normally distributed and that the error terms are statistically independent of practically everything in sight. Such assumptions are most familiar from factor analysis and the Thurstone school of scaling.

When the problem is phrased in this way, the question immediately arises as to whether we can arrange a choice situation which renders preference scaling similar to psychophysical scaling in the sense that the underlying set of alternatives has a lot of mathematical structure. Certainly, one cannot just copy the psychophysical assumption of a continuum but possibly the spirit of that model can be reproduced.

THE MODERN DECISION MAKING TRADITION

The idea now current for model building comes from a part of economics and statistics known as the theory of decision making under risk. A central observation of these theorists, in particular von Neumann and Morgenstern [7] and Ramsey [5] (who, although less influential than von Neumann and Morgenstern, predated many of their utility ideas by several decades), is that it is rather more rare than common to make choices between pure prospects, as has been the case in most preference experiments. Generally, one is confronted with prospects that are built up of several outcomes which are conditional upon the occurrence or nonoccurrence of certain future events. Let me be more specific. Your wife suggests that you purchase tickets to a certain play for the evening of January 15. Is it fair to say that you must simply choose between spending $8 and seeing the play on that date versus spending nothing and, say, sitting home watching whatever television fare is available? Hardly. If nothing else, there is a certain possibility that you cannot go to the play that night even if you have the tickets—a pressing professional activity may arise or you may be ill. Let me call all such eventualities the event α. Thus, the choice will be among:

Spending $8 and not seeing the play if α occurs; or
Spending $8 and seeing the play if α does not occur.

versus

Spending nothing and not seeing television if α occurs; or
Spending nothing and seeing television if α does not occur.

This seems a little more realistic, and certainly the choice is more difficult now because it depends both upon how likely you think it is that α will occur and on how much you want to see the play.

Abstractly, such a mixed prospect will be symbolized as follows: if a and b are any two prospects and α is an event, the mixed prospect "a if α occurs or b if it does not" is denoted by $a\alpha b$.

There is, of course, no reason why the component prospects of a mixed prospect cannot themselves also be mixed prospects. To return to our theater example, suppose that one has taken the theater option and that α does not occur. Thus, one goes to the theater; but this is a mixed pleasure, depending upon the weather. One's enjoyment of the play is liable to be somewhat dampened if there is a sticky New York snowstorm to battle. So, in our symbolism, if b is actually the mixed prospect $c\beta d$, then the over-all mixed prospect is $a\alpha(c\beta d)$.

It is clear that, even when both the set of pure prospects and the set of events are finite, the set of mixed prospects that can be generated recursively in this manner is infinite. It is only more so when the set of events is infinite, as we shall assume. The possibility of this set having a lot of reasonable mathematical structure is clear, and we shall impose some structure later in this paper.

The price that we pay—and from many points of view it is really a gain—for making the choice model a little more realistic is that we have two, not one, scaling tasks. In addition to scaling subjective values, we are pretty well forced to obtain a scale of subjective probability for the events. Depending upon one's interest, attention is generally focused on just one of the two scales and the other appears only as a necessary technical device.

One thing is immediately clear: the two scales are thoroughly interlocked since subjective values must be attached to mixed prospects, and these depend upon the events. If we let u denote the subjective value scale and ϕ the subjective probability scale, then one of the simplest ways they can be interlaced would be for the subjective value of a mixed prospect to be given by the expectation of the subjective value of its components, i.e., the subjective value of each component prospect is weighted according to its subjective probability of occurring. In the language of utility theory, this is described by saying: the individual behaves as if he were maximizing expected utility. A good deal of effort has gone into determining conditions under which this expected value property is met, for, without it, any mathematical model based upon a subjective value scale becomes dreadfully complicated. In this paper, however, we are concerned with a slightly different issue; we suppose that our scales do, in fact, possess this very desirable property and then inquire into its consequences when it is coupled with certain other intuitively plausible axioms.

PREFERENCE DISCRIMINATION AND INDUCED PREFERENCE

We shall need some notation. First, the set of pure alternatives, finite or infinite, will be denoted by A and the set (actually, Boolean algebra) of chance events by E. If α is an element of E, then $\bar{\alpha}$ will denote the complement of α. The set of mixed prospects, generated in the way just described, will be denoted by G.

Axiom 1. For every a in G, $a\alpha a = a$.

In words, the mixed prospect in which a is the outcome whether or not α occurs is not distinguished as different from a itself. It is hard to quarrel with this, although, when combined with Axiom 11, it implies that the subjective probabilities of an event and of its complement sum to 1, which Edwards [1] has questioned.

If a and b are two mixed prospects from G, we suppose that there exists an objective probability $P(a, b)$ that the given individual will prefer a to b. As I indicated earlier, it is not easy to see how to estimate such probabilities in practice, but we need not concern ourselves about that when describing the model.

Although it is true that imperfect preference discrimination has been introduced in part to avoid the strong transitivity requirements of the von Neumann and Morgenstern theory, it would be folly to ignore the empirical evidence suggesting that preferences are approximately transitive. It is easy to go astray at this point by assuming certain inequalities among the three quantities $P(a, b)$, $P(b, c)$, and $P(a, c)$; apparently this is not strong enough. Our tack is a bit different. Observe that, in an induced sense, a is "preferred or indifferent to" b if for every c in G both

$$P(a, c) \geq P(b, c) \quad \text{and} \quad P(c, b) \geq P(c, a).$$

Whenever these two sets of inequalities hold, we shall write $a \gtrsim b$. It is easy to see that $\gtrsim$ must always be transitive, but that, in general, there will be alternatives which are not comparable according to $\gtrsim$. A basic restriction we shall make about preference discrimination is that such comparisons are always possible, i.e.:

Axiom 2. For every a and b in G, either $a \gtrsim b$ or $b \gtrsim a$.

This is a strong assumption, but I do not believe it to be nearly so strong as the corresponding ones in the traditional nonprobabilistic utility models. There, comparability is operationally forced by the demand that the individual make a choice, but transitivity is in doubt. Here, transitivity is certain and comparability is in doubt. Although it is plausible that Axiom 2 is met in some empirical contexts, the following example, due to Howard Raiffa, strongly suggests that this is not always the case. Suppose that a and b are two alternatives of roughly comparable value to some person, e.g., trips from New York City to Paris and to Rome. Let c be alternative a plus \$20 and d be alternative b plus \$20. Clearly, in general,

$$P(a, c) = 0 \quad \text{and} \quad P(b, d) = 0.$$

It also seems perfectly plausible that, for some people,

$$P(b, c) > 0 \quad \text{and} \quad P(a, d) > 0,$$

in which event a and b are not comparable, and so Axiom 2 is violated. In one respect this example is special: c differs from a, and d from b, by the addition of an extra commodity which is always desirable; therefore, we may expect perfect discrimination within each of these two pairs. As we shall see, there are theoretical reasons for believing that the occurrence of perfect preference discrimination may require a somewhat different model than when it never occurs.

Let us say that a and b are indifferent in the induced sense, and write $a \sim b$, whenever both $a \gtrsim b$ and $b \gtrsim a$. We next argue that certain two-stage gambles should be indifferent.

Consider the mixed prospect $(a\alpha b)\beta c$, where a, b, and c are pure alternatives. If one analyzes what this means, one sees that outcome a results if both α and β occur, i.e., if the event $\alpha \cap \beta$ occurs; b results if both $\bar{\alpha}$ and β occur, i.e., if $\bar{\alpha} \cap \beta$ occurs; and c results if $\bar{\beta}$ occurs. A similar analysis of the prospect $a(\alpha \cap \beta)(b\beta c)$ shows that a, b, and c occur under exactly the same conditions. Thus, there is no difference between the two mixed prospects and it is reasonable to argue that a person should be indifferent between them. We shall demand that this holds not strictly but only in the weaker sense of induced preference.

Axiom 3. If a, b, and c are in A and α and β are in E, then

$$(a\alpha b)\beta c \sim a(\alpha \cap \beta)(b\beta c).$$

Actually, the results that we shall state depend only upon the weaker assumption

$$(a\alpha b)\beta b \sim a(\alpha \cap \beta)b,$$

which follows from Axiom 3 by setting $c = b$ and then using Axiom 1.

LIKELIHOOD DISCRIMINATION AND QUALITATIVE PROBABILITY

Suppose that our subject must decide between the two prospects $a\alpha b$ and $a\beta b$. He can simplify his choice by asking himself which alternative, a or b, he prefers, and which event, α or β, he considers more likely to occur. Of the four combinations, two should lead to preference for $a\alpha b$ over $a\beta b$:

1. a is preferred to b, and α is deemed more likely to occur than β.
2. b is preferred to a, and β is deemed more likely to occur than α.

By assumption, the probability that he will prefer a to b is $P(a, b)$. If we suppose that his discrimination as to the likelihood of events is statistically independent of his preference discriminations, and that it is governed by a probability $Q(\alpha, \beta)$, then the probability that he will both prefer a to b and deem α more likely to occur than β is $P(a, b) Q(\alpha, \beta)$. Similarly, the probability that he will both prefer b to a and deem β more likely to occur than α is $P(b, a) Q(\beta, \alpha)$. Since these two cases are exclusive of each other, the sum of the two numbers should give the probability that he will prefer $a\alpha b$ to $a\beta b$.

The important assumption made in this argument is that the two discrimination processes are statistically independent. This seems reasonable when and only when the subject believes the two prospects a and b to be "independent" of the events α and β, for, if alternative a depends on α and he believes α is likely to occur, then he is really forced to compare the outcome of a which arises when α occurs with $a\beta b$, in which case his preference between $a\alpha b$ and $a\beta b$ may be different from what it would be if a were independent of α. There is at least one case when it is plausible that the subject should deem a and b to be independent of α and β, namely, when a and b are pure alternatives having nothing to do with chance events. We shall assume that our conclusion holds in that case.

Axiom 4. There is a probability $Q(\alpha, \beta)$ for every α and β in E such that, if a and b are in A,

$$P(a\alpha b, a\beta b) = P(a, b) Q(\alpha, \beta) + P(b, a) Q(\beta, \alpha).$$

There is, as yet, no direct evidence as to whether these two discriminations actually are statistically independent. Conceptually, we clearly separate preferences among alternatives from likelihood among events, and it seems reasonable that people attempt to deal with these as distinct, independent dimensions. On the other hand, casual observation indicates that people do play long shots, and such behavior appears to violate the axiom. At the least, the axiom seems sufficiently compelling as a dictum of sensible behavior to warrant its investigation, and it can be looked on as a generalization of related, but nonprobabilistic, assumptions found in other work, e.g., in Ramsey [5] and in Savage [6].

Our next axiom is comparatively innocent. Let me state it first and then discuss its import.

Axiom 5. For every a and b in G,

$$P(a, b) \geq 0 \quad \text{and} \quad P(a, b) + P(b, a) = 1.$$

For every α and β in E,

$$Q(\alpha, \beta) \geq 0 \quad \text{and} \quad Q(\alpha, \beta) + Q(\beta, \alpha) = 1.$$

There exist at least two alternatives a^* and b^* in A such that $P(a^*, b^*) > \frac{1}{2}$.

First, we have supposed that the P's and Q's are actually probabilities in the sense that they lie between 0 and 1 inclusive, and we have supposed that the subject is forced to make choices between alternatives and between events. That is, he cannot report that he is indifferent between a and b. Experimentally, this is known as the "forced-choice" technique, and it is in standard use. It may be worth mentioning that, if one allows indifference reports in the sense of only demanding $P(a, b) + P(b, a) \leq 1$, then the mathematics leads to two quite distinct cases —one we shall describe here, and another one somewhat like it but apparently less realistic. The final condition simply demands that the situation be nontrivial in the sense that not all pure alternatives are equally confused with respect to preference.

From Axioms 4 and 5, it is trivial to show that

$$Q(\alpha, \beta) = \frac{P(a\alpha b, a\beta b) + P(a, b) - 1}{2P(a, b) - 1},$$

for every a and b in A such that $P(a, b) \neq \frac{1}{2}$ [by Axiom 5, at least one such pair (a^*, b^*) exists]. This expression is useful because it permits one to determine whether a given set of preference data do satisfy the independence assumption and, if they do, to estimate $Q(\alpha, \beta)$.

In complete analogy to "induced preference," we may define a relation on the set of events E. We write $\alpha \gtrsim \beta$ if

$$Q(\alpha, \delta) \geq Q(\beta, \delta) \quad \text{and} \quad Q(\delta, \alpha) \geq Q(\delta, \beta)$$

for every δ in E. We shall refer to this as the "qualitative probability" (induced by Q) on E. One might expect us now to impose a compa-

rability axiom like Axiom 2 on qualitative probability, but this is unnecessary as it is a consequence of our other axioms. Rather, an entirely
different assumption, peculiar to the notion of probability, is required.
We shall suppose that the subject is certain that the universal event e
of the Boolean algebra E will occur. For the moment, we will demand
that no event have a qualitative probability in excess of e or less than
its complement.

Axiom 6. If e is the universal event in E, then

$$e \gtrsim \alpha \gtrsim \bar{e} \quad \text{for every } \alpha \text{ in } E.$$

THE UTILITY AND SUBJECTIVE PROBABILITY FUNCTIONS

So far, our technique of study has been similar to that normally employed in utility theory, but now we depart from that tradition by
assuming that utility and subjective probability functions exist having,
among others, properties like those that are traditionally established.
Of course, neither of these two functions, however we choose them, can
be a complete representation of the assumed data in the same sense
that traditional utility functions are. We no longer have a simple
transitive relation to be represented numerically but rather a set of
probabilities. The role of what we shall continue to call the utility and
subjective probability functions will be a partial and—as we shall see—
comparatively simple representation of the probabilities. It is analogous to using a statistic such as the mean or standard deviation to give
a partial description of a probability distribution.

We shall suppose that there exists at least one real valued function u
on G, called the utility function, and at least one real-valued function
ϕ on E, called the subjective probability function, and that the following axioms are met.

Axiom 7. u preserves the induced preference relation on G, and ϕ
preserves the qualitative probability on E, i.e.,

$$u(a) \geq u(b) \text{ if and only if } a \gtrsim b, \quad \text{for } a \text{ and } b \text{ in } G$$

and

$$\phi(\alpha) \geq \phi(\beta) \text{ if and only if } \alpha \gtrsim \beta \quad \text{for } \alpha \text{ and } \beta \text{ in } E.$$

As this sort of condition is very familiar in all of utility theory, I need
not comment on it.

Axiom 8. $\phi(e) = 1$ and $\phi(\bar{e}) = 0$.

This prescribes more clearly the role of the universal event e. It is an event which is subjectively certain to occur, and its complement is subjectively certain not to occur.

Given a subjective probability function ϕ, we may follow the usual terminology for objective probabilities and say that two events α and β are (*subjectively*) *independent* if and only if $\phi(\alpha \cap \beta) = \phi(\alpha) \phi(\beta)$. It is clear that we cannot ascertain which events are independent until we know the subjective probability function ϕ, and thus it would appear as though we were rapidly getting ourselves into a circle. However, it turns out that all of our final conclusions can be stated without reference to independent events provided only that Axiom 4 can be extended in a certain way and that there are enough independent events—so many that no exhaustive check would be possible anyhow. These conditions will be formulated as Axioms 9 and 10.

Earlier, when we introduced Axiom 4, describing the statistical independence of the two discrimination processes, we held that it should be met whenever the two prospects a and b are "independent" of the events α and β, without, however, specifying what we might mean by this except that it should hold for all pure alternatives. We now extend Axiom 4 as follows:

Axiom 9.   If a and b are in A, and α and β are events which are subjectively independent of event γ, then

$$P[(a\gamma b)\alpha b, (a\gamma b)\beta b] = P(a\gamma b, b) Q(\alpha, \beta) + P(b, a\gamma b) Q(\beta, \alpha).$$

Axiom 10.   The subjective probability function ϕ shall have the property that, for all numbers x, y, and z, where $0 \leq x, y, z \leq 1$, there are events α, β, and γ in E such that:
  (a) $\phi(\alpha) = x$, $\phi(\beta) = y$, and $\phi(\gamma) = z$.
  (b) α and β are both subjectively independent of γ.

This axiom postulates a very dense set of independent events, so dense that every conceivable subjective probability is exhibited at least twice. Put another way, we are making a continuum assumption about the individual being described via the axioms. Although this type of assumption is not often made so explicit, it is nevertheless implicit whenever the assumption is made that any objective probability can be realized.

Axiom 11.   These two subjective scales satisfy the expected utility hypothesis in the sense that, for a and b in A, and α in E,

$$u(a\alpha b) = \phi(\alpha) u(a) + \phi(\bar{\alpha}) u(b).$$

This, except for the restriction to pure alternatives, is a familiar feature of utility theory. Although no restrictions are usually stated when the expected utility hypothesis is made, it is always tacitly assumed that it only holds for mixed prospects whose component events are independent of the event α of the hypothesis. In utility theory, of course, independence is meant in the usual objective sense. For our purposes, it is sufficient to assume the hypothesis only for pure alternatives which are trivially independent of events.

CONCLUSIONS ABOUT THE SUBJECTIVE SCALES

On the basis of these eleven axioms, the following conclusions can be established as to the form of the discrimination functions and the subjective scales. First of all, Q must depend only upon the difference of the subjective probabilities of its two events. Put more formally, there exists a real-valued function Q^* of one real variable such that

$$Q(\alpha, \beta) = Q^*[\phi(\alpha) - \phi(\beta)].$$

This result is interesting because of its connection with the old psychological problem mentioned on p. 146.

Actually, we can give a much more explicit result than that ϕ is a Fechnerian sensation scale: we can describe the mathematical form of Q. There are three cases. In the first, there is a positive constant ϵ and Q is of the form

$$Q(\alpha, \beta) = \begin{cases} \frac{1}{2} + \frac{1}{2}[\phi(\alpha) - \phi(\beta)]^{\epsilon} & \text{if } \alpha > \beta \\ \frac{1}{2} & \text{if } \alpha \sim \beta \\ \frac{1}{2} - \frac{1}{2}[\psi(\beta) - \phi(\alpha)]^{\epsilon} & \text{if } \beta > \alpha. \end{cases}$$

The second is the discontinuous function

$$Q(\alpha, \beta) = \begin{cases} 1 & \text{if } \alpha > \beta \\ \frac{1}{2} & \text{if } \alpha \sim \beta \\ 0 & \text{if } \beta > \alpha, \end{cases}$$

which results from the first case by taking the limit as ϵ approaches 0. This represents perfect likelihood discrimination. The third is the function obtained by taking the limit as ϵ approaches infinity, and it represents almost total lack of discrimination.

It is easy to see that, in the first case, but not in the other two, one can express ϕ in terms of Q, namely, as

$$\phi(\alpha) = [Q(\alpha, \bar{e}) - Q(\bar{e}, \alpha)]^{1/\epsilon}$$

or, more usefully, as

$$\phi(\alpha) = \begin{cases} \frac{1}{2} + \frac{1}{2}[2Q(\alpha, \bar{\alpha}) - 1]^{1/\epsilon} & \text{if } Q(\alpha, \bar{\alpha}) > \frac{1}{2} \\ \frac{1}{2} & \text{if } Q(\alpha, \bar{\alpha}) = \frac{1}{2} \\ \frac{1}{2} - \frac{1}{2}[1 - 2Q(\alpha, \bar{\alpha})]^{1/\epsilon} & \text{if } Q(\alpha, \bar{\alpha}) < \frac{1}{2}. \end{cases}$$

Similar results hold for u and P over the set A of pure alternatives. First, P can be shown to be a function only of $u(a) - u(b)$ for a and b in A. Second, assuming a Q of the first type above and letting ϵ be the constant determined there, then

$$P(a, b) = \begin{cases} \frac{1}{2} + \frac{1}{2}[P(a^*, b^*) - P(b^*, a^*)][u(a) - u(b)]^{\epsilon} & \text{if } a > b \\ \frac{1}{2} & \text{if } a \sim b \\ \frac{1}{2} - \frac{1}{2}[P(a^*, b^*) - P(b^*, a^*)][u(b) - u(a)]^{\epsilon} & \text{if } b > a, \end{cases}$$

and

$$u(a) = \begin{cases} \left[\dfrac{P(a, b^*) - P(b^*, a)}{P(a^*, b^*) - P(b^*, a^*)} \right]^{1/\epsilon} & \text{if } a > b^* \\ 1 - \left[\dfrac{P(a^*, a) - P(a, a^*)}{P(a^*, b^*) - P(b^*, a^*)} \right]^{1/\epsilon} & \text{if } b^* > a, \end{cases}$$

where a^* and b^* are mentioned in Axiom 5. Any positive linear transformation of u is equally acceptable.

Thus, we have the following situation. If the axioms are accepted and if it is assumed that discrimination of events is neither perfect nor totally absent, then the mathematical form of the model is completely specified except for a single parameter ϵ which appears to reflect the individual's sensitivity of discrimination; and the two subjective scales can be inferred from the empirical estimates of the probabilities P. The subjective probability scale is unique, and the utility scale is unique except for its zero and unit. There is only one trouble with all of this: it is extremely doubtful that people satisfy all the axioms.

An example, again due to Howard Raiffa, and a theorem will formulate our doubts. Although the mathematical argument used to establish our results rests heavily on steps involving independent events, the final results can be shown to hold for events whether or not they are independent, so we need not worry about independence in a counterintuitive example. Consider the two chance events: rain on Wall Street at time t, and rain on both Wall Street and 34th Street at time t. Since the locations are not widely separated, both being in New York City, it is highly likely that if it rains on Wall Street if will also rain on 34th Street, so the subjective probability of rain on Wall Street alone will only be slightly larger than rain at both places. Yet, if one is asked which is more likely, it seems silly ever to say the latter. If so, we have $\phi(\alpha)$ and $\phi(\beta)$ very close and $Q(\alpha, \beta) = 1$. If people actually behave in this way when making choices, then at least one of our axioms must be false.

AN IMPOSSIBILITY THEOREM

Casual observation suggests that there are many situations, e.g., those involving gambles of money, in which these conditions can be satisfied. First, there are at least three prospects a, b, and c which are perfectly discriminated with respect to preference, i.e., $P(a, b) = P(b, c) = P(a, c) = 1$. This will hold, we are sure, when all other things are equal and $a = \$10$, $b = \$5$, and $c = \$1$. Second, there are at least two events, α and β, which are neither perfectly discriminated nor equally confused, i.e., such that $Q(\alpha, \beta) \neq 0$, $\frac{1}{2}$ or 1. The impossibility theorem asserts that these two assumptions are inconsistent with the eleven axioms we have previously stated.

This result seems disturbing, for most of the assumptions on which it is based have, by now, acquired a considerable respectability. Yet, clearly, they cannot all be satisfied. The task of reappraising them is quite delicate, for there are numerous reasons for supposing that they are not terribly far from the truth. For example, the derived form of the discrimination function for events is sufficiently similar to much discrimination data to suggest that we are not completely afield.

It would appear that six of our assumptions are subject to the greatest doubt. Of these, three (Axiom 2, requiring that every pair of mixed prospects be comparable by the induced preference relation; Axiom 3, requiring that two prospects which decompose in the same way be indifferent in the induced sense; and Axiom 4, requiring that the two discrimination processes be statistically independent for pure alternatives) are subject to direct experimental study. The other three (Axiom 9, requiring that Axiom 4 hold for certain mixed prospects involving subjectively independent events; Axiom 10, requiring that certain triples of independent events be extremely dense; and Axiom 11, requiring that the expected utility hypothesis be true for pure alternatives) are impossible to study directly. Because of this, one can expect that most attempts to get out of the bind will be concentrated on the second three.

Since much of decision theory is so dependent upon the expected-utility hypothesis, special attention will undoubtedly be given to

Axioms 9 and 10. There is the intriguing possibility that these subjective scales are discrete rather than continuous, as has generally been assumed, which would make them more in accord with the way people seem to classify, say, events: impossible, not very likely, etc. In that case, Axiom 10 might be abandoned. On the other hand, Axiom 9 when coupled with our definition of independence may be the source of difficulty. As the axiom seems reasonable for one's intuitive idea of subjectively independent events, it may be the definition that should be altered.

As it stands, two conceptual features of this theory are of interest. First, by making the assumption that the two discrimination processes are statistically independent, it has been possible to deal simultaneously with both subjective value (utility) and subjective probability. Second, by using axioms which are closely related to those of traditional utility theory and the independence assumption (Axiom 4), it has been possible to demonstrate that both utility and subjective probability form sensation scales in the Fechnerian sense. In psychophysics it has been argued, though never fully accepted, that subjective experience must be represented by such scales; however, the defining condition is neither simple nor has it been derived from other assumptions. The traditional practice has been to postulate this condition as an *a priori* definition of subjective sensation, and, of course, many have objected that it is much too sophisticated to be accepted as a basic axiom. Whether a model that parallels this one and that arrives at sensation scales as a consequence, not as a postulate, can be developed for psychophysical problems is not known.[4]

For a fuller statement of this theory and for proofs of the assertions, see [2].

REFERENCES

1. Edwards, Ward, "The Theory of Decision Making," *Psychological Bulletin,* **51,** 1954, pp. 380–417.
2. Luce, R. D., "A Probabilistic Theory of Utility," *Econometrica,* **26,** 1958, pp. 193–224.
3. ———, *Individual Choice Behavior,* John Wiley & Sons, New York, 1959.

[4] Since this was written, I have developed a model, based upon a single plausible axiom (aside from those of ordinary probability theory), which is a probabilistic generalization of transitivity, that establishes the existence of sensation scales for arbitrary sets of alternatives whenever discrimination is not perfect; see [3].

4. Luce, R. D., and H. Raiffa, *Games and Decisions,* John Wiley & Sons, New York, 1957.
5. Ramsey, F. P., *The Foundations of Mathematics,* Harcourt, Brace and Co., New York, 1931.
6. Savage, L. J., *Foundations of Statistics,* John Wiley & Sons, New York, 1954.
7. von Neumann, John, and Oskar Morgenstern, *Theory of Games and Economic Behavior,* 2nd ed., Princeton University Press, Princeton, 1947.

PART

III

SOME PROBLEMS
IN THE PHYSICAL SCIENCES

8

PHILOSOPHICAL PROBLEMS CONCERNING THE MEANING OF MEASUREMENT IN PHYSICS

Henry Margenau [1]

EUGENE HIGGINS PROFESSOR OF PHYSICS AND NATURAL PHILOSOPHY
YALE UNIVERSITY

1. The trouble with the idea of measurement is its seeming clarity, its obviousness, its implicit claim to finality in any investigative discourse. Its status in philosophy of science is taken to be utterly primitive; hence the difficulties it embodies, if any, tend to escape de tection and scrutiny. Yet it cannot be primitive in the sense of being exempt from analysis; for if it were, every measurement would require to be simply accepted as a protocol of truth, and one should never ask which of two conflicting measurements is correct, or preferable. Such questions are continually being asked, and their propriety in science indicates that even measurement, with its implication of simplicity and adroitness, points beyond itself to other matters of importance on which it relies for validation.

Measurement stands, in fact, at the critical junction between theory and the kind of experience often called sensory, immediate, or datal. The cover-all term for this latter type of experience is—most unfortunately and misleadingly—"observation." This word is vague

[1] Aided by The National Science Foundation through research grant NSF-02257.

enough to hide a variety of problems; its penumbra of meaning overlaps that of measurement, and the two are often confused, a circumstance which further aggravates the analysis here to be conducted. What should be clear upon very little critical inspection is the following: If observation denotes what is coercively given in sensation, that which forms the last instance of appeal in every scientific explanation or prediction, and if theory is the constructive rationale serving to understand and regularize observations, then measurement is the process that mediates between the two, the conversion of the immediate into constructs via number or, viewed the other way, the contact of reason with Nature.

Theories are welded in two places to the P-plane (if I may introduce a term to designate the "perceptory" or "protocol" phase of experience, i.e., the kind just called observation), and both unions are measurements. In the simplest instance, certain quantities (e.g., position and velocity of a moving object) are measured; the results are then fed into a theory (e.g., Newtonian mechanics); here, through logical and mathematical transformations, a new set of numbers arises (e.g., position and velocity, or some other variable relating to the object at some other time) and these numbers are finally, again through measurement, confronted with P-facts. No scientific theory can have but a single contact with the P-plane—if it makes that claim it is called "magic." To change the metaphor, measurement enables both embarkation and debarkation of a theoretical traveler at the shore of empirical fact. Ordinarily, these operations are without difficulty and without interest. But when the sea is rough, they present problems and require special consideration. Fundamental reorganizations of theory, like seismic disturbances at the bottom of an ocean, produce troubled seas, and nowhere in modern physics has there occurred a greater revolution of thought than in quantum mechanics. Here the landing has been difficult, and the problem of measurement clamors for understanding and solution with particular urgency.

2. In this paper I attempt to prepare an understanding, but make no claim of providing a complete solution of the problem. In this attempt, the first step is to clear away the debris of older misconceptions. Most philosophers and many scientists regard measurement as a simple "look-and-see" procedure, requiring at the most a careful description of apparatus and the recording of a number. In doing so, they ignore two things. First, the relevance of the number obtained, its reference

to something that is to be measured, and its physical dimension. For the apparatus and the act alone do not tell us that the measured number represents a length, an energy, or a frequency; this identification involves the use of certain rules of correspondence with preformed theoretical constructs which greatly complicates the meaning of measurement. In the second place, a single measured number is devoid of significance except as a tentative indication, acceptable only under the duress of conditions that forbid the repetition of a measurement. Generally, measurements must form an aggregate to be of importance in science.

Eddington's persuasive claim of the reducibility of all measurements to pointer readings on a scale is equally fallacious. It is contradicted by the obvious possibility, indeed the increasingly prevalent method, of counting events without the use of pointer or scale—by the existence of "yes-or-no" measurements performed while watching a signal. Merely to see whether a spectral line occurs in a given region of a photographic plate may, in certain cases, constitute an important measurement. Clearly, one must beware of oversimplifying the meaning of that term.

3. Let us look briefly at the collective aspect of measurement. As was said, a measured number by itself signifies nothing that could safely be interpreted by means of rational constructs. If an aggregate is at hand, and only then, the theoretical significance of the measurements can be assessed. For in that case only do we have facilities for determining the error, or the measure of precision, of the results and can know what to do with them theoretically. But the discernment of errors raises further problems that need to be discussed.

An empirically "true" value of a measured quantity does not exist. What passes for truth among the results of measurement is maximum likelihood, a concept that attains meaning if a sufficient statistical sample of differing measured values is available. When such a sample is obtained, the physicist can plot a distribution curve that represents the quintessence of the intended measurement, since this curve reveals and determines the answer sought. It tells in the first place whether the set of values under inspection is trustworthy or whether it is to be rejected because of some manifest bias of the distribution. A simple, although not always applicable test for acceptability, is to see if the distribution is Gaussian. But to justify this or any other test is to invoke some sort of uniformity of nature, to appeal to "randomness" of the observations (a term so far not susceptible of rigorous mathematical definition); in short, it introduces the entire group of annoyances known to philosophers as "the problem of induction."

When the absence of bias has been established, the search begins for that value which is to be regarded as the most acceptable result of the series of measurements. Ordinarily one chooses for this distinction the value at the top of the distribution curve, reasoning that, if an infinite number of measurements were available, that value would occur most often. But this presumably most popular value is not in reality among the measured set, and its selection is attended by some uncertainty. For it is possible to draw an infinite number of error curves to approximate the finite collection of measurements under treatment, each error curve having a slightly different maximum. The choice of this maximum again introduces a need for considerations transcending any simple meaning of measurement.

4. The difficulties thus raised culminate in two questions regarding the manner in which sequences of measured values approach the ideal of truth, in so far as that ideal is revealed through measurement. The first concerns internal, the second external convergence.

To explain the first, let me suppose that a measurement is repeated N times with the same apparatus. The N results enable the construction of an error curve which fits them best according to some mathematical criterion, and the curve has a maximum M_N, as well as a certain width at half maximum W_N, called the half-width. As a matter of experience, W_N remains approximately constant as N increases, and may, therefore, be considered as a sort of instrumental uncertainty attached to the apparatus employed. The quantity M_N will fluctuate as N increases, and the question of internal convergence of the measurements is whether a limit $\lim_{N \to \infty} M_N$ exists. Experience answers this question affirmatively: we know of no instance where internal convergence fails. It is true that the meaning of the term "limit" must be changed from its strict classical understanding to the modern stochastic one in order to justify the foregoing statement; but this is a small price for a most satisfying nod of nature.

External convergence has to do with the behavior of W_N when different measuring apparatus are employed in a sequence of sets of measurements. Is it possible, at least within reasonable limits, to choose different devices of increasing instrumental precision in such a way that W becomes smaller and smaller, falling each time within the range of all

preceding W? In other words, does $\lim_{S \to \infty} W^S$ approach 0? In writing
this formula, we have omitted the subscript N because, as we have seen, W does not depend on it; but we have added the superscript S to designate the Sth measuring apparatus employed, these different apparatus being arranged in the order of increasing instrumental precision. Thus, if we are to measure a length, $S = 1$ might designate a carpenter's rule, $S = 2$ a carefully calibrated yardstick, $S = 3$ a vernier caliper, $S = 4$ a traveling microscope, $S = 5$ an interferometer device, etc. To be sure, external convergence cannot be tested in as simple and exhaustive a way as internal convergence because apparatus are not infinitely available. The interesting fact, however, is that despite this difficulty we already are aware of an important failure of external convergence: $\lim_{S \to \infty} W^S$ does
not approach zero when the measurements involve atomic systems. An accurate account of this failure is given in Heisenberg's uncertainty or indeterminacy principle of quantum mechanics, which we are thus led to consider.

5. According to the textbook version [1], two canonically conjugate quantities, such as position and momentum of a particle, or the energy of a physical system and the time at which it possesses this energy, cannot be measured simultaneously with unlimited precision. The story is that a measurement of one "inevitably" disturbs the other, and the argument then becomes inductive, appealing to a profusion of experimental situations in which the physical effect of a position measurement is to *alter* the momentum of the particle. Just why a change in the magnitude of the momentum should preclude its simultaneous measurement is supposed to be obvious, or at any rate is deemed a question too silly for the physicist to answer. This stereotyped attitude with its logical myopia has neither been dislodged by the clear evidence that one is often able to measure rapidly varying quantities with considerable success, nor by the patent possibility of making simultaneous measurements upon position and momentum of any particle, including an electron, with actually existing apparatus. Even the famous gamma-ray microscope, the *pièce de résistance* against every doubt afflicting the argument just offered, permits simultaneous measurements of both position and momentum, for there is no reason whatever why one cannot bombard an electron at the same time with many short- and long-wave gamma rays and wait until one gets a simultaneous return. True, there are hazards and idealizations in this proposal, and one may have to wait a very long time, but these difficulties are hardly of a

different sort from those encountered in the accepted "thought experiment," although they are now compounded and thereby aggravated.

Clearly, it is *not* impossible to make measurements of canonically conjugate quantities as nearly simultaneously as we please if measurement means putting a question to nature and getting a unique answer. What the uncertainty principle means to assert is that this answer—when interpreted in detailed fashion following the precepts of Newtonian mechanics, in a manner which pretends to follow the course of the interaction between photon and electron in every visual particular—makes no sense. It makes no sense on two accounts: first, in that the two numbers comprising the answer contain no reference to any definite instant of time at which both were present, since the measuring process does require a finite time. This, in itself, is not disturbing because the very essence of quantum mechanics enjoins us from employing classical models, visual interpretations of atomic happenings, and the fact remains that we get two numbers. The unique feature of quantum mechanics, as of the uncertainty principle, lies in the failure of what we have called external convergence. Hence, and this is the second reason why the answer alluded to above makes no sense, when the measurement is repeated, even with apparatus of indefinitely increasing refinement, the values obtained remain scattered over a nonshrinking range; they approach no limit, but their variances or probable errors, i.e., $W^s(q)$ for position and $W^s(p)$ for momentum, satisfy the relation $W^s(q) \cdot W^s(p) > ah$, where h is Planck's constant and a a number of order 1. Somehow, the uncertainty relation adverts to some disposition inherent in the state of the electron which manifests itself in the statistical distribution of the measurements made upon it, provided a sufficient statistical sample of measurements is at hand. We shall see below that this disposition is introduced into the situation, not by the act of measurement, but by a prior procedure to be called the preparation of the electron's state, and that it has its locus not so much in human manipulations as in the very essence of the electron.

Many physicists regard the fine distinctions made above as idle and unprofitable embellishments of what everybody knows, or else they disagree with the analysis for reasons never specified. It seems to me, however, that, if the preceding analysis is correct, the *philosophic* significance of the uncertainty principle, and indeed of quantum mechanics as a whole, is profoundly modified. For if the usual version holds, the principle amounts to a proscription of certain kinds of measurement; it says that certain P-plane experiences are impossible; it limits the field of actual empirical occurrences. Now it is my view that any physical theory which places a ban on possible *observational* experiences mortgages the future of science in an intolerable way. For it is the unconquerable mood of science that it will accept any "historically" valid fact of experience and see what it can do with it within its system of explanation, and if a contradiction arises, it is the theoretical system that is sacrificed.

The situation is quite different with respect to the structure of the concepts employed in physical explanation. Here proscription seems quite in order and is indeed practiced at every turn. We agree to use causal theories in preference to noncausal ones; we subject equations to covariance with respect to the Lorentz group; we rejected an unobservable elastic ether although, as Poincaré pointed out, it could be made to satisfy all observations. The interpretation of uncertainty advocated here places that important principle squarely among the methodological devices in terms of which we agree to describe observational experience. It is properly silent with respect to what can possibly be measured but speaks with eloquence and convincing force of the manner in which the measurements relate themselves to theoretical constructs. In the terms of my own earlier publications, it generates a rule of correspondence, and not a blackout on the P-plane. Uncertainty implies no ban on measurements; it prescribes the structure of certain theories. Nor does it throw a particularly revealing light on the philosophical nature of measurement.

6. There is a mathematical fiction that has tended in some respects to preserve, in others further to confound the naive metaphysical conception that a measurement disturbs a physical system in a predeterminable way. It was used persuasively by von Neumann and later by others who were able to derive from this fiction the correct formalism of quantum mechanics, thus adding another example to the vast array of scientific instances in which correct conclusions were deduced from insupportable premises.

Specifically, the story is this. Quantum mechanics associates operators or matrices with measurable physical quantities. We know, for example, what matrices correspond to the position, the momentum, the energy, etc., of a so-called particle. One of the simplest and mathematically most interesting matrices is the so-called statistical matrix P which satisfies the equation $P^2 = P$. For reasons to be given below, this is called the projection matrix, and it can be constructed quite easily in the following way. Suppose we are given a complex column vector **a** of unit length, so that its components behave in accordance with the normalizing relation $\sum_i a_i a_i{}^* = 1$. From every such **a** one can construct a P. To form the elements ρ_{ij} of the projection matrix all one needs to do is multiply together two of the components a_λ; precisely, $\rho_{ij} = a_i a_j{}^*$. The defining equation is then satisfied, since $(\rho^2)_{ij} = \sum_\lambda a_i a_\lambda{}^* a_\lambda a_j{}^* = a_i a_j{}^* = \rho_{ij}$. Furthermore, the eigenvalues of P are easily seen to be 1 and 0, suggesting that the matrix ought to correspond to some physical quantity which is characterized by presence or absence, yes or no, success or failure, or some other two-valued aspect. Could it refer to measurement, in the sense that measurement asks whether a specified value is present or not?

The temptation to connect P with measurement is further strengthened by another remarkable coincidence, which we present first in mathematical terms. Suppose that **x** is a column vector. Then $(P\mathbf{x})_i = \sum_\lambda a_i a_\lambda{}^* x_\lambda = (\sum_\lambda a_\lambda{}^* x_\lambda)\, a_i = (\mathbf{a}^+ \cdot \mathbf{x}) a_i$, $\mathbf{a}^+$ being the adjoint of the vector **a**. Thus the result of operating on a vector **x** with P yields $P\mathbf{x} = (\mathbf{a}^+ \cdot \mathbf{x})\mathbf{a}$. But $\mathbf{a}^+ \cdot \mathbf{x}$ is the scalar product of a unit vector $\mathbf{a}^+$ and the initial vector **x**, whereas **a** is another unit vector. Hence P, when acting on **x**, changes the direction of **x** into that of the unit vector **a** from which P was constructed, and it diminishes the magnitude of **x** to that of its component along $\mathbf{a}^+$. In somewhat simpler language, P "projects" a vector on which it acts upon a specified direction.

Is this not exactly what measurement does to the state of a physical system? If before the measurement the state is given by a vector **x** (in Hilbert space), then, after the measurement, **x** has been converted into a state characteristic of the measured value, namely **a**, but multiplied by a coefficient $(\mathbf{a}^+ \cdot \mathbf{x})$ indicating the probability that this will happen. The suggestion is very strong that the interesting matrix P be taken as the counterpart of the physical process called measurement.

In plainer language, this assignment entails the following conclusions. If a physical system is in a quantum state which is not an eigenstate of the observable to be measured, then a measurement of that observable causes the system to be suddenly transformed into some eigenstate of the observable. The plausibility of this correspondence between P and a measurement is further attested to by the fact that a second measurement following upon the heels of the first can cause no further change in the state of the system, a fact which is mirrored by the property of P: its iteration has no further effect, $P^2\mathbf{x} = P\mathbf{x}$. In the sequel I shall speak of the postulate here outlined, in connection with the mathematics which suggested it, as the *projection postulate*. It claims that a measurement converts an arbitrary quantum state into an eigenstate of the measured observable.

7. The physical case in favor of the projection postulate has been argued most strongly and succinctly by Einstein who, curiously, did not believe that the present form of the quantum theory was satisfactory. In 1935 he, in collaboration with B. Podolski and N. Rosen, attempted to show that quantum theory cannot describe reality. As a sequel to this well-known publication, I wrote a short article pointing out that Einstein's difficulties, and his so-called paradox, at once vanish when the projection postulate is dropped, whereas the power of quantum mechanics remains unchanged. In a personal answer to my paper Einstein wrote: [2]

The present form of quantum mechanics is adjusted to the following postulate, which seems inevitable in view of the facts of experience:

If a measurement performed upon a system yields a value m, then the same measurement performed immediately afterwards yields again the value m with certainty.

Example: If a quantum of light has passed a polarizer P_1, then I know with certainty that it will also pass a second polarizer P_2 which has its orientation parallel to the first.

This is true independently of the way in which the quantum is produced, hence also in the case in which prior to the passage of the first polarizer (P_1) the probability for the polarization direction perpendicular to that of P_1 was not zero (for instance the case in which the quantum of light comes from a polarizer P_0 whose polarization direction forms an acute angle with that of P_1).

For these reasons, the assumption is in my opinion inevitable that a measurement modifies the probability amplitudes of a state, that is, produces in the sense of quantum mechanics a *new* state which is an eigenstate with respect to the variables to which the measurement refers.

8. Here is the physical argument in a nutshell, simple and beguiling. *If* the photon passes through P_1, then it will surely pass through P_2, P_3, and any number of other polarizers if they are set parallel to P_1. But is the passage through P_1 a measurement? Whatever the meaning of this operation, it must provide a positive answer and not merely a hypothetical one. Now to remove the *if* from Einstein's proposition, the observer must see whether the photon did, in fact, pass through P_1. For this purpose, he may use his eye, a photocell, or some other device that will register the photon's presence. In other words, P_1 plus photocell constitute a measuring instrument; P_1 alone merely *prepares a*

---

[2] Private letter from which an excerpt is published here (in translation) with permission of the literary executors of Professor Einstein's estate.

state. The example shows the need for a very clear distinction between (1) the preparation of a state and (2) a measurement. In classical physics, the two are ordinarily the same, but in quantum mechanics they often differ.

A careful study of the situation considered by Einstein will doubtless lead to an account such as this. To the left of P_1 (assuming for definiteness that the photon is known to be on the left of the polarizer), the photon is in a state of known or unknown character, a state which is supposedly not an eigenstate of its spin (polarization). Whether or not that state has been prepared by human intervention is of no interest; it is *un*prepared with respect to the inquiry concerning its spin which is about to be conducted. To the right of P_1 the state *is* prepared; it is an eigenstate of the spin. Thus P_1 prepares the state, but it does not perform a measurement, since P_1 does not tell me whether a photon passed through P_1. This is the important character of the act called "preparation of state" in quantum mechanics: that *it determines the state of a physical system but leaves us in ignorance as to the incumbency of that state after preparation;* it may be a state without a system; i.e., no photon may be present on the right of P_1.

To perform a measurement, a photocell must be placed to the right of P_1, and the combination, P_1 plus photocell, is a measuring instrument, a device which says categorically that a photon with definite and known spin did in fact exist. But this measurement did *not* produce an eigenstate of the spin; indeed it destroyed that state—more than that, it destroyed the photon! Yet it was a good measurement despite its violation of the projection postulate. In contradistinction to the preparation of a state, a measurement certifies that *some system responded to a process, even though we are left in ignorance as to the state of the system after the response.*

These are the bare requirements of (1) preparation and (2) measurement, requirements which in some sense complement each other. However, there are numerous physical operations which combine the two requirements and may therefore be regarded as both—preparation and measurement. This contingency is very common in macroscopic affairs (and in classical physics) where a machine which turns out nuts or bolts according to specifications may indiscriminately be said to prepare or to measure them. For we know of the finished product that (1) if it is present, it is in a certain state and (2) that it is, in fact, present.

In atomic physics there are likewise instances in which a single operation prepares a state and measures. To be sure, for the measurement of photon spins I have not been able to find such an example, as I see no practical way in which the photon can register its presence and retain its polarization. A photon's position, however, can easily be measured in two ways, one effecting a measurement only, and another effecting both a measurement and a preparation of state. The first occurs when the position is determined by means of a photographic plate, where a blackened grain is at once position record and tombstone of the photon, and where projection into an eigenstate has certainly not taken place. The second is a measurement through the Compton recoil of a charged particle, where the photon is preserved and the state at the moment of recoil is a definite eigenstate of the position (delta function). Here it is possible that another charged particle, situated near the first immediately after the measurement, might suffer a collision and thereby signify the persistence of the state produced by the measurement. Similar preparation-measurement operations can be made upon the position of a charged particle itself (instead of the photon); indeed, a visible cloud chamber track is nothing but an extended series of such dual events. It would appear, then, as if in this latter class of operations the projection postulate stood aright, as if it characterized some, though not all, measurements.

But there are complications even here. Although quantum mechanics permits the preparation and the measurement of a position eigenstate, it takes back with one hand what it has given with the other, since it requires that such an eigenstate cannot persist for any finite time; according to Schrödinger's equation, the state function diffuses with infinite speed. Only for a sufficiently indefinite position measurement do we have an opportunity of testing what is not truly an eigenstate!

Thoughts of this kind, when properly entertained against the seductive surface plausibility of the projection postulate, indict it severely and raise the hope that one might get along without it. Such hope, strange to say, is not frustrated when a positive effort is made to build the foundation of quantum mechanics without the postulate; indeed, it becomes perfectly clear on very little consideration that the postulate is *never needed at all*. Suppose we drop it and assign to the individual measuring act no power beyond yielding a number. Instead of making it produce a state, we let it terminate our inquiry concerning the state in question, i.e., the state existing prior to the measurement. With this minimal function, measurement still satisfies its purpose in quantum mechanics. Alone, a single measurement is devoid of significance, as it should be. Performed on an ensemble, however, it generates the distribution discussed in Section 3 and permits the collective treatment necessary for the theoretical interpretation of the measured observable. Commitments with respect to any subsequent effect of the measurement on the system are superfluous.

The ensemble which enters the discussion at this point is either a physical assemblage of copresent systems, all similarly prepared, which respond simultaneously to the measuring act, or it is a temporal sequence of identical state preparations upon an individual system, each preparation being terminated by a measurement.

In conclusion of this section, let it be said that its contents can hardly be taken as a definitive solution of the problems under study; rather, they suggest the desirability of an unbiased, careful, and exhaustive survey of all classes of physical measurements that does not prejudge their nature in favor of some mathematical conviction.

9. Current disbelief [2] in the correctness of the present formulation of quantum mechanics has its source at least partly in the grotesque claims of the projection postulate. De Broglie, for example, bases one objection upon the improbability of the "reduction of a wave packet" occurring on measurement. The phrase, "reduction of a wave packet," adverts to the projection attending the position measurement of an electron. Suppose the energy of this entity is known exactly, not necessarily by any measurement that has actually been made upon it but by the manner in which it was produced (e.g., photoelectric effect). Its state is then represented by a wave function which extends with equal amplitude throughout all space. If a position measurement now succeeds in determining its actual place, the wave will have been "reduced" or, to put the matter more graphically, will have collapsed upon the measured locus, having taken on the value zero everywhere except at one point—provided we accept the projection postulate. This sudden transformation, for which there is no precedent in all of physics, has raised many eyebrows and has led men like De Broglie to assert that the state function cannot represent any physical reality. For if it carries information, the instantaneous collapse violates relativity theory; on the other hand, it might be said to confirm the claims of the advocates of telepathy.

To save the quantum theory in view of these infelicities, it has been customary to deny real status to the electron's state function and to regard it as a measure of knowledge which can, in fact, do peculiar things. This avenue is unquestionably open. It leads, however, to the equally unpleasant consequence that physics has seriously begun to describe human knowledge, a subjective aspect of the mind, in terms of differential equations involving physical constants. The point I wish to make is that we are not forced to this conclusion. A removal of the projection postulate removes De Broglie's difficulty, as it eliminates Einstein's. The state function then refers to an objectively real probability like the probability of tossing a head with a penny, a quantity which retains the value ½ even when a throw has yielded a head.

10. The last item to be discussed under the heading of physical measurement and its philosophic interpretation is not directly related to the projection postulate; it has to do with another paradox which measurement has been illicitly called upon to resolve. The second law of thermodynamics asserts that every isolated physical system, such as a gas contained in an absolutely rigid container, increases its entropy. The unusual case in which the entropy remains constant is not of interest here. This means that the system changes its internal state in a certain way, the change leading to conditions of greater and greater probability.

But in quantum mechanics, an isolated system, which cannot exchange energy with its surroundings, reaches very rapidly a state in which its energy is definite, if it has not been left in an eigenstate of the energy to begin with. Unfortunately, such a state is a stationary one, i.e., a state in which the system will continue indefinitely. How it can possibly satisfy the second law thus becomes problematic.

Our pragmatists resolve the difficulty in this way. The state of a truly isolated system, they say, is uninteresting because it cannot be known. To become known, the state must undergo a measurement. But a measurement "opens" the state, interferes with it, and raises the entropy every time it occurs. The second law does not refer to truly isolated systems, but to systems repeatedly subjected to measurements. The latter act becomes the *deus ex machina* which saves the second law from being trivial or false.

This solution is highly unsatisfactory to me, for I like to think of the second law of thermodynamics as a pronouncement which is valid independently of intervention. That is to say, measurement should not again be given sacramental unction and expected to perform a redemptive act. Band [3] has pointed out a better way out of the dilemma: it is simple, obvious and devoid of mysticism. He shows that to assume a perfectly rigid enclosure is a classical falsification of the quantum situation. Such an assumption violates the uncertainty principle, which requires a connection between momentum and position of the walls just sufficient to supply the mechanism that drives the system to more probable states. The process which "opens" the system is not measurement but the inevitable character of nature which is present even in the absence of an observer.

Is it meaningful to speak of the uncertainty principle as exhibiting a fundamental trait of nature, a character independent of observation? Is not the uncertainty principle merely that basic postulate which, when incorporated into the quantum theory at the very beginning, automatically takes cognizance of interactions and allows us to forget the effect of measurement ever after? If this is the case, does not the argument of the preceding section contradict itself because it denies the need of human intervention when the very axioms of quantum mechanics already include its effects?

Indeed, it may be that such questions cast doubt upon the considerations of this section; to me, these questions appear to be among the most important unsolved problems of the philosophy of physics. Quite apart from their answers, however, there remains an unambiguous issue in the present consideration. The entropy of an isolated system either increases in discrete steps whenever measurements are made or it increases in continuous fashion as we wait, even before a measurement occurs. Our point is that the second alternative is realized, and this matter is open to test.

In concluding, I wish particularly to call attention to one other line of investigation designed to eliminate the logical difficulties here uncovered. It is Landé's approach [4], which, though different from the present sketch and more analytic in detail, clearly and sensitively moves to a similar end. I owe Professor Landé gratitude for much inspiration.

REFERENCES

1. A. March, *Quantum Mechanics of Particles and Wave Fields,* New York, John Wiley and Sons, 1951.
2. Reference is here made to the studies of De Broglie, Bohm and others. These are reviewed and carefully answered by W. Heisenberg in *Niels Bohr and the Development of Physics* (Pauli, Rosenfeld, and Weisskopf, eds.), New York, McGraw-Hill Book Co., 1955.
3. William Band, *A New Look at von Neumann's Operator and the Definition of Entropy* (unpublished).
4. A. Lande, *Foundations of Quantum Theory,* Yale University Press, 1955, and numerous later articles.

9

ARE PHYSICAL MAGNITUDES
OPERATIONALLY DEFINABLE?

Arthur Pap

ASSOCIATE PROFESSOR OF PHILOSOPHY
YALE UNIVERSITY

The question chosen as title of this paper may strike the reader as peculiar. For it is often said that an operational definition of a concept is a definition in terms of operations of measurement. To be an operationist, many scientists would say, is to insist that scientific concepts be made precise and empirically applicable by defining them in terms of measuring operations. Does it not follow, then, that, if any concepts are operationally definable, then concepts of physical magnitudes are? However, the widely used term "operational definition" needs clarification. I shall specify in the course of this paper a sense in which such terms as "length," "mass," "temperature," etc., are not operationally definable in so far as they enter into the mathematical formulation of physical laws; but I will also specify a sense in which they must be operationally definable if they are to have any physical significance.

OPERATIONAL DEFINITION AS CONTEXTUAL
DEFINITION OF CLASSIFICATORY PREDICATES

Although operationism was originally a program of concept formation aimed at quantitative sciences, the term "operationism" nowadays tends to connote the *empiricist* postulate that any descriptive term,

177

whether quantitative or not, which is cognitively significant must either designate something that is directly observable or else be definable in some way on the basis of terms of the latter kind. In the correspondingly broad sense of "operational definition," an operational definition specifies the sort of observations that are relevant to decide the question whether the defined term is applicable in a given situation. I am here adopting Carnap's [1] terminology in distinguishing classificatory predicates like "long," "warm," "heavy" from comparative predicates like "longer," "equally warm," "heavier," and from metrical terms (functors) like "length (of x cm)," "temperature (of x degrees)," etc. Many classificatory predicates used in formulating empirical laws do not designate directly observable qualities but seem to be definable in terms of observables in a straightforward fashion: such are the classificatory *disposition* predicates like "soluble," "magnetic," and "electrically charged." Thus: x is soluble in liquid $L =_{df}$ if at any time x were immersed in L, then x would dissolve in L. This kind of definition is contextual in the sense that it defines a predicate in the context of a particular form of statement containing it; it is a rule for translating statements containing the disposition predicate into synonymous statements that do not contain it. It is operational only in the sense of telling us by what kind of observations we may hope to confirm or disconfirm directly a statement of the form "x is soluble in L." If we happen to observe an immersion of a solid object in a liquid L, we can decide whether it is soluble in L just as easily as if we had intentionally immersed it ourselves. In this respect the word "operational" is unfortunate, for it suggests experimental activities whereas the definiens need not mention experimental activities at all. To illustrate further, Einstein's definition of distant simultaneity has been cited by Bridgman as a classical example of operational definition. It can be formulated as a contextual definition as follows: Spatially separated events E_1 and E_2 happen simultaneously $=_{df}$ if light rays are emitted from the places of E_1 and E_2 at the times when the events happen there, one light ray going from E_1 to E_2 and the other in the opposite direction, then they will reach the mid-point simultaneously. This definition mentions emissions of light rays, but it does not mention experimental physicists flashing light signals and receiving light signals at the mid-point. Or consider the following contextual definition of magnetism: x is magnetic at $t =_{df}$ if a small iron body is in the vicinity of x at t, then it will accelerate towards x at t. According to this definition the occurrence of an acceleration under certain conditions confirms the statement that a particular object is magnetic regardless of whether those conditions are intentionally instituted by an experimenter or just happen to be realized without experimental design.

OPERATIONAL DEFINITION IN THE FORM OF REDUCTION SENTENCES

If the logical constant "if-then" by means of which such contextual definitions are formulated is construed in the sense of material implication, then, as Carnap first pointed out in "Testability and Meaning" [2], such definitions are wholly inadequate. Since a material implication with a false antecedent is true,[1] such definitions entail that any object has at time t any disposition that is defined in terms of a "stimulation" to which the object is not exposed at t: all bodies are magnetic and electrically charged at those times when they are sufficiently distant from test particles, wooden objects are soluble in liquids in which they are never immersed, etc. In order to avoid this paradox, Carnap proposed that disposition terms be introduced into scientific languages by reduction sentences, such as: If a small iron body is in the vicinity of x at t, then x is magnetic at t if and only if the iron body accelerates towards x at t. Unlike definitions in the usual sense of the term, they do not have the form of an equivalence, and dispositional statements accordingly are not *translatable* into a language whose descriptive predicates are exclusively observable predicates;[2] though, according to the theory of "Testability and Meaning," truth conditions for dispositional statements can be formulated in such an "observation language." But it would be a perfectly sound objection to this argument in favor of reduction sentences that it is based on a misinterpretation of the expression "if-then." No causal statement of conditional form, such as, "if the vase is dropped on the floor, it will break," is ever meant as a material implication. Therefore Carnap should have concluded, not that disposition terms are not "definable" in the usual sense but that they are not so definable in terms of material implication; or more generally speaking, that causal implications cannot be analyzed by means of an *extensional* language.[3]

[1] This follows from the definition of material implication: "$p \supset q$" means that either "p" is false or "q" is true.

[2] The term "observable predicate" is used by Carnap in the sense of a predicate designating a directly observable quality or relation.

[3] An extensional language is a language satisfying the following conditions: (a) All molecular statements, i.e., statements containing statements as parts, like conjunctions, disjunctions, implications, are truth functions of the component

Is there, however, something else to be said in favor of reduction sentences, even after the weakness of the argument from the "paradoxes of material implication"[4] has been conceded? Indeed, it has been argued (by myself among others [4]) that the use of reduction sentences can be justified by the consideration that they specify the meanings of disposition terms only partially, relative to specific test conditions; which feature reflects the actual use of disposition terms by scientists. Thus our sample reduction sentence does not completely specify the meaning of "magnetic" because it provides us with no criterion for using the term in a situation where x is far removed from small iron bodies. Yet, it is by no means meaningless to characterize such an object as magnetic or nonmagnetic because there are other tests for magnetism, formulated by other reduction sentences, as for example: if x moves through a closed wire loop at t, then x is magnetic at t if and only if an electric current[5] flows in the loop at t. Some have objected to this method of incomplete meaning specification because it blurs the distinction between analytic statements, which elucidate the meaning of a term, and synthetic (factual) statements about the things designated by the term [5]. Why not operationally define, they say, magnetism by means of one of these tests and then formulate an empirically confirmable law to the effect that a magnetic body so defined has such and such other dispositions? But such a reconstruction surely is not a reconstruction of the scientists' actual usage of the terms in question. For suppose a physicist were asked what he would say in the following situation: a small iron object which is close to x accelerates towards x but when x is moved through a closed wire loop, immediately after the close of this experiment, the most accurate tests fail to detect a flow of electric current through the wire. If the operational definition referring to test particles expressed the complete meaning of statements of the form "x is magnetic at t," the scientist would have to say that undoubtedly x was magnetic at that

statements, i.e., their truth values are uniquely determined by the truth values of the component statements; (b) the truth value of nonmolecular statements depends only on the extensions, not the intensions, of the constituent predicates. For a comprehensive discussion of the problem as to whether disposition concepts are analyzable by means of an extensional language, see [3].

[4] The "paradoxes of material implication" are the theorems: $\sim p \supset (p \supset q)$; $q \supset (p \supset q)$, i.e., a false proposition materially implies any proposition and a true proposition is materially implied by any proposition.

[5] The term "electric current" is not an observable predicate but is, in turn, reducible to such predicates.

time but that the law of magnetic induction of electric currents had been refuted. But I am sure he would feel that, though the observed facts force him to revise some of his assumptions about magnetism, he could without logical inconsistency choose to retain the mentioned law and to give up instead the proposition relating magnetism to acceleration of surrounding particles.[6]

Nevertheless, I have lately convinced myself that this argument from "surplus meaning," as it might be called, can be satisfactorily countered by Bridgman's principle "different operations define different concepts" as long as we are dealing with classificatory, nonmetrical disposition concepts. The point is that one could consistently speak of distinct though extensionally equivalent disposition concepts,[7] each of which is completely defined by a particular kind of test, and reflect the multiplicity of concepts by a more differentiating terminology than the one customarily used. Instead of saying that the same disposition manifests itself in different ways, we might say that there are two distinct dispositions D_1 and D_2, each completely defined by a certain stimulus-response sequence (in a generalized sense of "stimulus" and "response") such that, as a matter of empirical fact, anything which has D_1 has D_2, and conversely. This approach has the advantage of avoiding a logically objectionable feature of pairs of reduction sentences for the same disposition term, namely, that a conjunction of analytic statements entai's a synthetic (factual) statement. The conjunction of "$Q_1 \supset (D \equiv Q_2)$" and "$Q_3 \supset (D \equiv Q_4)$" entails "$\sim (Q_1 \cdot Q_2 \cdot Q_3 \cdot \sim Q_4)$"; the negated conjunction "$(Q_1 \cdot Q_2 \cdot Q_3 \cdot \sim Q_4)$," however, is logically possible. It is, for example, logically possible that a body which attracts a small iron body should fail to generate an electric current in a closed wire loop through which it moves. But if we put "D_1" in the first reduction sentence and "D_2" in the second, we cannot formally deduce the mentioned synthetic (factual) consequence; we would require the further premise "$(x)(D_1(x) \equiv D_2(x))$," which is itself synthetic and not deducible from the pair of reduction sentences.[8] If the generalization "$(x)(D_1(x) \equiv D_2(x))$" is highly confirmed, the scientist tends to identify the dispositions, just as we speak on the prescientific level of identical shape qualities that manifest themselves to both sight and touch though, obviously, there are distinct visual and tactual qualities that are not intrinsically connected (as we discover when a stick that looks bent feels straight). But if the

---

[6] I have argued the same point at greater length in [4]. Carnap has more recently endorsed this argument in a very clarifying paper [6].

[7] Two concepts are extensionally equivalent if they apply to the same objects.

[8] I am indebted to Professor H. Mehlberg for calling this logical point to my attention.

operational definitions (in the form of contextual definitions or of reduction sentences) for "D_1" and "D_2" are not logically equivalent, these
terms are not synonymous in spite of their extensional equivalence.

Philosophers of science who, following in the tradition of the earlier
logical positivists, want to split systems of scientific statements into
analytic statements, which elucidate the meanings of symbols, and
synthetic statements, which have "factual content," may feel relief at
this stage of my argument. But they should not praise the day before
the sun sets. For it will be shown that Bridgman's principle "different
operations define different concepts," which I invoked in order to
rescue the analytic-synthetic distinction on the level of qualitative
observation language (extended by reduction sentences introducing
qualitative disposition terms), breaks down the moment we begin to
do quantitative science.

PHYSICAL MAGNITUDES AND
THE LANGUAGE OF OBSERVABLES

The construction of a metrical concept presupposes a serial ordering
of the objects characterized by some value or other of the magnitude
in question. In the case of length, for example, we have to define in
terms of observables what it means to say that one object is longer
than another, and the definition must be such that, as a matter of
empirical fact, the defined relation is transitive. Similarly, an equality
relation with respect to the magnitude in question must be defined
in terms of observables, and it must be empirically shown that this
relation is transitive.[9] If by "operational definition" of a physical
functor [10] is meant just such interpretations, by reference to observable relations, of the corresponding *comparative* terms, it is of course
undeniable that physical functors are operationally definable—whether
the operational definition takes the form of a contextual definition or
of a set of reduction sentences.

But the question here at issue is whether the metrical term itself,
which designates a numerically determinable magnitude, can be re-

[9] For a detailed and precise explanation of the "topological" presuppositions,
see [7].

[10] A functor differs from a predicate in that its atomic statement form is an
equation with object variables and a numerical variable: for example, length
$(x, t) = y$ cm, where x ranges over objects that have some length or other, t over
times, and y over measure numbers. If what is characterized by values of the
functor are space-time points, then the atomic statements have the following
form: $F(x, y, z, t) = u$.

duced to observable predicates. Now, to give such a reduction for the term "length," for example, would mean to formulate in observational terms distinct sufficient conditions for the truth of all admissible substitution instances of the statement form "length$(x, t) = y$ cm." In so far as physical functors are used to formulate numerical laws, their numerical variable is usually *continuous,* as required especially by the applicability of the calculus. But since every measuring instrument, no matter how sensitive it may be, has a finite "least count," only a finite number of determinate forms of a determinable quality can be distinguished by measurement. Continuity is a mathematical idealization which measurement, by its very nature, cannot verify. It would be boring if I were to belabor this simple and well-known argument against the reducibility of physical functors to observational terms [7, 8]. But before turning to a more important and less publicized argument against such reducibility, I would like to rebut an apparently simple answer to it. One might say that to the extent that two such metrical statements as (a) "the length of this rod is 20.74893652 cm" and (b) "the length of this rod is 20.74893654 cm" are empirically significant, they are simply synonymous; their last decimals, with respect to which they differ, just have no experimental significance. In general, a metrical statement has no definite empirical meaning unless the measuring instrument by means of which it is testable is characterized, and once this is done, so the operationist might reply, it will become clear that infinitely many metrical statements that look mathematically incompatible are just synonymous *qua* verifiable statements. However, this answer overlooks that, even if (a) and (b) are construed as referring to the outcome or average outcome of measurements performed with a fixed instrument of fixed sensitivity, measurements are conceivable which would constitute *indirect* evidence for the truth of one and falsehood of the other. This is simply because differences smaller than the least count may become detectable through addition. In order to admit of fundamental measurement, a magnitude must be additive. For the example of weight, this property of additivity consists in the fact that, if the weight of a body A is x grams and the weight of a body B is y grams, then the weight of the physical sum of A and B is $x + y$ grams. Now suppose two statements about the weight of A, p and p', which according to the criterion of empirical synonymy I am criticizing, are empirically synonymous, and statements q and q' about the weight of B which by the same criterion are likewise synonymous. It may easily happen that, by means of the principle of additivity of weight, we can deduce from the conjunction of p and q a statement about the weight of the physical sum of A and B which is *not* empirically synonymous with the corresponding consequence of the conjunction of p' and q'. *Mutatis mutandis,* the same holds for addition of length or of any other additive magnitude. Surely we must conclude from this that the proposed criterion of empirical synonymy of metrical statements is untenable.

But the most important argument against operational definability of physical functors, in the specified stronger sense, arises from reflection on the interplay between measurement and calculation which is characteristic of theoretical physics. Consider, for example, the ascription of a tremendously high temperature to the sun. If the meaning of a physical statement is determined by the operations appropriate for its verification, then "temperature" cannot mean in this context what it means when we speak of, say, the temperature of our bedroom, for the operations by which the temperature of the sun is discovered are partly calculations (Bridgman's "pencil and paper operations") on the basis of laws that have been extrapolated beyond the range within which they were confirmed by measurement. Suppose that, as consistent operationists, we accordingly use different functors for temperatures that can be determined by calculation only and for temperatures that can be determined by measurement: $T^c(\text{sun}) = x$ °K, and $T^e(\text{surface of the earth}) = y$ °C. Similarly, operationist univocality would require different symbols for the measurable mass of a football and for the computable masses of planets and electrons, say, "mass^e (football)," "mass^c(earth)," and "mass^c(electron)." But this analysis cannot be reconciled with the actual procedure of theoretical physics for a very simple reason. The physicist deduces the values of $T^c(\text{sun})$ and mass^c(earth) and mass^c(electron) from empirically verifiable statements about observables by means of equations whose variables range over both measurable and only *computable* values of *one and the same magnitude.* If the Stefan-Boltzmann law, for example, were formulated in terms of T^e, then it could not be used to calculate $T^c(\text{sun})$; if the laws of mechanics were formulated in terms of mass^e, as direct inductions from experiments with manipulable bodies, then they could not be used to calculate mass^c(earth), and so on. In short: unless one is justified in regarding the mass of the earth, the mass of an electron, and the mass of a football as determinate forms of one and the same determinable property, one cannot justify extrapolation of numerical laws for the purpose of calculating values of physical variables which are not accessible to measurement.[11]

THEORETICAL DEFINITION AND PARTIAL INTERPRETATION

The semantic question we have to face now is how a physical functor "F" can be regarded as univocal if, for some substitution instances of the statement form "$F(x) = y$" (y ranging over real measure numbers), a truth condition can be formulated in the observation language, whereas for other substitution instances this cannot be done. In denying that, for example, a truth condition for the statement "the mass of an electron equals x grams" can be formulated in the observation language, I do not, of course, mean to deny that the statement has a high probability relative to certain statements describing experimental results. What I deny is that the statement is a deductive consequence of statements that can be formulated in the observation language, on the obvious ground that the deduction presupposes *theories* in terms of which the experimental data are interpreted. The answer I propose to the above question is that "F" is univocal, provided its theoretical definition is the same no matter whether a statement of the form "$F(x) = y$" is directly verifiable by measurement or only indirectly confirmable by means of the described procedure of extrapolation of confirmed laws that relate F to other magnitudes. A theoretical definition is here contrasted with an *interpretation* in terms of observables.[12] It should be noted that an interpretation of a physical functor, unlike

[11] Discussion of some nice and pertinent questions regarding the precise difference between measurement and calculation must be omitted because of space limitation. Certainly the physicist's language does not clearly distinguish between measurement of a quantity $f(x)$ and calculation of $f(x)$ on the basis of direct measurement of x and a law expressing $f(x)$ as a function of x. Thus he speaks of a measurement of atmospheric pressure though he is really calculating it, in dynes per square centimeter, from the height of the barometric mercury on the basis of hydrostatic principles. Or he speaks of "measuring" the force of gravity in terms of the period of a pendulum. Nevertheless, it is clear that some of the values of a magnitude M to which a law relating M to other magnitudes is assumed to apply are not measurable in the same direct way as other values. This is the only distinction my argument requires, and it cannot be blurred by deciding to call "indirect measurement" what I call "calculation based on measurement and numerical laws."

[12] This contrast is similar to H. Margenau's contrast between "constitutive definitions" that relate a magnitude mathematically to other magnitudes and "epistemic definitions" that describe a method of measuring the magnitude [9].

a theoretical definition, cannot be expressed in the form of an equivalence. It either amounts to a "rule of correspondence" (to borrow a term from both Carnap [6] and Margenau [9]) which tells us how *comparative* statements involving the functor may be empirically tested, or to one which describes a procedure of measurement for a finite and discrete set of values of the functor. What is not possible is the formulation of a universal equivalence: $(x)\,(y)\,[\,(F(x) = y) \equiv (\ldots\ldots\ldots\ldots)\,]$, where the dots on the right of the equivalence sign are filled in with a statement form that can be constructed out of the primitives of the observation language (note that the observation language does not contain real-number variables). Since the word "definition" ordinarily suggests an equivalence, I prefer not to speak of operational definition here, but of rules of correspondence. To illustrate: the definition of the absolute temperature of a body as the average kinetic energy of its molecules is theoretical. Rules of correspondence for "temperature" are: if $T(x, t) > T(y, t)$, then, if contact is established between x and y at t, y becomes warmer and x colder at t; if $T(x, t) = 40°$ C, then, if a centigrade thermometer is brought into contact with x at t, the top of its mercury will coincide with the mark 40 when equilibrium is reached. The above example of theoretical definition happens to be an explicit definition, but a theoretical definition may also have the form of a postulate, or set of postulates; indeed, it cannot be explicit if the theoretical term in question is a primitive, such as length, time interval, and perhaps mass, in classical mechanics. The equation "$F = m \cdot a$" may be regarded as a theoretical definition of force, but the way the term "theoretical definition" is here used this is compatible with also regarding it as a theoretical definition of "mass." If one prefers, one may call it a postulate of mechanics which, jointly with other postulates, implicitly defines the magnitudes that are mathematically related by it. The meaning of a physical functor is determined by both the equations relating it to other functors and the rules of correspondence for it or for other functors to which it is functionally related. If physicists should abandon the rule of correspondence according to which two bodies have equal mass if they extend a spring by equal amounts (provided the spring's position in the gravitational field is unchanged), they would thereby change the meaning of "mass." But they would also change the meaning of "mass" if they abandoned the postulate that the mass of a body which is acted on by a constant force is inversely proportional to the body's. acceleration. Similarly, if the operational criterion of temperature difference, formulated above, were revised, the meaning of "temperature" would therewith be changed; but there would be equally good reason for saying that the meaning of "temperature" had changed if the rules of correspondence were kept unchanged but the theoretical definition in terms of kinetic energy were given up. It is in this sense that the meaning of a physical functor is determined by both the postulates of the deductive system and the rules of correspondence.

It is not at all paradoxical to say that an explicit definition of a term X by means of a complex expression containing a term Y partly fixes the meaning of Y. For by virtue of the logical or mathematical relations expressed by the definition any *interpretation* of X, the defined expression, will delimit the possible interpretations of Y. Thus the kinetic theory of gases contains the term "number of molecules" (n) as a primitive. It is difficult to imagine how this term could be operationally defined, the way number concepts applicable to macro-objects are operationally definable in terms of the process of counting. But n enters into the explicit definitions of pressure, density, and temperature, which functors are partially interpreted in terms of measuring operations; and by virtue of both the rules of correspondence for these explicitly defined functors and their explicit definitions in terms of n, measurements become inductively relevant to hypotheses about the number of molecules contained in a given volume of gas. Note that a physical theory like the kinetic theory of gases is "partially interpreted" in a twofold sense: the primitive terms like "number of molecules" and "displacement of a molecule" are not interpreted by rules of correspondence at all, and the explicitly defined functors of the theory, like pressure and temperature, are not completely interpreted by rules of measurement.[13]

THE BREAKDOWN OF THE ANALYTIC-SYNTHETIC DISTINCTION FOR PARTIALLY INTERPRETED SYSTEMS

Since it is the laws or theories themselves which, jointly with rules of correspondence of whatever form, determine the meanings of the physical functors, it is hopeless to try to reconstruct a quantitative scientific theory dualistically as a system of statements some of which are analytic (i.e., explanatory of the meanings of terms) and some of which have factual content. (In order to obviate the objection that

[13] That it is quite all right, from the point of view of logical empiricism, for physicists to leave some primitive theoretical terms uninterpreted, provided they interpret more complex concepts that are defined by means of them, was first stated by Carnap [10]. See also Nos. 7 and 8 of [7].

surely a statement like "momentum equals mass times velocity" is merely a nominal definition and says nothing about nature, let us suppose that no abbreviatory physical terms are used and the theory is written out in primitive notation. It goes without saying that such physical definitions as Mach's definition of mass or the definition of absolute temperature in terms of kinetic energy of molecules are not nominal if by a "nominal definition" we understand a stipulation that a short expression is to abbreviate a longer one.) Take, for example, the equation relating the average velocity of the molecules to the absolute temperature of the gas. Since temperature is measurable independently of any assumptions about kinetic energies of molecules, and the average kinetic energy of the molecules of a given mass of gas can be calculated within the framework of the kinetic theory, independently of measurements of temperature, there is, as it were, independent access to the two sides of the equation. Therefore it is wrong to say the equation in question is purely analytic, just an explicit definition of temperature in terms of micromagnitudes. The equation definitely is "in principle falsifiable" by measurements: if Boyle's law, for example, should, even as an approximative law, be refuted by measurements, the physicist *might* decide to give up this equation and to retain the other postulates of the kinetic theory. On the other hand, this equation is a postulate which partially defines temperature as well as the mechanical functors that are in the kinetic theory extended to microstates, and in that sense the equation is "analytic." The postulates of the theory and the rules of correspondence have *both* an analytic and a predictive explanatory function. Thus the equation under discussion makes it possible to deduce the general gas law, which was already confirmed by direct measurement, from the dynamic and statistical postulates of the kinetic theory; but, at the same time, the equation gives a physical meaning to the term "velocity of a molecule," for which no rules of correspondence are given, by connecting it functionally with a functor which is directly (though incompletely) interpreted by rules of correspondence. The same double function is performed by the equation relating the macromagnitude pressure to the microvariables: P on area A = instantaneous force on area A divided by $A = (nm \, d\bar{v}/dt)(1/A)$. It expresses one of the assumptions in terms of which the macrobehavior of gases is explained by the kinetic theory and, at the same time, endows "n," "m," and "$\bar{v}$" with physical meaning by linking them to a complex construct for which there is a rule of correspondence (indications of a pressure gauge). It would, of course, be methodologically unenlightened to belittle this equation as a nominal definition which, like all nominal definitions, is theoretically dispensable. For if the variable "pressure" does not occur in the theory, it is impossible to deduce empirical laws containing that variable from the theory.

Another instructive example is the definition of time in mechanics. The required rules of correspondence here include an operational criterion of equality of time intervals and an operational criterion of distant simultaneity (of events happening in the same system). The theoretical definition consists in the postulates relating time to mechanical vectors, some of which are themselves defined in terms of the time variable (they are implicit functions of the time, in the language of physicists), foremost the equation according to which the force acting on a mass m is proportional to the change of velocity of m and inversely proportional to the time during which it acts on m. Now, according to the kind of logical analysis of scientific theory I am criticizing, an operational definition of time equality in terms of some standard clock is an assignment of empirical meaning to a term of the theoretical language and *therefore* not a synthetic statement that can significantly be supposed to be confirmable or disconfirmable. But it is precisely because the (partially) interpreted term is linked by the postulates of the theory to other terms that are likewise (partially) interpreted that conceivable observations can be described which *might* lead the scientists to change the rule of correspondence and keep the postulates unaltered. In fact this did happen when physicists deduced from the laws of mechanics that were first established by means of time measurements based on the assumption of strictly uniform rotation of the earth that, because of tidal friction, it cannot be the case that the earth's rotation around its axis is strictly uniform. It may be replied that in so concluding physicists decided to change their operational definition of time equality because another definition would lead to better agreement of observations with the simple mechanical laws they wished to retain, and that this is different from rejecting a synthetic statement as having been empirically disconfirmed. But the reply is utterly unilluminating because it is not clear how one is to distinguish between rejecting, on empirical evidence, a synthetic postulate which contains a theoretical term, and changing the meaning of the theoretical term in the light of the empirical evidence. One more illustration may be in order to clarify this point. As is well known, even if measurements of the interior angles of a light triangle yield a non-Euclidean sum, it does not follow that the physically interpreted axioms and theorems of Euclidean geometry are false. For one may instead reject the assumption that light rays are straight and postulate "disturbing" forces. Now, suppose the question were raised whether in denying that light rays in gravitational fields travel in straight lines (in the Euclidean sense of "straight") one would simply be changing the physical meaning of "straight"—changing what Reichenbach has called a "coordinative definition"—or would be rejecting an empirical hypothesis (rectilinear propagation of light rays) in order to restore agreement between the total system of empirical hypotheses and the results of measurement. In the absence of a criterion for distinguishing rejection of an empirical hypothesis formulated by means of theoretical term T and reinterpretation of T, this question must be pronounced a pseudo question.

That one can deny the statement "all fathers are happy" without changing the meanings of the terms "father" and "happy" whereas one cannot deny the statement "all fathers are parents" without changing the meaning of either "father" or "parent" (assuming the logical constants to be used normally), I do not wish to controvert. But the attempt to impose this same semantic distinction on the statements of a partially interpreted theoretical language, like the language of theoretical physics, is foredoomed to failure. No observation statement, or conjunction of observation statements, can logically contradict any single statement of such a language; only the entire system, including both theoretical postulates and rules of correspondence, can be so contradicted. It is idle to dispute whether a revision of the system that is made to restore agreement with experience amounts to rejection of a synthetic statement as false or to a change of meanings until a sharp analytic-synthetic distinction for partially interpreted theoretical languages can be defined. Of this possibility I am strongly skeptical.[14]

REFERENCES

1. R. Carnap, *Logical Foundations of Probability,* Chicago, University of Chicago Press, 1950, Chapter 1.
2. ———, "Testability and Meaning," *Philosophy of Science,* 1936, 1937. (Reprinted by the Graduate Philosophy Club, New Haven, Yale University.)
3. A. Pap, "Disposition Concepts and Extensional Logic," *Minnesota Studies in Philosophy of Science,* **II** (Feigl, Scriven and Maxwell, eds.), Minneapolis, University of Minnesota Press; 1958.

[14] In this respect I find myself in complete agreement with the conclusions reached by C. G. Hempel [11].

4. A. Pap, "Reduction Sentences and Open Concepts," *Methodos,* **V,** No. 17, 1953.
5. G. Bergmann, "The Logic of Psychological Concepts," *Philosophy of Science,* April 1951.
6. R. Carnap, "The Methodological Character of Theoretical Concepts," *Minnesota Studies in Philosophy of Science* (Feigl and Scriven, eds.), **I,** Minneapolis, University of Minnesota Press, 1956, pp. 68–69.
7. C. G. Hempel, "Fundamentals of Concept Formation in Empirical Science, III," *Int. Encyclopedia of Unified Science,* **II,** No. 7, Chicago, University of Chicago Press.
8. ――――, "The Concept of Cognitive Significance: A Reconsideration," *Proc. Am. Acad. Arts Sci.,* **80,** No. 1, 1951.
9. H. Margenau, *The Nature of Physical Reality,* New York, McGraw-Hill Book Co., 1950, Chapter 12.
10. R. Carnap, "Foundations of Logic and Mathematics," *Int. Encyclopedia of Unified Science,* **I,** No. 3, pp. 56–69. The relevant part of this monograph is reprinted in Feigl and Brodbeck, *Readings in the Philosophy of Science,* "The Interpretation of Physics," New York, Appleton-Century-Crofts, Inc., 1953.
11. C. G. Hempel, "A Logical Appraisal of Operationism," *The Scientific Monthly,* October 1954.

10

THE QUANTUM THEORETICAL
CONCEPT OF MEASUREMENT

John L. McKnight

ASSOCIATE PROFESSOR OF PHYSICS
THE COLLEGE OF WILLIAM AND MARY

As a preliminary to the modern theory of measurement with which this paper is chiefly concerned, it is desirable to review a few of the characteristics and implications of classical physics to illustrate the far-reaching changes that have taken place in our conception of nature as a result of the development of quantum mechanics.

1. The basic assumption underlying classical physics is that the observer may stand quite outside any physical system and may measure state variables of that system without affecting the system itself. The observer and the observed system are radically separate.

Thus the external world is viewed classically as a concrete scientific object which has certain "primary qualities" inherent in it. These are independent of whether any observation of them is attempted or not. Whether any act of measurement takes place or not, the classical mechanical system has a definite position, energy, velocity, and so on. Furthermore, these definite values are independent of one another as far as measurement is concerned. They can be measured to any degree of accuracy and the results can be combined to give a complete, coherent, and detailed description of the state.

2. Quantum mechanics necessitates the abandonment of the radical separation of the observer and the observed. The system observed

and the system of the observer form together in their interaction a larger single system in a broad sense. The interaction profoundly affects the value of the variable measured. Whereas in classical physics adequate corrections and compensations can eliminate the disturbance caused by measurement, in quantum mechanics this is no longer possible. Quantum theory simply does not contain the measured properties that may be individually traced in detail through a process.

In many cases, in fact, the act of measurement destroys the system in question, much as many biological measurements destroy the cell on which they are performed. In any case, the act of measurement often changes the value of the observable in a way that makes impossible the classical idea of an independent nature we could know directly. The act of measurement may fatally disrupt the prior existing state.

3. For example, let us attempt to measure the momentum of a free electron by means of some instrument. The detector of this instrument uses the electron to trigger some macroscopic event, and, in so doing, reduces the energy of the electron to the point where it is captured and becomes indistinguishable from the electrons already in the material of the detector. Thus the free electron has disappeared in the act of measurement. What then have we measured? We have only the interaction of a certain apparatus and an electronic system as the result. Further interpretation will help to clarify this seemingly ambiguous outcome of measurement.

An important distinction was made by Margenau [1] in 1937 between the preparation of a state and measurement. Let us consider in detail the apparatus described above, i.e., let us consider a beta-ray spectrometer. One common type uses a magnetic field normal to the path of the electron's flight, which gives to the electron a deflection proportional to its momentum. The electron is detected by means of a Geiger counter, which operates by an electron's triggering of an avalanche of ions, causing a count to register. In operating the counter, the state of the electron is destroyed. Two elements are thus seen to be necessary for this process: the preparation of the state by means of the magnetic field and the measurement of the end of the electron's path through the apparatus by means of the counter, which may be moved to encompass all of the end points resulting from the momenta we wish to measure.

Margenau [1] states that the uncertainty arises in the preparation of the state and not in the measurement utilized to give a number. Even if the Geiger counter were not present, the path of the electron would be prepared in such a way that it would either arrive or would not arrive at the place where the counter would have been put. The act of measurement is distinct from the preparation of the state, since the latter alone, in this case the magnetic field, would yield no experimental data.

The uncertainty resulting from the preparation of the state is reflected in the state function, which is such after a preparation that the way in which we limit the selection of momenta, i.e., the sharpness of the momentum state, affects the sharpness of definition of the particle's position. This is true whether we actually perform the measurement or not. An ensemble of measurements will reveal standard deviations such that the product of the deviations will be equal to or greater than $h/4\pi$, where h is Planck's constant of action.

4. A most important theoretical discussion of the theory of measurement occurs in the last chapter of von Neumann's *Mathematical Foundations of Quantum Mechanics* [2]. Here he investigates the transformation properties of a set of matrices corresponding to states of the quantum system. He notes particularly two types of operations that may be performed on quantum-mechanical systems. The first of these is represented by the energy operator of Schrödinger which, when it is applied to the quantum-mechanical state function, produces a purely causal and continuous transformation. The second results from the projection operator which brings about a sudden acausal and irreversible transformation. The former he would place in the system external to the observer, the latter, in the interaction of the observer and the observed. The world is thus sharply divided into the world outside the observer and the system of the observer himself. At the juncture of these, there is a discontinuity which is reflected in the apparent breakdown of any causality across the boundary.

Von Neumann's theory says that the process of measurement carries the pure state over into a mixture. The crucial details relevant for the present discussion are outlined in the following section.

5. In the theory of measurement, however, no operator is known in classical physics; measurement is taken as primitive. Thus, if we are to have a theoretical operation to describe the measurement process, it must be introduced, ad hoc, into the theory. Following the Heisenberg matrix formulation, a projection operator P_ν is introduced as characteristic of measurement, the operator giving the projection of the state vector to which it is applied onto a particular eigenstate [3]. It transforms the state on which it is applied into an eigenstate ϕ_ν. Thus, $P_\nu\Psi$

$= \mathbf{\phi}_\nu$ where ν is an index identifying the particular eigenstate realized. If the serial order of the appearance of the eigenstates is not noted, then the final state may be represented as an ensemble of pure eigenstates. Each eigenstate appears in the final ensemble a number of times which is in keeping with its probability of being found in measurements performed on a system in the initial state $\mathbf{\Psi}$. Since, however, von Neumann says that the act of measurement carries the state over into the particular eigenstate measured $\mathbf{\phi}_\nu$, the resulting state after measurement must be described as a mixture. A statistical mixture operator $\mathbf{W}$ may be found which, when it operates on the $\mathbf{\Psi}$-function, gives a mixture.[1]

6. This creation of a particular eigenstate by measurement seems contrary to the actual results of such a measurement. If the measurement prepared a pure eigenstate, the same value would result upon repeated measurement of the same system. In practice, however, the same measurement repeated on a system we have measured with the result $\mathbf{p}_\nu$ will *not* give us the same value. The measurement actually disrupts the system on which it is performed. Only in an ensemble of measurements performed on an aggregate of systems all in the same initial state $\mathbf{\Psi}$ can we deduce even the state *prior* to measurement. After the measurement, no further measurement is possible. In an ensemble of measurements obtained by this procedure, the results derived by the use of von Neumann's theory are correct. Confusion has arisen in the interpretations of the theory in which individual events have been considered rather than ensembles.

7. Let us consider the alternative mentioned in Section 3 [1]. We define the measurement of a state variable of a system as the interaction of the system and a suitable apparatus so as to produce a number which may be correlated, by means of the theory, with the variable. The important result is the number; any experiment which does not result in a number (this includes a yes-or-no answer as a special case) is not rightly to be called a measurement.

Not all measurements are, however, significant. If they are to be significant, it is necessary that, when they are used in one coherent theory, no contradictions result. It is sometimes said that the types of apparatus needed to measure two quantum variables are incompatible in that the use of one precludes the use of the other, but this is not true of our definition of measurement, for surely they do give numbers if used together. The criterion for their incompatibility is not an empirical one but rather a purely theoretical one. The numbers ob-

---

[1] For details concerning the projection operator, see [1].

tained are useless when we attempt to formulate results with respect to the quantum state of the system from them.

The difficulty seems to lie in not realizing that the so-called observables of quantum mechanics are not perceived facts, but rather are constructed from a theory which shows that they *arise* from the interaction of a particular quantum-mechanical system with a particular measuring apparatus. The variables which are the constructions of the theory are so related in the theory that the specification of one within given limits will affect the specification of the variable conjugate to it in accordance with the uncertainty relation. Thus any apparatus which performs a measurement on one variable may cause the measurement of some other variable to be dependent on the nature of the first measurement in a manner only statistically predictable. This frees quantum mechanics from the necessity of giving a detailed account of each individual interaction. In fact, although the heuristic value of describing the interaction in terms of classical models may be considerable, only statistical descriptions may be legitimately used in quantum mechanics. This is not at all a detriment to physics, since no one would be likely to submit the result of a single measurement as a contribution to a professional journal, but would endeavor, if at all possible, to collect many examples under the same conditions of the system measured in order to minimize any chance error. This is equally true for classical physics, but, in the older physics, we had no reason to believe that we could not describe all processes in detail if we so desired. Quantum physics renounces the possibility of detailed explanation in this sense.

If then the measurement itself gives no criterion of its validity, we may well look at the aforementioned stage called "the preparation of the state." The preparation arranges the ensemble impinging on the measuring apparatus. It is the actual interaction of the apparatus and some quantum mechanical system, with no question of a measurement being made. The preparation of a state modifies the probability distribution of the incident system's state function in such a way that one may interpose apparatus that will give directly a number dependent on the preparation preceding it.

At this stage the interaction of systems occurs, and here uncertainty enters, not in the measurement itself. The measurement occurs only if a number appears, but the quantum state is modified from the initial state, whether or not a measurement is made. Any other explanation runs the risk of reducing the statistical assertions of quantum mechanics to mere psychological measures of our lack of knowledge.

8. For example, suppose we wish to measure the position and momentum of an electron by means of the well-known conceptual experiment involving an X-ray microscope [4]. An incident monochromatic beam of photons, moving parallel to the axis of the optical system, is scattered by an electron in the object plane; see Fig. 1. In diagram A, the photographic plate is placed in the image plane to measure the end of the paths of photons scattered by a particular electron and thus to locate its position. To find a sharp value of the momentum of the electron, however, we must know the direction in which the photon was scattered by its interaction with the electron. To do this, the plate is placed, as shown in diagram B, in the *focal* plane. The interaction of the photon and the electron in the *object* plane prepares the state of both, and the interaction of the photon and the plate measures the photon state from which we infer, on the basis of the theory, the electron state we wish to know.

In diagram A, applying the usual laws of physical optics, we may determine the position of the electron in the object plane within a region of horizontal extent $\Delta q \sim \lambda/\sin \alpha = c/\nu \sin \alpha$. Here, α is the angle subtended by the lens as seen from the object plane. A photon prepared by the interaction with the electron may be scattered into any angle up to α and still reach the lens and be focused in the image. The photon in being scattered, however, transfers momentum to the electron in amounts from 0 up to $\Delta p \sim (h\nu/c) \sin \alpha$. This, then, is the uncertainty introduced in the electron's momentum by the interaction with the photon which localized the electron's position within

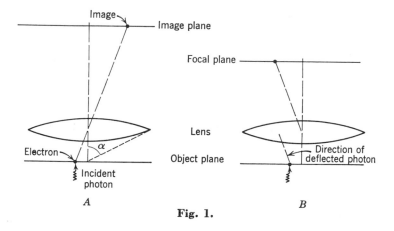

Fig. 1.

$\Delta q \sim \lambda/\sin \alpha$. Hence, Δq and Δp satisfy the uncertainty relation $\Delta q \cdot \Delta p \sim h$.

On the other hand, if we wish to find the electron's momentum sharply, we must know the direction in which it deflected the photon, i.e., we must collect all of the photons which leave the object plane at the same angle. Now, a *parallel* beam of photons is focused at one point in the *focal* plane whose location gives the angle at which they were scattered by the electron. Knowing the direction, we know exactly the lateral momentum transferred to the electron, and, therefore, the uncertainty in the momentum, Δp, is very small. Being badly out of focus, however, the photon image which shows the position of the electron is a blur and Δq is very large. If we know the precise initial electron state, we know accurately its final state. Both of these states will have a significant spread in position values. In diagram A, contrastingly, the probability distribution of the initial electron state is supposed to collapse on measurement into a region close to about the measured location of the electron in the object plane.

These assertions are incompatible with one another if one claims that the *measurement* creates the electron's measured state. Instead, the preparation of the electron state by collision with a photon also prepares a photon state that carries information within itself which we may measure in more than one way. Thus we may also make inferences as to the electron's state in more than one way. The prepared state is independent of measurement.

Our information about the single event of one photon being scattered by an electron is *not* likewise independent of measurement. The single event is completely inadequate for the formation of decisions as to the quantum-mechanical state of the system. Full note must be taken of the statistical nature of the quantum theory; therefore, the discussion of a single event must be abandoned.

Quantum mechanics discards the notion of tracing through the detail of individual events and gains the power of definite and verified statistical pronouncement. In the case of the X-ray microscope, the interaction between the photon and the electron modifies the state functions of both and introduces an uncertainty in the momentum-position pair of variables. Viewing this now for the result of many measurements, with the plates in the image plane in some and in the focal plane in others, we see two immediate valid conclusions that seem to strengthen our view. If the momentum is sharp, all the photons will be deflected at the same angle to the axis, but this parallel beam will give no image in the *image* plane. Similarly, if the position is definite, then the lens must be infinite in diameter and photons pass through it at all angles up to the right angle, and no image forms in the *focal* plane. Limiting α by making the lens finite is a further preparation of the photon state which sharpens the momentum but increases the diffraction in the position image. Given one definite preparation, however, the measurements are potentially fixed for any position of the plate. The plate's position does not reflect back on the preparation. Since we would, in practice, measure a large number of systems all in the same initial state, for each of the possible plate positions, we may, so to speak, eat our cake and have it too, if only we do not try to account for the individual bites in detail.

9. The primary statement of the uncertainty principle was that given by Heisenberg in 1927 [5]. The product of the statistical deviations of the measured values of quantities whose quantum-mechanical operators are noncommuting is of the order of Planck's constant, h. These pairs of variables are those which are canonically conjugate in classical mechanics.

We have seen earlier how this finds application in the X-ray microscope example, and I shall assume that the reader is familiar with more examples of this type. It is especially to be noted, however, that this uncertainty arises at the preparation of the state and not in its measurement. It is produced by the interaction of two physical systems which prepares a state whose statistics are such that the uncertainty relation holds true.

Von Neumann has shown that the uncertainty relation follows directly from the postulates of quantum theory [2, p. 230ff.]. Thus its status is quite independent of measurement and is not to be confused with the error introduced in the measurements of classical physics by the interference to the system caused by imperfect measuring instruments. Neither is it, if we hold the quantum theory as it is understood by most physicists, a measure of our ignorance of the true state of the system due to our crude measuring methods.

The uncertainty is inseparable from the quantum concept itself and is contained in the definition of the state function. The nonexistence of independent classical variables of state within the quantum-mechanical state function precludes the possibility of their independent prediction. If we do measure them, their values spread.

Bohr [6] was one of the first to propose an interpretation of this apparent peculiarity of nature. His view is that it expresses the complementarity of certain pairs of variables. If the values of each member of the pair are established and are permitted by the uncertainty relation, then the resulting description is said to be complete. The same principle is applied to the duality of the wave and particle descriptions of the electron and to many pairs of observables and modes of description in physics and in the biological and social sciences. This complementarity of mutually exclusive descriptions gives one a convenient balm to soothe one's conscience about not being able to formulate exact solutions. One may, however, question the philosophy of despair to which this interpretation tends to lead. It provides too easy a stopping point; if one finds two descriptions or observables that seem to contradict one another, but each seems valid within its own limits of application, the temptation is strong to call them complementary and move on to greener fields. In the early years of the quantum theory, this concept saved many physicists from following lines of investigation likely to be fruitless, but now, when problems are arising at the very roots of the theory, in nuclear studies, perhaps the crutch should be removed and the scholar should take the risk of stumbling while walking unfamiliar paths.

Born [7] differs from Bohr in the interpretation of complementarity when he emphasizes the fact that one description exhausts its own criterion but cannot suffice to give the real object of physics. He holds that a number of views are necessary to establish some sort of perspective. One view cannot give the full proportions and two perspectives may seem quite incompatible, but, in reality, both may be embraced by a more adequate concept. This is a more encouraging interpretation but, at present, not universally adopted.

Lenzen [8] and others place the uncertainty at the boundary of the observer and thus introduce a strongly dualistic universe. Complementarity becomes more of a psychological principle and reduces physics to a level which would stifle hope for the solution of any of its problems.

Schlick [9] ascribes the limiting effect of complementarity to our methods of measurement and goes on to assert that nothing is, in principle, unknowable. Von Laue [10] extends this and concludes that our concepts and measuring techniques are too limited, but we need not recognize any limits to our knowledge of nature.

Such attitudes seem preferable to those of certain logicians who see complementarity as grounded in the theory of probability and arising from the underlying irrationality of quantum-mechanical description and logic. Some of these, notably Reichenbach [11], advocate a multivalued logic as a solution to the problem. Mme. Destouches-Février [12], in fact, says that only a logic of an infinite number of values can make quantum mechanics noncontradictory. Such approaches as yet have not reached a sufficient level of development to allow application to the crucial problems of quantum theory and are regarded as uninteresting by many physicists.

In spite of the numerous alternative interpretations, the Bohr principle of complementarity remains the one most used by practicing physicists. It is the easiest to understand, and reconciles the human desire for an interpretation of quantum mechanics in terms of macroscopic models with the postulates of quantum theory which would exclude such visualization. Nonetheless, Bohm [13] and of late De Broglie [14] have attempted to reformulate quantum mechanics in terms of "hidden variables" which may not be measured, but which would allow a detailed description of the evolution of states. If an experiment could be devised which would depend on these variables, the basic postulates of quantum mechanics would need reformulation. The behavior of an atomic system would be describable in more than the Ψ-state of the present formulation. No such experiment has been found, and since the "hidden variables" method is far more complex than the conventional one for the problems which it can solve, it has not been enthusiastically received in spite of the admitted attraction of a detailed description.

10. An approach which may be helpful in mitigating the dilemma of complementarity has been suggested by Margenau [15]. It may be called the latency theory of the quantities subject to physical measurement. One notes that there is a unique theoretical state function for an electron which may be used to give any of its observable properties. This state function can evolve in time and undergo transformations that are continuous and causal. It does not, however, contain any of the classical variables of state in an explicit form. One must operate on this state function with some mathematical operator functions to find the expectation values of the classical variables of state. For instance, the operator $(h/2\pi i)(\partial/\partial x)$ when applied to the state function gives the expectation value of the momentum in the x-direction.

Similarly, in experimental physics, one must bring to bear some apparatus which will interact with the electron to perform a measurement. If we wish to measure the variable, momentum, we must use the beta-ray spectrometer mentioned earlier. To speak of the electron's momentum without any consideration of its measurement is meaningless. The electron has momentum only potentially.

Similar analyses may be made of the other classical state variables, none of which are "contained" in the state function. These variables may be said to be latent in the state function and arise only in the act of measurement. They are like Locke's secondary qualities, which are not in the object as are the primary qualities but arise in the act of observation. An example would be the blue color of a book which has meaning only in reference to an observer.

As science has advanced, the primary qualities have become converted into secondary qualities. Color, hardness, and the like were thought by the ancients to be primary but today are accepted without a doubt as secondary. Position and momentum are even now believed to be primary by the common-sense observer, but they are in conflict with one another in quantum theory in a way that no independently existing qualities could be. It is proposed therefore that we deny the inherent position and momentum and view them as secondary qualities that *arise* if we make a measurement.

These latent observables are not identical with the "disposition predicates" mentioned by Pap. They differ in that, whereas it is possible to imagine the continuing existence of the observable represented by a disposition predicate even when no observation is being made, the physical theories connected with the latent observable make it logically contradictory to attribute the variable to the system at any time when it is not being observed.

The latency interpretation removes the mystery associated with the uncertainty principle and takes the numbing sting out of the principle of complementarity. It allows us to retain a causal universe and, at the same time, to accept the haziness of nature revealed by quantum mechanics. First, we accept the quantum-mechanical state function Ψ as the fundamental and real attribute of the physical system. Then, if the variables of classical physics are not in the state function, and if they arise only on the application of noncommuting operators corresponding to these variables, there is no reason whatsoever to expect the resulting values to be independent. Their dependence is, in fact, given explicitly by the uncertainty relation. The step of abandoning the classical variables to the realm of potential, latent qualities may seem drastic, but the success of these as primary qualities in situations in which classical physics is applicable is, after all, no guarantee of their adequacy in quantum theory.

REFERENCES

1. Margenau, H., "Critical Points in Modern Physical Theory," *Phil. Sci.*, **4**, 1937, pp. 337–370.
2. von Neumann, J., *Mathematical Foundations of Quantum Mechanics*, Princeton, Princeton University Press, 1955, p. 417.
3. *Ibid.,* p. 75ff.
4. Ludwig, G., *Die Grundlagen der Quantenmechanik*, Berlin, Springer Verlag, 1954, p. 126ff.
5. Heisenberg, W., "Über den anschaulichen Inhalt der quantentheoretischen Kinematik und Mechanik," *Z. f. Physik*, **43**, 1927, pp. 172–198.
6. Bohr, N., "The Quantum Postulate and the Recent Development of Atomic Theory," *Nature*, **121**, 1928, pp. 580–590.
7. Born, M., "Physical Reality," *Phil. Quart.*, **3**, 1953, pp. 139–149.
8. Lenzen, Victor F., "The Interaction between Subject and Object in Observation," *Erkenntnis*, **6**, 1936–37, pp. 326–335.
9. Schlick, M., "Quantentheoric und Erkennbarkeit der Natur," *Erkenntnis*, **6**, 1936–37, pp. 317–326.
10. von Laue, M., "Über Heisenbergs Ungenauigkeitsbeziehungen und ihre erkenntnistheoretische Bedeutung," *Die Naturwissenschaften*, **22**, 1934, pp. 439–441.
11. Reichenbach, H., *Philosophic Foundations of Quantum Theory*, Berkeley, University of California Press, 1944.
12. Detouches-Février, P., "Manifestations et sens de la notion de complementarité," *Dialectica*, **2**, 1948, pp. 382–412.
13. Bohm, D., "A Suggested Interpretation of the Quantum Theory in Terms of 'Hidden' Variables," I. *Phys. Rev.*, **85**, 1952, pp. 166–179; II. *Ibid.*, pp. 180–193.
14. De Broglie, L., *La physique quantique restera-t-elle indeterministe?*, Paris, Gauthier-Villars, 1953.
15. Margenau, H., "Advantages and Disadvantages of Various Interpretations of the Quantum Theory," *Physics Today*, **7/10**, 1954, pp. 6–13.

11

MEASUREMENT OF RARE EVENTS

E. J. Gumbel

COLUMBIA UNIVERSITY

The word "measure" will be used in the popular and not in the technical sense which it acquired in modern mathematics. We consider the analysis of rare events by classical and recent probabilistic methods. Laplace claimed that the calculus of probabilities is nothing but mathematics applied to common sense. However, common sense is an ambiguous notion, since it often yields nonsensical results such as, "The earth is flat and the sun 'rises' every day."

CALCULUS OF PROBABILITIES

Probability theory arose from questions which are the exact opposite of the problems to be considered later. The gamblers who, in the Renaissance and the following centuries, belonged to the upper classes, asked the scientists for policies on how to bet safely in the long run. The techniques used then were dice casting and card playing. The vice of gambling and the questions asked by such intelligent people as the Chevalier de Méré were fruitful to the development of probability theory whereas the virtue of the insurance business contributed much less. Both roads continue to exist today in different forms: playing at the stock market and the respectable business of investment. The most remarkable recent contribution in this respect arose from the question: Can business forecasters forecast? The answer obtained by the Cowles Commission at great cost was in the negative.

The shock encountered by the inability of the learned statisticians to realize the existence of the great depression of the 1930's is still in our minds. These and similar failures—for instance, the population forecasts in the 1940's, which overlooked the "baby-boom"—must arise when methods designed for a stable situation are applied to situations which are essentially unstable, i.e., not in statistical control. The mathematics were all right, but the social assumptions were utterly wrong. Forecasts are valid in the trivial case when the prophet can insure his forecasts to become true: The statement that a certain stock will rise in the central market will become true if this piece of news is believed by a sufficiently large number of prospective buyers.

Successful applications of probability calculus to physics, astronomy, biology, and, under certain restrictive conditions, to economics [6] are so well known that it is unnecessary to insist upon details. Still, the objection remains that the basic probabilities are generally unknown. As soon as we want to apply them, they have to be estimated, but this holds also for physical quantities which, too, are unknown and have to be estimated—with the help of the calculus of probabilities.

In all these cases, the calculus is concerned with mean values, and its validity in this respect is generally recognized. No insurance business ever went bankrupt through the fault of the actuary. However, we have to insist on a logical limitation. Whatever effort we may make, probability theory is a closed system. From given probabilities, we derive new probabilities, and these present no way to security except as a limiting process or as a triviality.

RARE EVENTS

Unlimited variates have been used in the calculus of probabilities since the discovery of the normal distribution. Is such a notion admissible? Real objects which can be measured are always finite. In using this notion, we admit the existence of giants and dwarfs for a variate which may be of the order of a few centimeters. This is a shocking physical obstacle and certainly defies common sense. However, this notion implies, at the same time, that the probabilities for the existence of such monstrosities are extraordinarily small. Hence, the use of an unlimited variate and, in particular, of the normal distribution leads to the logical and practical question of whether the calculus of probabilities holds within this realm which, for simplicity's sake, is now called the "rare event."

The main attack against the validity of probability theory in such cases was not frontal, but arose for a side issue linked to a discontinuous variable, and was concerned with the question of independence of rare events. Curiously enough, there have been two opposing views, sometimes brought forward by the same people. One school claims that rare events should occur less frequently than foreseen by the calculus. If the tossing of a coin has shown a series of heads, then "common sense" will be inclined to believe that the next throw should be a tail. Since the probability for a sequence of heads diminishes with its length, there should even be an upper limit to this length. After reaching it, we should be sure that the opposite event will happen. The classical refutation brought forward, for example, by Poincaré is: The dice or the roulette wheel have neither memory nor moral obligation.

Another school claims a "law of the series," expecting the rare events to be more frequent than foreseen by the theory. In reality, the alleged duplicity is created by the publicity. A rare event evokes interest. Its repetition is published just because the event has happened.

Both views, if correct, must, in the last resort, lead to a system of gaining at roulette. Of course this is possible, provided some fault in the system has been found out, which is tied to systematic deviations from the chance distribution of the numbers, and provided that sufficient capital to face the risks is available. However, the bank has its safeguard against this possibility by putting a limit to the sums at stake. "Foolproof" systems for winning at roulette are sold to victims who do not ask why the inventor did not put the system to his own use instead of selling it; they have never worked.

The first scientific study of rare events is due to Poisson who, incidentally, did not realize the importance of his discovery. If the probability p in an alternative becomes very small, and the number of trials n is very large, such that the product n times p is finite, Poisson's law gives the probability $w(x)$ that the event happens $x = (0, 1, 2 \ . \ . \ .)$ times. For half a century this theorem remained nothing but a mathematical curiosity. The first to realize its importance was L. von Bortkiewicz in his famous example of the number of Prussian soldiers killed yearly by the kick of a horse. This rare event showed a remarkable regularity corresponding closely to Poisson's formula. This law can also be derived independent of the notion of rare events, and has now become one of the cornerstones of modern probability theory. It also holds for the lengths of a series in an alternative, and has been generalized for dependent events with small or large contagion.

The classical scheme for dependent events was given by Markov, who introduced the probabilities of transition from one stage of a given system to the next one. This theory of Markov chains could be put to good use in climatology in order to test, say, the story of the ground hog, or apparent irregularities in seasonal developments, e.g., for temperature drop in the beginning of May.

The Poisson law disposes of the question of the number of rare events but not with their size. This question is linked to the notion of an unlimited distribution of a continuous variate, the main tool in statistical analysis. Do large values of the variate connected with extraordinary small probabilities correspond to reality? Is infinity for the normal distribution equal to 3, 4, or 5 sigmas? Is the procedure to disregard observations which fall outside of the 3σ limit justified? It will be shown that this is not the case. If the discharges of the Hudson River follow some unlimited distribution, will the river ever top the Empire State Building? It is impossible that the improbable could never happen but it is easy to show that very improbable events are linked to such large periods of time that they will never be observed. An event with probability p happens in the mean, i.e., for a large series of observations, once in $1/p$ trials. Thus the probability of an event is linked to the number of observations. The generalization of this relation to a continuous variate is as follows: Let $F(x)$ be the probability of a chance variate to be equal to or smaller than x. Then $1 - F(x)$ is the probability of a value larger than x. Its inverse

$$(1) \qquad\qquad T(x) = \frac{1}{1 - F(x)}$$

is called the return period. This notion, which comes from engineering practice, has its appropriate place in statistics, where the return period is practically equal to the number of observations. An extraordinary small probability corresponds thus to an extraordinary high return period, too large to be realistic. But a value outside of the 3σ limit in a normal distribution happens in the mean once in 370 observations. This is a small number in industrial production.

The most radical proposition concerning small probabilities has been made by a very conservative Frenchman, the late Borel. He stated that there is a unique law of probabilities, namely, that sufficiently rare events will not be observed, and he proposed definite scales where such probabilities should be excluded. These are:

$$\text{For the human scale} \qquad < 10^{-6}$$

$$\text{For the terrestrial scale} \quad < 10^{-15}$$

$$\text{For the cosmic scale} \qquad < 10^{-50}$$

Finally, 10^{-500} should definitely be taken as identical to zero.

It follows that $x \geqq 10$ should be excluded in the Poisson law. This distinction between the different scales permits exceptions to the irreversibility of certain physical phenomena. The increase of entropy is valid on a terrestrial scale. Can we conclude that it must also hold on a cosmic scale? The idea of an expanding universe suggests repulsion as a property of matter. This has not been observed on a terrestrial scale, and according to modern physics would imply the existence of negative matter in the cosmos. This would be an extraordinary exception to the important observation that the stars are composed of exactly the same elements as found on earth.

The theory of rare events deals with the number of such events. Their sizes, however, fall within the domain of the theory of extreme values, which is explained in the following section.

THEORY OF EXTREME VALUES

If we arrange n measurable observations in increasing magnitude, these values are called order statistics, x_m. The first, x_1, is the smallest, the last, x_n, is the largest one. Both may have occurred more than once. If we repeat the same number of observations under the same circumstances, we will not obtain the same values. Thus, there is a distribution of the order statistics depending on the initial distribution, the sample size, n, and the rank m.

Since the time of Laplace it has been well known that the order statistics in the neighborhood of the median are normally distributed under not very restrictive conditions. However, this will not hold for the smallest and the largest value, henceforth called "extremes." In addition to the extremes proper, we may speak of the mth extremes from the bottom or from the top, if m is either very small compared to n or of the same order as n.

The main practical difficulties within the theory of extreme values are the same as for all statistical procedures. They are the result of two assumptions: first, that the observations are independent, and, second, that we know the theoretical distribution from which the given observations are samples. In most cases, the observations are dependent, and a good fit of a certain theoretical distribution does not exclude that another distribution is valid.

If all observations are independent, then the probability for all of them to be equal to or less than a given value x is

$$(2) \qquad\qquad F^n(x) = e^{n \lg F(x)}$$

The whole theory of extreme values is centered around the analysis of this simple and exact expression. The first consequence is that the largest value of a statistical variate is not fixed, but is a new statistical variate. If the initial distribution is limited (or not), possesses all moments (or not), the same holds for the largest value.

If the initial probability function $F(x)$ and n are known, Equation 2 can be used for the analysis of observed extremes. However, as a rule $F(x)$ is unknown, and in many cases the only observations we have at our disposal are the extremes themselves. Therefore we have to find a method of disposing of the initial distribution. Since the largest and smallest values are linked by a symmetry relation, valid also for asymmetrical initial distributions, it is sufficient to study the largest value. If the number of observation increases, the largest value will increase too, and the probability $F(x)$ will converge to unity. Its logarithm converges to zero. In consequence, the exponent in Equation 2 becomes an indeterminate expression. Its value cannot be obtained by the usual procedure. Instead, we have to postulate certain properties of the initial distribution in order to attribute a value to the indeterminate expression. Thus we must make some assumption about the behavior of the initial distribution towards large values of the variate. It is quite important that we do not need any assumption for the neighborhood of the mean.

Three types of initial distributions have been worked out by Fréchet [2], Fisher [1], and von Mises [7], which lead to three and only three distributions of extremes [3].

1. The first type is called the exponential type. Then the probability of a value larger than x converges to zero for large values of the variate in about the same way as the exponential function e^{-x} converges to zero. Most of the distributions used in statistics, such as the normal, the exponential, the gamma distribution, and the unlimited distributions of the Pearson type, belong to this category. In this case, all moments of the initial distribution and of the distribution of the extreme values exist. But the inverse is not true. The existence of

moments does not imply that the distribution is of the exponential type.

2. Other distributions, which are also unlimited, have a very long tail such that the variate lacks some of the higher moments. Since this is the case for Cauchy's distribution, this type may be called the Cauchy type. It has been studied by Fréchet [2] to whom belongs the priority of this line of research. However, this type is rarely used in statistics.

3. There are certain distributions having an upper or lower limit. Then the largest value, too, has an upper limit and the smallest a lower limit. The limits enter as parameters in the distribution of the extremes and have to be estimated. All moments exist for these distributions.

The theory of extreme values [5] has been studied from two aspects. In the first procedure, a stability is postulated, namely, that the unknown distribution of the largest values should be identical to the initial distribution except for a linear transformation of the variate. In consequence, the maximum of the largest values should have the same distribution as the largest value proper except for a linear transformation. In this method, the initial distribution and the distribution of the largest value are both unknown. The postulate leads to a functional equation that has been solved, first by Fréchet [2] for the second type, and later by Fisher and Tippett [1] for the three types.

The second procedure, first used by the late von Mises [7], starts from a known initial distribution and shows that the distribution of the largest value converges to a certain expression. This method can be generalized in such a way that, instead of using a given initial distribution, we only request that its type is known. Both procedures lead to three and only three expressions for the asymptotic distribution of largest values. The symmetry principle leads then to the corresponding three asymptotic distributions of smallest values, and a further generalization leads to the three asymptotic distributions of the mth's extreme values. Similar studies have been made for the range.

For a given set of observations, it can generally be decided to which type of initial distributions they should be attributed. The rapidity of the approach of the distribution of largest values to the asymptotic form is different for different distributions. It is quick for the exponential distribution but slow for the normal one.

The three asymptotic distributions contain a parameter of location and a parameter of scale. The location parameter is a quantile u_n, defined by the equation

(3) $$F(u_n) = 1 - 1/n$$

This parameter can also be interpreted as that largest value which corresponds to the probability $1/e$. The parameter of scale can be interpreted as a function of the standard deviation of the largest value. In addition, the second and third type of asymptotic distributions contain a lower or an upper limit respectively which may be zero. Thus we have two or three parameters to estimate. They originate from the initial distribution. In particular, the upper and lower limits of the initial distribution are also the upper and lower limits respectively of the distribution of extreme values. If the initial distribution is known, the parameters can be calculated therefrom.

However, in most cases the initial distribution is unknown and the parameters in the distribution of extreme values have to be estimated from the observed extremes alone. This problem is greatly facilitated by the construction of a probability paper which can be used for all six distributions of extremes (three largest and three smallest values). The variable is traced on a linear scale for the first asymptotic distribution and on a logarithmic scale for the second and third distributions. The probability scale is obtained from tables published by the National Bureau of Standards [8]. In addition to these two scales, the paper also shows the return periods. Such papers are used, among others, by the Geological Survey and the Weather Bureau. They reduce the analysis of extreme values to the fitting of straight lines and lead to a graphical test for the validity of these theories.

Thus, this theory fulfills three different tasks. First, it gives a test for the type of initial distribution. This knowledge may be of importance for many statistical problems.

Second, the comparison of a single outlier to the expected largest value may lead to the acceptance or rejection of a particular extreme observation. However, it is much better to compare an observed series of such extreme values, each taken from a large sample of the same size to the theoretical distribution, and thus derive a test for the regularity of the extreme observations.

Third, the return-period scale on the probability paper may be used to forecast extreme values as a function of time or area. The use of probability paper allows the interpretation of largest values as a function of time if the observations are made in equal intervals.

ENGINEERING APPLICATIONS OF EXTREME VALUES

The usual applications of statistical methods are based on mean values. However, there is a vast domain where, in contrast to popular opinions, the extremes are much more important. This holds foremost in engineering applications of statistical methods. A bridge must withstand the usual discharges of a river, but, it must also be safe for the largest discharge to be expected within a given period. We are not interested in the flood at a certain time but only within a certain period. Thus we want to know the largest value of a certain statistical variate, the daily discharge as a function of time, the number of years. The notion of return period, previously introduced, takes care of this problem, since the distance between two largest annual discharges is approximately one year. The floods of many hundreds of rivers, analyzed by this method, have led to a good fit of the theory of extreme values to the observations. Therefore, this theory may be used for the forecast of floods as a function of time. The rivers know the theory of extreme values, although many engineers still ignore it.

The most probable largest flood within a hundred years may arrive tomorrow. Taking into account these probabilities, we can calculate the risk for a structure to fall before the end of the design period. This method leads to a numerical evaluation of the risk, in contrast to the usual talk of calculated risk without numerical basis.

The building code is another example for the application of extreme value theory. We want a building to withstand the strongest wind to be expected within a given period. An application of the theory to economic problems is given in [6].

A hydraulic problem of smallest values is posed by the droughts, defined as the smallest values of the discharges during a year. A forecast for the droughts is necessary for the construction of reservoirs which should not be empty even in the driest year to serve their purpose, say, for irrigation. Since the discharges are non-negative, the asymptotic theory of smallest values with a variate limited to the left becomes the appropriate tool for analysis. Again, a very good fit of the theory has been obtained for many rivers.

A fruitful application of the extreme-value theory exists in fatigue life and fatigue stress. The static stress is a very old notion that must have been known even in prehistoric times when primitive men constructed their huts. We speak of dynamic strength when a load is applied during a number of cycles. This notion became of major importance for the construction of railways. Axles broke under loads much smaller than those for which they were built to carry in the static case. Great accidents were the consequence. Today, this problem is decisive for the safety of aircraft structures where failures may be due to overloading. The most famous of such accidents were those incurred by the British airplanes called Comets. In 1854, a Royal British Commission investigated the railway accidents, in 1954 the airplane accidents. It is pathetic to compare the two inconclusive reports. They attribute the failure to a vague notion called fatigue. Consequently, the first task is to attribute an exact meaning to this notion. This is obtained by a simulating procedure.

In testing, a load rotates about a piece of metal up to fracture. Since "identical" pieces tested in the same manner under the same load and by the same machine break at different numbers of cycles, the number of cycles at fracture N becomes a statistical variate, having the dimension of time. Thus, the notions used for life, considered as a statistical variate, are appropriate for fatigue. We can construct a survivorship function for constant stress (load per unit of surface) and get consecutive survivorship functions for increasing stresses. Their sequence gives a criterion for the homogeneity of the observations.

In a similar way, fatigue strength, the stress at fracture for a constant number of cycles, may be considered as a statistical variate. In the corresponding experiment, the test is stopped after a certain number of cycles and repeated for different stresses.

Two boundary values in these survivorship functions are of specific interest: the minimum life, the number of cycles as a function of the load, such that the probability of survival is equal to unity and the endurance limit, a load so small that the probability of survival is equal to unity even for an unlimited number of cycles. Both values cannot be observed. However, they can be estimated by extrapolation if the survivorship function is known.

Physical considerations and analogies to life table functions have led to the use of the asymptotic theory of smallest values. It gives a good representation for fatigue life and fatigue stress. The minimum life and the endurance limit enter as parameters in the probabilities of survival as a function of the number of cycles, and the probability of permanent survival as a function of the stress. The consistent estimation of these parameters presents some analytical difficulties, but they are minor as compared to the difficulties due to the lack of reliable observations based on a sufficiently large number of specimens and repeated for a sufficiently large number of stresses. For example, it can be shown by purely logical considerations (apart from any specific statistical theory) that none of the observations on permanent survival now available can be used for the estimation of the endurance limit. Even in such a rational science as engineering, there is inertia based on vested interests in the use of old-fashioned textbook formulae—although the costs of one single major failure exceed by far the costs of systematic large-scale experiments.

RARE EVENTS AND THE OCCULT SCIENCES

Within our short lives, the elders among us have seen spectacular technical developments such as the electric light, automobile, airplane, radio, television, radar, all of which are linked to or produced by the progress of science and seemed impossible for previous generations. The great physicist, Helmholtz, has proved that man will never be able to fly, and his proof is still correct because he could not foresee the invention of the internal-combustion engine and the light motor.

We have seen the transformation of matter into energy, a procedure considered technically impossible by previous generations. So why should we doubt that other wonders will appear in the future? Astrology, telepathy, and similar occult sciences promise us such new knowledge. Why should we reject it, and thus restrict the road to progress? The adherents of these arguments are victims of several basic fallacies.

First, no recognized scientist shares today the belief of the 18th century that the major domain of knowledge is explored. On the contrary, every problem solved only leads to the discovery of other unsolved problems, and this is an endless procedure. The more we know the greater becomes our knowledge of our ignorance. Therefore, the claim of adherents of occult sciences that classical science believes to know everything reminds one of the fight of Don Quixote against wind mills which he considered to be giants.

Second, the claim of the occultists of exploring the supernatural is wrong. Everything unknown exceeds our knowledge of nature. Nature will never be totally known. The domain of ignorance has nothing to do with the supernatural. The supernatural of today is the natural of tomorrow. The mystic properties that the Greeks attributed to electricity are now the basis of everyday life. The claim of the occultist to be able to explore the supernatural is even an imposture, so far as they use instruments, tables that turn, rods that move, maps of the stars, etc. Instruments, even of the most fantastic structure, can only reach physical realities, just as classical instruments. Let us admit, for argument's sake, that forces exist that influence the instruments of the occultists, then these forces too belong to the natural, and nowhere else.

Third, there is one and only one criterion for the validity of the claims of the occultists, namely, that a new fact could be established for which it can be proved that no person living today is aware of it, and that this new fact can be checked by procedures independent of the methods of discovery. The great physicist Oliver Lodge wrote a whole book on life after death, based on the revelations of a turning table. It revealed that the dead live in houses, which could not be built without the existence of gravity forces; that they speak, i.e., possess a vocal chord. They even eat, thus have a digestive apparatus. In other words, life after death is the life on earth. Such experiments should be checked by professional magicians and not by physicists or, what is worse, philosophers. There is a long list of sorcerers who have deceived many scientists, but nearly every medium has later been unmasked. The few systematic experiments have not been accepted as successes by the nonbelievers.

The following experiment would be decisive: Fermat claimed to have found a simple proof for his famous theorem that the equation

$$(4) \qquad x^n + y^n = z^n$$

has no solution in positive integers x, y, z for any value of n greater than 2. The theorem seems to be true, but nobody has been able to give a complete proof. Let us ask Mr. Fermat to dictate his proof to a turning table. This would constitute a fact unknown to anybody living today and could be checked by contemporary mathematics.

The marvelous techniques claimed by the occult scientists are by no means new. They belong to old traditions and return from time to time. Astrology is the mother, and not the daughter, of astronomy. Alchemy is the mother, and not the daughter, of chemistry. The body of astrology is built on the celestial structure as known to antiquity. It claims that apparent positions of planets within nonexisting entities of stars at the time of birth influence human fate. If such strong influences on earthly phenomena exist, the corresponding forces would enter into each physical, chemical, and biological experiment. But these experiments have been successful and have led us to a broad knowledge of physical and chemical forces and of biological factors existing on earth.

A word has to be said about "extrasensory" powers. To begin, the name cannot be accepted, because it is based on the absurd assumption taken from antiquity that only five senses exist. Probably the senses cannot be numbered, and, even if we admit such a procedure, the number five is certainly wrong.

In the animal kingdom there exist senses which are poorly developed in mankind. Some dogs find their way back even if separated by kilometers of unknown roads. Birds migrate thousands of kilometers and return to their starting point. Similar senses, although in very small intensities, may exist in mankind too, bodily functions which are still unknown, but certainly *not* extrasensory.

The late Richard von Mises brought out the following argument: Smell is badly developed in human beings as compared to dogs or cats. In a long evolution, we can think of the extinction of this sense, so that man could no longer smell the difference between a rose and asafoetida of the same shape. A few individuals may be left who still conserve a remnant of smell, which would be considered "extrasensory" power. In the same way, people may exist with ways of perception which are badly developed among the rest of humanity. But there is nothing supernatural or extrasensory in this notion.

To find out whether such people exist, random numbers, shapes of colored graphs, and three-dimensional objects should be put in a radio station in front of a person who claims to be able to influence people at a distance. The "sensitive" people in the audience should be asked to give an exact description of the objects. A similar experiment made in Berlin's radio station many years ago led to utmost failure.

There are people who claim to be able to find hidden treasures, not only by inspection of the location but even from a map. The following experiment was designed by these "radiesthetists." A treasure consisting of gold pieces was put into a room of a ten-room apartment. Eighty-six participants were asked to state where the gold was hidden. Then the coins were transported into another room, and so on, without ever being returned to a room previously used. A physical procedure of detection (if available) would have led to about 10 right answers. In reality, the number of successes varied only from 0 to 4, and corresponded to the probabilistic theory of coincidences, i.e., a choice by pure chance.

Here are the results, published in 1938 [4].

Successes	Radiesthetists	Chance
0	31	32
1	33	32
2	14	16
3	7	5
4	1	1
≧ 5	0	0
	—	—
	86	86

Scientific results must be repeatable, but the results of the occult scientists, even if we exclude deceit, are erratic and isolated, and no new fact has ever been established by these methods. As long as this is not the case, we have to reject these procedures.

REFERENCES

1. Fisher, R. A., and L. H. C. Tippett, "Limiting Forms of the Frequency Distribution of the Largest or Smallest Member of a Sample," *Proc. Cambridge Phil. Soc.* **24,** 1928, p. 180.
2. Fréchet, M., "Sur la loi de probabilité de l'écart maximum," *Ann. Soc. polon. Math.,* **6,** 1927, p. 93.
3. Gnedenko, B. V., "Sur la distribution limite du terme maximum d'une série aléatoire," *Ann. Math.,* **44,** 1943, p. 423.
4. Gumbel, E. J., "Gli eventi compatibili," *Gior. Ist. ital. Attuari,* **VI,** 1938.
5. ———, *Statistics of Extremes,* New York, Columbia University Press, 1958.
6. ———, and Littauer, S. B., "An Application of the Theory of Extreme Values to Economic Problems," *Ann. Math. Statistics,* **21, 1,** 1950.
7. Mises, R., von, La distribution de la plus grande de *n* valeurs, *Revue Math. Un. Interbal.,* **1,** 1936, p. 1.
8. National Bureau of Standards, "Probability Tables for the Analysis of Extreme Value Data" (preface by E. J. Gumbel), *Appl. Math. Ser. No. 22,* 1953.

IV

SOME PROBLEMS
IN THE SOCIAL SCIENCES

12

INCONSISTENCY OF PREFERENCES
AS A MEASURE
OF PSYCHOLOGICAL DISTANCE

Clyde H. Coombs [1]

PROFESSOR OF PSYCHOLOGY
UNIVERSITY OF MICHIGAN

Inconsistency of judgments has long been one of the behavioral manifestations serving as a foundation stone for psychological measurement. Fechner [1] and Thurstone [2] built theories and systems of psychological measurement based on measures of inconsistency. A fundamental assumption common to both workers is that the degree of inconsistency is monotonically related to psychological distance. Fechner further assumed that "equally often noticed differences are equal," and Case V of Thurstone's law of comparative judgment makes the same assumption. Thurstone further assumes in his ϕ (γ) hypothesis that the function relating inconsistency to psychological distance is the integral of a normal curve. These systems have both been used extensively for the purpose of scaling stimuli on some attribute which they have in common.

[1] This research was carried out while I was a Fulbright Research Scholar at the University of Amsterdam, 1955–1956. Professor H. C. J. Duijker, Director of the Institute of Psychology, very generously made the facilities of the laboratory available, and Professor A. De Groot and his students contributed greatly to discussions before and after the experiment. I am particularly indebted to Mr v.d. Broecke who served as research assistant.

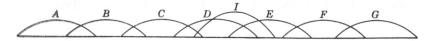

Fig. 1. Discriminal distributions of stimuli (A, B, $\cdots$, G) and a distribution of an individual's ideals (I).

Quite aside from the usefulness and validity of these systems in such psychophysical problems, the recent development of a theory about preferential choice [3] raises the question of the relation of inconsistency to psychological distance for such data. The theory leads to the inference that inconsistency of preferential judgments is not monotonically related to psychological distance and, in particular, is a function of two variables (as will be shown), one of which is psychological distance, and that the relation is monotone only if the second variable (here called *laterality*) is held constant.

Consider the case of a unidimensional latent attribute generating preferential choices. The stimuli are conceived as having a distribution of discriminal processes[2] on this attribute; and the individual whose preferences are being obtained is also conceived as having a distribution of *ideals* (Fig. 1), an ideal being a point from which the individual evaluates the stimuli and states as his preference the stimulus which is nearer his ideal. Thus, for any judgment of preference, we consider that the individual has an ideal point, each stimulus is represented by a point drawn from its distribution, and the judgment reflects which stimulus point is nearer the ideal point.

Let us signify by the term "unilateral pair" a pair of stimuli whose discriminal distributions are both on the same side of the scale relative to the distribution of ideals, and by the term "bilateral pair" a pair of stimuli whose discriminal distributions are on opposite sides of the distribution of ideals. There may be stimuli whose discriminal distributions overlap the distribution of ideals but these will be neglected in the following treatment.

The inconsistencies of an individual's preferences between unilateral pairs as compared with bilateral pairs will be of a different order of magnitude according to this model. In the case of unilateral pairs, only the overlap of the discriminal distributions of the stimuli will generate inconsistency, whereas the inconsistency of judgments between

[2] Discriminal processes is Thurstone's term for what might synonymously be called *perceived magnitudes*.

bilateral pairs will be generated by the variance of the individual's distribution of ideals as well as by the discriminal dispersions.

This may be visualized more clearly if the individual is seen as folding this scale at his ideal point, and, as this folding point varies between successive judgments, the discriminal distributions of unilateral pairs will move nearer to or farther from him in unison, whereas those for bilateral pairs will move in opposite directions.

The implication of this model is that the transformations of inconsistency measures into psychological distance measures must be different, depending upon whether the inconsistency is between unilateral pairs or bilateral pairs. The experiment reported here was designed to test this prediction.

METHOD

Subjects. The subjects (S) were two male and two female psychology students at the University of Amsterdam; all were naive with respect to the experimental problem.

Stimuli and Apparatus. The stimuli were 12 gray chips prepared by a commercial photographer by exposing photographic paper for different periods of time. They varied in arbitrary steps from almost white to almost black.

An apparatus was constructed to present the stimuli in sets of four at a time in a rectangular arrangement of circular chips with 3-inch diameters and 9 inches between centers (not diagonally). The chips were exposed through a 16-inch-square mat, painted white, in which the four 3-inch circular holes were cut. The rest of the apparatus was painted black. Figure 2 is a photograph of the apparatus with the sliding cover open to show a presentation of four stimuli. The cover was closed between presentations. Figure 3 presents the apparatus with the entire front removed, showing the four large aluminum disks on which the chips were pasted. The disks could be rotated from the rear to present any combination of four stimuli desired.

Stimulus Sequence. There are 495 combinations of 12 stimuli taken 4 at a time. In these 495 presentations each stimulus is presented 165 times, each pair 45 times, and each triple 9 times. This suggests the possibility of arranging the 495 presentations in three sequences of 165 each such that each stimulus, each pair, and each triple would occur one-third of its respective total number of occurrences in each of the three sequences. An exact solution was not found, so an approxi-

Fig. 2. Front of apparatus with sliding cover open.

mate one was selected which was quite close; thus, in the case of the 66 pairs of stimuli, 32 pairs each occurred 15 times in each sequence and 28 pairs were distributed over the three sequences with frequencies of 14, 15, and 16. Only one pair of the remaining six pairs differed from the optimal distribution by as much as three in one sequence (e.g., its distribution over the three sequences was 13, 14, and 18).

Procedure. The four S were seated in two rows of two each, 3 and 4 yd respectively from the apparatus. All of the 495 presentations were run on each of two successive evenings in a well-lighted laboratory room. The instructions, of course, were in Dutch and were given to the S in written form and read aloud. Essentially, the S were told that they would see a presentation of four greys which they were to rank from the most preferred as a representative grey to the least preferred. The instructions also indicated how they were to record their judgments on the data sheets provided.

Treatment of the Data. The data from each of the S are analyzed separately as each S is a separate experiment. The first task of the analysis was to see if there was a predominant ordering of the stimuli from most preferred to least preferred for each S. This was arrived at as follows: each pair is imbedded in 90 sets of four stimuli, and from the S's ranking of each set of four a paired comparison on each pair is implied. Thus for each pair the relative frequency with which

Fig. 3. Front view of apparatus with front panel removed.

one member of a pair is preferred is tabulated. The 90 replications on each pair, however, are not to be interpreted as 90 independent paired comparisons because the S ranked four stimuli at a time which imposed transitivity on the imbedded six paired comparisons.

Information theory provides a way of computing the amount of information in these 90 replications: in any given set of four stimuli, the number of ways they can be ordered is $4! = 24$. So the information in any presentation, assuming equal probability for orderings, is $\log_2 24 = 4.58$ bits per presentation. These are distributed over six paired comparisons so that each has, on the average, 0.763 bits of information. Accumulating the information for any pair over its 90 replications gives a total of 68.67 bits of information per paired comparison. Thus the 90 replications may be regarded as the equivalent of 68.67 independent replications on any pair, a matter relevant to the reliability of the percentages.

Defining the dominant preference on any pair to be that which occurred more than 50 per cent of the time yields the paired comparison preferences of each S over the 66 pairs. If these are transitive, one has the rank order of the individual's preferences from most to least preferred. This rank order is called an I scale. If the order of the stimuli on this I scale can be obtained by folding the stimulus scale of greys which goes from light to dark, then the condition that preferences for greys are generated by a single dimension of brightness is satisfied in so far as these data could test it. This means that the I scale could be unfolded and the laterality of stimuli be determined. For example, let the stimuli be labeled alphabetically from A to L in order of decreasing brightness, and suppose an individual's rank-order I scale was $GFEDHICBJAKL$ where G is the most preferred and L the least. Clearly such a preference scale could be obtained by folding the scale A to L in the neighborhood of stimulus G.

The laterality of the stimuli with respect to the distribution of an individual's ideals having been determined, the further determination of which pairs are bilateral and which are unilateral immediately follows. To test the hypothesis that the transformation of inconsistency into psychological distance is on a different scale of measurement for bilateral pairs than for unilateral pairs, the stimuli on the I scale were taken in subsets of three ordered stimuli at a time. Thus, from the rank-order I scale given above, EDI, CBA, and DHC are examples of three such triples. These also illustrate three different kinds of triples defined as follows:

Unilateral triples—in which all three stimuli are unilateral to the distribution of ideals, e.g., *CBA, IJK,* etc.

Bilateral adjacent triples—in which the two stimuli from one side are adjacent in the *I*-scale rank order of the three, and the third stimulus from the other side is either first or last, e.g., *DHJ, ICB,* etc.

Bilateral split triples—in which the two stimuli from one side are separated in the rank order by the stimulus from the other side, e.g., *DHC, JAK,* etc.

If a monotone transformation of inconsistency into psychological distance exists, then, for *any* ordered triple of stimuli from the *I* scale, the percentage of preferences of the first over the third should be at least as great as the percentage of the first over the second, or the second over the third, within the reliability with which the percentages were determined. The theory proposed here asserts that this will not always be the case; in particular, it will tend not to hold for bilateral adjacent triples; in general, it should hold for unilateral triples; and it will hold for bilateral split triples especially.

Consider the following illustration of a bilateral adjacent triple from the former example *ICB.* This is the rank order of preference, hence, the distance from *I* to *B* should be at least as great as that from either *I* to *C* or *C* to *B.* If we were to find that the percentage of preferences of *I* preferred over *B* (a bilateral pair) was 66 per cent and the percentage of preferences of *C* over *B* (a unilateral pair) was 92 per cent, such data would violate the hypothesis of a monotone transformation of inconsistency into psychological distance. Such results are anticipated, however, where *I* and *B* are a bilateral pair and where *C* and *B* are a unilateral pair, because the measure of the inconsistency on a bilateral pair is a function of the variance of the distribution of ideals *in addition to* the discriminal dispersions of the stimuli; whereas the measurement of inconsistency on a unilateral pair is a function only of the discriminal dispersions of the stimuli.

RESULTS

Rank Orders of Preferences. Tables 1 through 4 contain the inconsistency data of the four *S.* Each entry is the percentage of times that a subject preferred the stimulus corresponding to that row over the stimulus corresponding to that column. The stimuli are labeled from *A* to *L* in order of decreasing brightness. The fact that a permu-

TABLE 1.   Inconsistency of Preferences for S 1

	G	F	E	D	H	I	C	B	J	A	K	L	No. of Preferences
G		52	67	72	64	76	91	89	99	100	100	100	819
F			83	83	74	80	98	99	100	100	100	100	869
E				50	67	64	92	97	97	100	100	100	735
D					61	63	90	100	91	100	100	100	720
H						68	50	72	100	99	100	100	650
I							54	66	97	99	100	100	598
C								92	94	100	100	100	550
B									83	100	94	100	417
J										83	99	100	289
A											62	97	160
K												100	130

Note: Entries represent percentage of times the row was preferred to the column.

tation of each table exists such that all the entries on one side of the diagonal are at least as great as 50 per cent implies that the 66 paired comparisons are transitive for each S, and the order of the columns corresponds to the rank order of that S's dominant preferences, his I scale.

TABLE 2.   Inconsistency of Preferences for S 2

	J	I	H	G	F	E	D	K	C	B	L	A	No. of Preferences
J		51	59	61	68	84	88	94	90	94	100	100	801
I			52	77	96	97	96	82	100	99	100	100	852
H				86	93	99	100	87	100	100	100	100	858
G					93	98	99	80	100	100	98	100	760
F						96	99	67	100	99	100	100	639
E							59	50	88	99	50	100	466
D								56	93	99	96	100	453
K									53	67	99	99	452
C										92	93	100	325
B											97	100	223
L												80	92

TABLE 3.   Inconsistency of Preferences for S 3

	F	G	E	D	H	I	C	J	B	K	L	A	No. of Preferences
F		70	91	87	74	80	94	93	100	100	100	100	891
G			68	78	52	73	94	99	97	100	100	100	802
E				53	51	60	89	87	100	93	99	100	696
D					53	57	93	83	100	97	100	100	689
H						63	76	97	99	99	100	100	722
I							80	92	88	100	100	100	654
C								54	90	82	89	100	440
J									64	94	99	100	407
B										52	76	100	261
K											97	100	251
L												99	126

Inspection of these rank-order I scales reveals that three of them can be obtained by folding the stimulus scale of greys, satisfying a condition for unidimensionality of the latent attribute. The one exception is that of the fourth S, for whom stimuli D and E are reversed. We see from Table 4 that this S preferred D to E 51 per cent of the time, which represents a split of 46 to 44 out of the 90 replications. Looking at the data from all the S on this pair of stimuli, it is evident that they were very close together, and this reversal is not significant.

TABLE 4.   Inconsistency of Preferences for S 4

	G	F	H	I	D	E	J	C	B	K	L	A	No. of Preferences
G		53	63	66	86	79	97	92	94	97	99	99	832
F			62	62	87	87	90	96	99	93	99	100	829
H				54	63	68	94	80	89	97	99	97	734
I					64	61	98	80	82	100	100	99	722
D						51	60	93	99	87	96	99	616
E							71	94	99	84	96	99	628
J								57	63	94	100	91	446
C									93	68	93	100	416
B										58	84	100	291
K											100	73	266
L												53	79

Test of Monotonicity. Given the I scale of each subject, a breakdown into unilateral triples and bilateral adjacent triples was made, and these were examined to see how many of each kind satisfied the necessary condition for the existence of a monotonic transformation of inconsistency into psychological distance. If the distribution of the individual's ideals overlaps the discriminal distributions of stimuli, the definition of unilateral and bilateral pairs involving such stimuli breaks down. Consequently, the first two stimuli on each I scale were dropped in the following analysis, and the results were based on the remaining ten stimuli. The 45 paired comparisons that remain for each S were divided into those which were between bilateral pairs and those between unilateral pairs. The bilateral pairs were then examined to see how many of them violated monotonicity in a bilateral adjacent triple, and the unilateral pairs were examined to see how many of them violated monotonicity in a unilateral triple.

The results for each S are presented as fourfold tables in Table 5 with x^2 tests of significance. Obviously, the combined results are highly significant.

A given paired comparison enters into many triples and, hence, may satisfy or violate monotonicity in more than one. There is, of course, some dependency among such figures so that no statistical test is available, but it is instructive to see the figures anyway. Table 6 presents a count of the number of each of the three kinds of triples (bilaterals split, unilaterals, and bilaterals adjacent) for each S and the number of such triples that violated monotonicity. The theory predicts that

TABLE 5.   Relation of Laterality to Monotonicity

	$S\,1$		$S\,2$		$S\,3$		$S\,4$	
	Mon. Satisfied	Mon. Not Satisfied	Mon. Satisfied	Mon. Not Satisfied	Mon. Satisfied	Mon. Not Satisfied	Mon. Satisfied	Mon. Not Satisfied
Bilateral adjacent triples	15	10	9	7	12	13	6	19
Unilateral triples	19	1	27	2	18	2	14	6
p	<0.02		= 0.01		<0.01		<0.01	

**TABLE 6.   Number of Each Kind of Triple and Number
Violating Monotonicity**

Subject No.	Bilaterals, Split		Unilaterals		Bilaterals, Adjacent	
	Total No.	No. Violating Monotonicity	Total No.	No. Violating Monotonicity	Total No.	No. Violating Monotonicity
1	34	0	20	1	66	18
2	24	0	56	2	40	24
3	38	0	20	2	62	29
4	38	0	20	10	62	48
Combined	134	0	116	15	230	119

the frequency of violations should increase from a rare event with bilaterals split to a common event with bilaterals adjacent.

DISCUSSION

These results, although clearly indicating that the relation of inconsistency to psychological distance is dependent upon laterality, by no means imply that inconsistency cannot be used to measure psychological distance.   Given that monotonicity is satisfied with laterality held constant, there may exist a valid transformation of measures of inconsistency into measures of psychological distance.   The different transformations for different laterality would still presumably belong to the same family of curves.   For example, if a normal curve transformation were suitable such as is used with the law of comparative judgment, or as the standard deviation of the distribution of differences is used as the unit of measurement, then there would be reason to expect that this standard deviation would have one value for unilateral pairs and a larger value for bilateral pairs.   It would be like measuring psychological distance with a foot rule for unilateral pairs and with a yard stick for bilateral pairs.   Some interesting theoretical and experimental problems arise here.

SUMMARY

A measurement of inconsistency has long been a basis for measurement of psychological distance as, for example, with the *jnd* concept in psychophysics.   This experiment is an intensive study of the relation of measures of inconsistency to psychological distance in the context of *preferential choice* as distinct from the context of psychophysical discrimination. A theory was tested which predicts that measures of inconsistency of preferential choice are not monotonically related to psychological distance unless another condition, called laterality, is held constant. A series of 12 shades of grey were presented in sets of four at a time to each of four S who indicated their preferences among the stimuli as best representing their concept of grey. Each individual's concept of grey turned out to be an intermediate grey with lighter greys on one side and darker greys on the other. The hypothesis was tested that inconsistency between pairs of greys whose members were both on the same side of the S's ideal would be of a different order of magnitude than inconsistency between pairs whose members came from opposite sides of the S's. Each S constituted a separate experiment and the hypothesis was sustained for each of them. The significance of this test for converting inconsistency measures into psychological distance measures was discussed.

REFERENCES

1. Boring, E. G., *History of Experimental Psychology*, New York, Appleton-Century-Crofts, 1929.
2. Thurstone, L. L., "A Law of Comparative Judgment," *Psych. Rev.*, **34**, 1927, pp. 273–286.
3. Coombs, C. H., "A Theory of Psychological Scaling," Ann Arbor, University of Michigan Press, 1952. *Engineering Research Institute Bulletin No. 34* (a monograph).

13

EXPERIMENTAL TESTS

OF A STOCHASTIC

DECISION THEORY[1]

Donald Davidson

ASSOCIATE PROFESSOR OF PHILOSOPHY
STANFORD UNIVERSITY

Jacob Marschak

PROFESSOR OF ECONOMICS
COWLES FOUNDATION FOR RESEARCH IN ECONOMICS
YALE UNIVERSITY

INTRODUCTION

Common experience suggests, and experiment confirms, that a person does not always make the same choice when faced with the same options, even when the circumstances of choice seem in all relevant respects to be the same. However, the bulk of economic theory neglects the existence of such inconsistencies; and the best known theories for decision making, for example, those of von Neumann and Morgenstern [1] or

[1] Research undertaken by the Applied Mathematics and Statistics Laboratory, Stanford University, under contract Nonr-225(17), NR 171-034, with the Office of Naval Research, and by the Cowles Commission for Research in Economics under contract Nonr-358(01), NR 047-006, with the Office of Naval Research.

The authors were helped by discussions with G. Debreu, E. Fels, L. Hurwicz, R. Radner, H. Raiffa, R. Summers, R. Savage, and P. Suppes.

Savage [2], base the existence of a measurable utility upon a pattern of invariant two-place relations, sometimes called "preference" and "indifference." This raises a difficulty for any attempt to use such theories to describe and predict actual behavior.

A number of ways of meeting the difficulty may be mentioned:

1. It is possible to insist on the normative status of the theory and construe all deviations as evidence of error on the part of the subject.

2. One may defend the descriptive accuracy of the theory and argue that it has been incorrectly interpreted; for example, by wrongly identifying two options (say winning $1 at time t and winning $1 at time $t + 10$ minutes) as the same.

3. One may interpret every case of inconsistency as a case of indifference: if the subject has chosen a rather than b but soon afterwards chooses b rather than a, this is interpreted as indifference between those two objects; if he chooses a rather than b, b rather than c, and c rather than a, this is interpreted as indifference between those three objects. In empirical application, this approach would probably make indifference all-pervasive.

4. An alternative approach is to define preference and indifference in terms of probabilities of choice. Mosteller and Nogee, in testing the von Neumann and Morgenstern axioms, considered a subject indifferent between two options when he chose each option half the time [3]; Edwards [4] has also used this method. In this approach probabilities of choice do not enter the formal axiomatic development.

5. A fifth strategy, explored in this paper, incorporates probabilities of choice into the axiomatic structure and exploits their properties in scaling utilities.

PRIMITIVE AND DEFINED NOTIONS

We now introduce various concepts needed for the subsequent discussion. It should be emphasized that strictness has in many places been sacrificed to perspicuity; we trust that the knowing reader can make the corrections needed for formal accuracy. First we list the primitive notions:

Primitive 1. A set A of *alternatives*.[2] A may include wagers (choices involving risk) as well as sure outcomes. In this and the following section,

2 We use the word "alternative," as is fairly common in the literature of decision theory, to mean one of two or more things or courses among which a person may choose.

we shall treat alternatives quite generally. In the section entitled "Stochastic Theory of Choice Between Subjectively Even-Chance Wagers" we shall use special properties of wagers.

Primitive 2. The *probability* $P(a, b)$ that the subject, forced to choose between a and b, chooses a. We assume, in what follows, for every a and b in A:

(a) $P(a, b) + P(b, a) = 1$.
(b) $P(a, b)$ lies in the open interval $(0, 1)$.

In a fully formalized exposition these assumptions would appear as axioms or theorems; in this paper we shall sometimes leave these assumptions tacit. Under a natural interpretation Primitive 2(a) has empirical content: it implies that, when a subject is asked to choose between a or b, he always chooses a or b. Normally, we are not interested in testing Primitive 2(a); rather, we attempt to make it true by enforcing a choice. Therefore we may want to state our experimental hypothesis as follows: if Primitive 2(a) is true for a given subject, then the other axioms hold; if Primitive 2(a) fails for a subject, we then reject the subject, not the hypothesis. Or we may want to include Primitive 2(a) in the hypothesis and reject the hypothesis for a subject who refuses an offered choice. For the experiments reported here, the issue is academic. All subjects were docile.

For the case where $a = b$, Primitive 2(a) has the consequence $P(a,a) = \frac{1}{2}$. Formal convenience dictates that we not exclude this case although we give it no empirical meaning.

Before commenting on Primitive 2(b), it will be useful to give some definitions.

Definition 1. a is *absolutely preferred* to b if and only if $P(a, b) = 1$. This concept corresponds to the psychologists' "perfect discrimination."

Definition 2. a is *stochastically preferred* to b if and only if $\frac{1}{2} \leqslant P(a, b) < 1$.

Definition 3. a and b are *stochastically indifferent* if and only if $P(a, b) = \frac{1}{2}$. Since we use the word "indifferent" in no other sense, we often omit the word "stochastically."

Definition 4. c is a *stochastic mid-point* between a and b if and only if $P(a, c) = P(c, b)$.

In situations in which it is natural to apply the theory, it is obvious that cases of absolute preference occur, violating Primitive 2(b). In particular, one would expect that when a and b denote respectively "receiving m dollars" and "receiving n dollars" (or, for that matter, m or n units of some commodity), then $m > n$ implies $P(a, b) = 1$. More generally, if m_1, n_1 are amounts of some commodity and m_2, n_2 are amounts of a second commodity, and $m_1 > n_1$, $m_2 \geq n_2$, then the alternative consisting of receiving m_1 and m_2 will be absolutely preferred to the alternative n_1 and n_2. This extends also to bundles consisting of three or more commodities.

In the experimental testing of stochastic theories of choice, various devices may be used to avoid comparisons of alternatives which yield absolute preferences. Papandreou et al. [5], using appropriate commodity bundles, avoided cases of the sort just mentioned. The methods used for avoiding comparisons apt to generate absolute preference in the experiments reported here are discussed in what follows.

As long as the assumption stated in Primitive 2(b) remains in force, it is not enough merely to avoid comparing alternatives one of which is absolutely preferred to another; the set A of alternatives to which the theory applies must contain no two such alternatives. Although we have no solution on hand, we shall mention in the next section the possibility of modifying the formal system to eliminate dependence on the assumption in Primitive 2(b).

GENERAL STOCHASTIC THEORY OF CHOICE

An important aspect of a general stochastic theory of choice lies in the fact that, without specifically considering wagers, it is possible to obtain forms of measurement stronger than a mere ordering by imposing plausible conditions on probabilities of choice. When conditions of sufficient strength are satisfied, it is possible to interpret a comparison of probabilities as a comparison of differences in subjective value or utility. This idea is captured in a general form by the following definition:

Definition 5. For a given subject, a real-valued function u is called a *utility function* on A (in the sense of Definition 5) if and only if, for every a, b, c, and d in A,

$$P(a, b) \geq P(c, d) \text{ if and only if } u(a) - u(b) \geq u(c) - u(d).$$

The technique of building a subjective scale on the basis of frequency of discriminated differences is common in psychophysics since Fechner [6]; however, the emphasis in psychophysics on relating the subjective (sensation) scale to a physical continuum (which is not assumed in utility measurement) tends to obscure the analogy. Discussion of the relation between psychophysical scaling and utility measurement will be found in Marschak [7] and Luce [8, 9].

There is a much used adage in psychophysics which may be taken as suggesting the principle underlying Definition 5: "Equally often noticed differences are equal [on the sensation scale] unless noticed always or never" (ascribed by Guilford [10] to Fullerton and Cattell). The final phrase of this adage enters a caveat which is clearly as pertinent in utility as in sensation measurement for, in our terms, the caveat concerns the case of absolute preference. Consider the case where $P(6\cent, 5\cent) = 1 = P(\$5000, \$0)$ and hence, by Definition 5, $u(6\cent) - u(5\cent) = u(\$5000) - u(\$0)$, which is intuitively absurd. The difficulty created by the existence of absolute preferences is thus clear. The approach to a solution which suggests itself is to add to Definition 5 the caveat "provided neither $P(a, b)$ nor $P(c, d)$ is equal to 0 or 1." This would require modification of the axiomatic conditions needed to prove the existence of a utility function. We have not attempted to carry out this modification, which may well not be trivial.

We now consider what conditions are sufficient for the existence of a utility function (in the sense of Definition 5). Fortunately, in approaching this question, we are able to depend on previous work because any theory which makes essential use of a four-place relation comparing intervals may, with fairly trivial modifications, be reconstrued as a theory in which the atomic sentences are all of the form $P(a, b) \geq P(c, d)$, as demanded by Definition 5.[3]

What constitutes sufficient conditions for the existence of a utility function depends, in part, on the nature of the set A. We therefore consider several cases:

Case (a). The set A contains a known finite number n of alternatives, $a_1, \cdots, a_n$. In this case, it is always possible, although perhaps tedious, to stipulate conditions on the probabilities $P(a_i, a_j)$ necessary and sufficient for the existence of a utility function. A simple example (for $n = 3$) will be treated fully later. In general, it suffices, because of Primitive 2(a), to consider those probabilities $P(a, b)$ that are $\geq \frac{1}{2}$; a given complete ordering of these numbers yields, by Definition 5, a sequence of $n(n - 1)/2$ inequalities of the form

$$u(a_g) - u(a_h) \geq u(a_i) - u(a_k) \geq \cdots \geq 0$$

involving a set of only n distinct unknowns, viz., the utilities of the n alternatives. Whether these inequalities have a solution can be answered separately for each of the possible $[n(n - 1)/2]!$ orderings of the probabilities.

---

[3] The modifications may allow for the special properties of probabilities, and for the fact that $P(a, b) \geq P(c, d)$ compares signed intervals whereas the quaternary relations taken as primitive in some theories compare unsigned intervals.

Case (b). The set A contains an arbitrary number of alternatives which are equally spaced in utility [such that for every a, b, c, and d in A, if a and b are adjacent in utility [4] and c and d are adjacent, then $P(a, b) = P(c, d)$]. The axioms are an obvious modification of the axioms in Davidson, Suppes, and Siegel [11, p. 31].

Case (c). It will be convenient to give two definitions. The first we owe to Professor Patrick Suppes.

Definition 6. A set A of alternatives is *stochastically continuous* if and only if it meets the following three conditions for every a, b, c, and d in A:

(i) There exists a stochastic mid-point between a and b.

(ii) If $P(c, d) > P(a, b) > \frac{1}{2}$, then there exists a g such that $P(c, g) > \frac{1}{2}$ and $P(g, d) \geq P(a, b)$.

(iii) (Archimedean condition.) If $P(a, b) > \frac{1}{2}$, then for every probability q such that $P(a, b) > q > \frac{1}{2}$, there exists a positive integer n such that $q \geq P(a, c_1) = P(c_1, c_2) = \cdots = P(c_n, b) > \frac{1}{2}$.

Definition 7. The *quadruple condition* is satisfied if and only if, for every a, b, c, and d in A, $P(a, b) \geq P(c, d)$ implies $P(a, c) \geq P(b, d)$.

It follows immediately from Definition 5 that, if a utility function exists on A, then the quadruple condition is satisfied in A. However, we are now in a position to assert more:

Theorem 1. *If A is stochastically continuous then a utility function exists if and only if the quadruple condition is satisfied.*

A proof of this theorem will not be given here. The general line of demonstration is as follows: Suppes and Winet [12] have given an axiomatization of utility based on a primitive concept which compares utility differences, and they have proved that, if certain axioms on a relation between two pairs of alternatives hold, then utility differences can be defined and, hence, a function analogous to a utility function (in the sense of Definition 5) exists. (See also Alt [13].) Suppes [14] has shown how to express these axioms in terms of relations between probabilities; the new axioms on probabilities (let us call them S) suffice to prove the existence of a utility function in the sense of Definition 5. The three conditions of Definition 6 are trivially equivalent to the continuity axioms of S. Finally, we have been able to prove that all the further axioms of S hold if the quadruple condition is satisfied [and provided, of course, the assumptions specified in Primitives 2(a) and (b) hold]. Hence

---

[4] Let $P(a, b) \geq \frac{1}{2}$; then a and b are said to be adjacent in utility if $P(a, b) \leq P(a, c)$ for every c with $P(a, c) \geq \frac{1}{2}$.

we know that, if the continuity and quadruple conditions of Definitions 6 and 7 hold, S holds, and there exists a utility function.

Case (d). A result similar to Theorem 1 was obtained by Debreu [15] under a different definition of stochastic continuity properties. Debreu has shown that there exists a utility function on A if the following conditions are satisfied:

(i) If a, b, c are in A and $P(b, a) \geq q \geq P(c, a)$, then there is a d in A such that $P(d, a) = q$.

(ii) The quadruple condition holds for A.

Case (e). The set A contains an unknown number (possibly finite) of alternatives. For this case, no axiom system is known, and it has been conjectured by Scott and Suppes [16] that under certain natural restrictions on the form of axioms no axiomatization is possible.

It may be noted that in Cases (b), (c), and (d), the axiom systems adequate to prove the existence of a utility function (in the sense of Definition 5) are adequate to prove also that any such function is unique up to a linear transformation (i.e., the existence of cardinal utilities).

We can submit to direct experimental test a set of the kind described in Case (a) containing a small, known, finite number of alternatives (let us call the set of alternatives under test T). If the quadruple condition is satisfied for every quadruple of alternatives in T, and T is a sample drawn from a larger set A, we may conclude—with a degree of confidence depending among other things on the size of the sample—that the quadruple condition holds for A. If our hypothesis is that a utility function on A exists, then we need further information about A; for example, we may know the (finite) number of its elements, Case (a), or we may hold that A is stochastically continuous, Cases (c) and (d).

In the experiment reported here, one hypothesis is that a utility function exists for the set consisting of all money wagers of a certain sort. If we can assume that A is stochastically continuous in the sense of Cases (c) or (d), e.g., because the money amounts which enter the wagers are, approximately, continuous variables, and if, on the basis of our sample T, we have concluded that the quadruple condition holds for A, then we can conclude, by Theorem 1, that there exists a utility function on A.

Actually, we did not test for the quadruple condition on our sample T. Instead, we tested for certain implications of that condition: if T does not satisfy such an implication, we reject the hypothesis that T satisfies the quadruple condition. Those implications involve triples (not quadruples) of alternatives and will be referred to as stochastic transitivity properties.

Even for relatively small finite sets of alternatives, the existence of a utility function in the sense of Definition 5 implies more than is implied by the quadruple condition alone. This fact suggests a view of the relation between experimental evidence and hypothesis which differs slightly from the one outlined in the preceding paragraphs. For each sample T drawn from A, we may test *all* the conditions necessary and sufficient for the existence of a utility function on T [the general method is given above in the discussion of Case (a)]. We then consider confirmation of the existence of a utility function on T as inductive evidence for the existence of a utility function on A. As will be shown, the condition of strong stochastic transitivity about to be stated gives necessary and sufficient conditions for the existence of a utility function on a set consisting of three alternatives.

Condition 1.

(a) *Weak stochastic transitivity* holds in A if and only if, for all a, b, and c in A,

$$\text{if } P(a, b) \geq \tfrac{1}{2} \text{ and } P(b, c) \geq \tfrac{1}{2}, \text{ then } P(a, c) \geq \tfrac{1}{2}.$$

(b) *Strong stochastic transitivity* holds in A if and only if, for all a, b, and c in A,

$$\text{if } P(a, b) \geq \tfrac{1}{2} \text{ and } P(b, c) \geq \tfrac{1}{2}, \text{ then } P(a, c) \geq \max [P(a, b), P(b, c)].$$

These terms are due to S. Vail [17]. (We sometimes omit the word "stochastic.") Clearly Condition 1(b) implies 1(a), but 1(a) does not imply 1(b); both are implied by the existence of a utility function and are, therefore, necessary conditions for the existence of such a function. Condition 1(b) is equivalent to:

Condition 2. If $P(a, b) \geq \tfrac{1}{2}$, then $P(a, c) \geq P(b, c)$.

Proof: To show that Condition 1(b) implies Condition 2, assume $P(a, b) \geq \tfrac{1}{2}$ and show that, by Condition 1(b), $P(a, c) \geq P(b, c)$ for each of the three possible cases:

1. $P(b, c) \geq \tfrac{1}{2}$; then $P(a, c) \geq \max[P(a, b), P(b, c)] \geq P(b, c)$.
2. $P(b, c) < \tfrac{1}{2} \leq P(a, c)$; then $P(a, c) \geq P(b, c)$.
3. $P(b, c) < \tfrac{1}{2}$, $P(a, c) < \tfrac{1}{2}$; then $P(c, a) > \tfrac{1}{2}$, hence $P(c, b) \geq \max[P(c, a), P(a, b)] \geq P(c, a)$, $P(a, c) \geq P(b, c)$.

It may be left to the reader to prove the converse, i.e., that Condition 2 implies Condition 1(b).

Consider three fixed alternatives, a_1, a_2, a_3 and label the three relevant probabilities $P(a_1, a_2) = p_1$, $P(a_2, a_3) = p_2$, $P(a_3, a_1) = p_3$. The two

TABLE 1. Specimen Stimulus Cards

For Testing Transitivity of Alternatives

	A	B			A	B			A	B
ZOJ	−5¢	+36¢		QUG	+36¢	−54¢		WUH	−54¢	−5¢
ZEJ	−21¢	−38¢		QUJ	−38¢	+22¢		XEQ	+22¢	−21¢

For Testing Transitivity of Utility Intervals

	A	B			A	B			A	B
ZOJ	−6¢	+5¢		QUG	+38¢	+31¢		WUH	+31¢	+38¢
ZEJ	+24¢	+13¢		QUJ	+13¢	+24¢		XEQ	+5¢	−6¢

kinds of transitivity condition applied to the set consisting of a_1, a_2, a_3 can then be expressed in the following symmetric form:

Condition 3.

(a) *Weak transitivity:* p_1, p_2, p_3 not all $\geq \frac{1}{2}$ or $\leq \frac{1}{2}$ unless they are all $= \frac{1}{2}$.

(b) *Strong transitivity:*

$$p_1 \geq \tfrac{1}{2} \text{ if and only if } p_2 + p_3 \leq 1,$$

$$p_2 \geq \tfrac{1}{2} \text{ if and only if } p_3 + p_1 \leq 1,$$

$$p_3 \geq \tfrac{1}{2} \text{ if and only if } p_1 + p_2 \leq 1.$$

In the experiment reported in this paper, we are concerned with triples of alternatives. It is therefore interesting to note that, if the set of alternatives consists of exactly three elements a, b, c, then the condition of strong stochastic transitivity is not only necessary for the existence of a utility function (as mentioned in the foregoing) but also sufficient. For, under strong transitivity, we may assume without loss of generality that $P(a, c) \geq P(a, b) \geq P(b, c) \geq \frac{1}{2}$. The corresponding inequalities between utilities (Definition 5) are: $u(a) - u(c) \geq u(a) - u(b) \geq u(b) - u(c) \geq 0$. These inequalities are satisfied, for example, by the following numbers: $u(a) = 1$, $u(c) = 0$, $u(b) =$ any number between, and including, 0 and 1.

In Table 1, the upper three cards show how we tested strong (and weak) transitivity experimentally. The subject made choices between the two columns on a card; the syllables on the left represent events determining the outcome of a wager. On the three cards there are altogether three alternatives (wagers) paired in each of the three possible ways. By testing whether Condition 3(b) holds for a sample consisting of a number of such triples of alternatives, we obtain evidence for or against the hypothesis that a utility function exists on the set A from which the sample is drawn.

STOCHASTIC THEORY OF CHOICE BETWEEN SUBJECTIVELY EVEN-CHANCE WAGERS

In this section we deal with a special case of the stochastic theory of choice, exploiting some possible properties of choices between wagers of a special sort, namely, those created by chance events with a "subjective probability of one half." The theoretical and experimental importance of the nonstochastic theory of choice for such wagers was first pointed out by Ramsey [18]; a formalization of the theory applied to finite sets, and reports of several experimental applications (including one with stochastic aspects) are given in Davidson, Suppes, and Siegel [11].

We assumed in the foregoing section that the set A of alternatives might contain wagers as well as sure outcomes; however, the formal developments made no use of this assumption.

Some additional primitive notions are needed.

Primitive 3. A set X of *states of the world*. The subsets of X are called *events*, denoted by E, F, $\cdots$ and forming a set $\mathcal{E}$.

Primitive 4. If a, b are in A and E is in $\mathcal{E}$, then aEb is the wager which consists in getting a if E happens, and getting b if E does not happen.

Definitions 1 through 4 are applicable to wagers; for example, when $P(aEb, cFd) = \frac{1}{2}$, we say that aEb and cFd are (stochastically) indifferent. We may presume that in certain cases absolute preference occurs. In particular, if a_1, a_2, b_1, b_2 are in A and $P(a_1, b_1) = 1 = P(a_2, b_2)$, then for any event E in $\mathcal{E}$, $P(a_1Ea_2, b_1Eb_2) = 1$.

Definition 8. An event E in $\mathcal{E}$ is an *even-chance event* if and only if, for every a and b in A,

$$P(aEb, bEa) = \tfrac{1}{2}.$$

If E is an even-chance event, we call aEb an *even-chance wager*. It is obvious that the notion of even chance involved in this definition is *subjective;* it makes no appeal to the objective probability of E. The justification for our terminology is simple. Suppose a subject prefers a to b. If he thinks E is more likely to happen than not, he will choose aEb more often than bEa; if he thinks E less likely to happen than not, he will choose aEb less often than bEa. Hence he will choose aEb and bEa equally often if and only if he thinks E is as likely to happen as not, i.e., E has a "subjectively even chance."

Definition 9. The subject is said to be *unbiased* if and only if, for any two even-chance events E and F and any a and b in A,

$$P(aEb, aFb) = \tfrac{1}{2}.$$

It is obvious that if this condition is satisfied and there exists a utility function u on A, then for any two even-chance events E and F and any a and b in A,

$$u(aEb) = u(bEa) = u(aFb) = u(bFa).$$

This justifies writing simply ab for aEb where E is any even-chance event; since we explicitly consider no other events, symbols for chance events need not enter our formalism.

The chief concern of this section may be stated by giving a more restrictive version of Definition 5:

Definition 10. A real-valued function u is an *even-chance wager utility function* (or a *utility function in the sense of Definition 10*) on A if and only if:

(a) u is a utility function on A in the sense of Definition 5;

(b) for every a and b in A and every even-chance event E, $u(aEb) = [u(a)]/2 + [u(b)]/2$.

Definitions 10(a) and (b) together express in stochastic form the usual hypothesis that a subject prefers the wager with the higher expected utility (applying this hypothesis to the case of even-chance wagers). Clearly, these conditions imply that $u(aEb)$ has the same value for all even-chance events E in $\mathcal{E}$, and that the subject is unbiased.

Now we wish to state conditions sufficient for the existence of an even-chance wager utility function. To this end we define the following condition:

Definition 11. The *even-chance mid-point* condition holds in A if and only if the subject is unbiased and, for every a and b in A,

$$P(a, ab) = P(ab, b).$$

(Definition 11 says ab is a stochastic mid-point between a and b; see Definition 4.)

We may now state a theorem analogous to Theorem 1:

Theorem 2. *If A is stochastically continuous, then an even-chance wager utility function on A exists if and only if the quadruple condition (Definition 7) and the even-chance mid-point condition hold in A.*

Proof: Suppose A is stochastically continuous. Then a function u on A such that $P(a, b) \geq P(c, d)$ if and only if $u(a) - u(b) \geq u(c) - u(d)$ exists if and only if the quadruple condition holds (Theorem 1). Hence the quadruple condition is a necessary condition for the existence of an even-chance wager utility function. And if the quadruple condition is satisfied, then a utility function in the sense of Definition 5 exists; hence:

$$P(a, ab) = P(ab, b) \text{ if and only if } u(a) - u(ab) = u(ab) - u(b),$$

that is,

$$u(ab) = \frac{u(a)}{2} + \frac{u(b)}{2}.$$

Therefore the quadruple and even-chance mid-point conditions together are necessary and sufficient for the existence of a utility function in the sense of Definition 10, provided A is stochastically continuous.

An alternative statement of sufficient conditions may now be considered. We define:

Definition 12. The *even-chance quadruple condition* holds in A if and only if, for every a, b, c, and d in A,

$$P(a, b) \geq P(c, d) \text{ if and only if } P(a, bc) \geq P(bc, d),$$

and assert:

Theorem 3. *If A is stochastically continuous then a utility function on A in the sense of Definition 10 exists if and only if the even-chance quadruple condition holds in A.*

Proof: It follows directly from Definition 10 that, if a utility function in the sense of that definition exists, the even-chance quadruple condition holds. We prove the sufficiency of the even-chance quadruple condition by showing that it implies both the even-chance mid-point condition and the quadruple condition, and then applying Theorem 2. By the even-chance quadruple condition we have (replacing b by a, and c and d by b):

1. $P(a, a) = P(b, b)$ if and only if $P(a, ab) = P(ab, b)$.

The right side of (1) (i.e., the even-chance mid-point condition) is true since the left side is true by Primitive 2(a). Using the even-chance quadruple condition again and Primitive 2(a), the following steps lead to the quadruple condition:

2. $P(a, b) \geq P(c, d)$ if and only if $P(d, bc) \geq P(bc, a)$.
3. $P(d, bc) \geq P(bc, a)$ if and only if $P(a, c) \geq P(b, d)$.

We may now establish:

Theorem 4. *If the even-chance quadruple condition holds in A, then for all a, b, c, and d in A,*

$$P(a, b) \geq P(c, d) \text{ if and only if } P(ad, bc) \geq \tfrac{1}{2}.$$

We establish Theorem 4 by noting that, if the even-chance quadruple condition holds, then $P(a, b) \geq P(c, d)$ is equivalent to $P(a, bc) \geq P(bc, d)$, which in turn is equivalent to $P(ad, bc) \geq P(bc, ad)$.

We have seen (in the proof of Theorem 3) that the even-chance quadruple condition implies the quadruple as well as the even-chance mid-point condition. On the other hand, it seems a safe conjecture that these two conditions in conjunction do not imply the even-chance quadruple condition unless the assumption of stochastic continuity is made. With the assumption of stochastic continuity, the implication does hold, as is easily seen from Theorems 2 and 3.

Theorem 4 thus states a strong principle. It interlocks, in effect, the utility scales obtained by comparing differences in utility by two separate methods.

Condition 4.

(a) *Weak stochastic transitivity for utility intervals* holds in A if and only if, for all a, b, c, d, e, and f in A,

if $P(bf, de) \geq \tfrac{1}{2}$ and $P(ae, cf) \geq \tfrac{1}{2}$, then $P(ab, cd) \geq \tfrac{1}{2}$.

(b) *Strong stochastic transitivity for utility intervals* holds in A if and only if, for all a, b, c, d, e, and f in A,

$$P(bf, de) \geq \tfrac{1}{2} \text{ if and only if } P(ab, cd) \geq P(ae, cf).$$

The analogy between the transitivity conditions for alternatives (Condition 1) and transitivity conditions for intervals (Condition 4) may be brought out as follows. If a utility function in the sense of

Definition 10 exists, then Condition 4(a) is equivalent to the statement (holding, identically, for any six numbers):

If $\qquad\qquad [u(b) + u(f)] - [u(d) + u(e)] \geq 0$

and $\qquad\qquad [u(a) + u(e)] - [u(c) + u(f)] \geq 0$

then $\qquad\qquad [u(a) + u(b)] - [u(c) + u(d)] \geq 0,$

and hence to:

Condition 5.

(a) If $u(b) - u(d) \geq u(e) - u(f)$ and $u(e) - u(f) \geq u(c) - u(a)$, then $u(b) - u(d) \geq u(c) - u(a)$.

Similarly, Condition 4(b) is equivalent to:

(b) $u(b) - u(d) \geq u(e) - u(f)$ if and only if $[u(b) - u(d)] - [u(c) - u(a)] \geq [u(e) - u(f)] - [u(c) - u(a)]$.

Now let the length of the utility interval $u(b) - u(d) = I$, $u(e) - u(f) = J$, and $u(c) - u(a) = K$. Then Conditions 5(a) and (b) become similar in form to Conditions 1(a) and 2:

Condition 6.

(a) If $I \geq J$ and $J \geq K$, then $I \geq K$.
(b) $I \geq J$ if and only if $I - K \geq J - K$.

Thus Conditions 4(a) and (b) may be interpreted as stating conditions on utility intervals analogous to Conditions 1(a) and (b) for alternatives (whether or not these alternatives happen to be wagers). However, it should be emphasized that in testing the transitivity of intervals we must make use of wagers; although we did use wagers in testing the transitivity of alternatives, this is not essential to the theory.

From Conditions 5(a) and (b), it is clear that the transitivity conditions for utility intervals are necessary for the existence of a utility function in the sense of Definition 10.[5] To obtain evidence whether such a function exists for a limited set of outcomes consisting of winning and losing small amounts of money, we tested certain implications of Conditions 4(a) and (b) for sextuples of outcomes which may be regarded as samples from the total set of outcomes. Let us designate six specific money outcomes, a_1, a_2, a_3, a_4, a_5, a_6, arranged in ascending

[5] We conjectured that, if the set of alternatives is stochastically continuous, then the conjunction of strong transitivity of alternatives and of strong transitivity of utility intervals is necessary *and sufficient* for the existence of a utility function in the sense of Definition 10. While this paper was in preparation, G. Debreu [19] proved a closely related theorem which seems particularly applicable to wagers in money amounts (or, more generally, in any continuous commodity amounts).

order by monetary value.   For reasons given in the next section, we considered the following probabilities only:

$$p_1 = P(a_1a_4, a_2a_3) \qquad p_2 = P(a_6a_3, a_5a_4) \qquad p_3 = P(a_5a_2, a_6a_1).$$

For these three probabilities the implications of Conditions 4(a) and (b) are just:

Condition 7.

(a) *Weak transitivity of utility intervals.* p_1, p_2, p_3 not all $\geq \frac{1}{2}$ or $\leq \frac{1}{2}$ unless they are all $= \frac{1}{2}$.

(b) *Strong transitivity of utility intervals:*

$$p_1 \geq \tfrac{1}{2} \text{ if and only if } p_2 + p_3 \leq 1,$$

$$p_2 \geq \tfrac{1}{2} \text{ if and only if } p_3 + p_1 \leq 1,$$

$$p_3 \geq \tfrac{1}{2} \text{ if and only if } p_1 + p_2 \leq 1.$$

It will be noted that Conditions 7(a) and (b) are identical with Conditions 3(a) and (b) where, of course, the three relevant probabilities are differently defined. If a utility function for the six outcomes $a_1, \cdots, a_6$ exists, Conditions 7(a) and (b) will be satisfied; but the converse is not in general true. The existence of a utility function in the sense of Definition 10 implies, even for six outcomes, more than is implied by the transitivity of intervals condition (for example, Theorem 4 is implied by the existence of a utility function but not by the transitivity of intervals condition); and the transitivity of intervals condition alone implies more for six outcomes than is tested by checking the relations given in Conditions 7(a) and (b) and with p_1, p_2, p_3 as defined above.

The second line of specimen cards in Table 1 illustrates the method used in testing Conditions 4(a) and (b). Before the three pairs of wagers on these cards were offered to the subject, it was verified that the chance events underlying the designed money wagers were even-chance events in the sense of Definition 8.[6]   This justified the assumption that all wagers on the cards were (for the given subject) even-chance wagers; therefore it could be tentatively assumed that, whenever the subject chose a wager (a column of a card), he could be interpreted as comparing two utility intervals, represented by the rows of the card. On the three cards illustrated, there are three pairs of identical rows: they correspond to the intervals I, J, and K in Conditions 6(a) and (b). (From Conditions 5(a) and (b) it is clear that interchange of rows or of columns in a given card does not matter, nor does the interchange of alternatives in one of the columns.)

---

[6] A more precise statement of the procedure used will be given in the next section.

EXPERIMENTAL DESIGN

The experiment to be described was designed to test the plausibility of the hypothesis that (for given individuals) there exists a utility function in the sense of Definition 10 (or at least, in the sense of Definition 5), defined over a set of alternatives consisting of winning and losing small amounts of money and of even-chance wagers constructed from the basic alternatives. The individuals were 17 students from an elementary logic class at Stanford University. The general hypothesis was tested by testing certain of its consequences: stochastic transitivity (weak and strong) of alternatives as applied to triples of alternatives (interpreted here as wagers), and stochastic transitivity (weak and strong) of utility intervals as applied to sextuples of alternatives.

The obvious way of testing a stochastic theory of choice is to estimate probabilities of choice from frequencies of choice observed when the subject is repeatedly offered the same alternatives. This method, common from psychophysical experiments, has been used with apparent success by a number of workers in decision theory. These workers (who include Mosteller and Nogee, Ward Edwards, and Papandreou) were, of course, aware of the memory effect, and used various techniques in the attempt to cope with it. In a pilot study for the present experiment, we found that, with wagers of the sort we wished to use, the subject almost always made the same choice when offered the same pair of alternatives; thus we would be forced to estimate almost every probability as 0 or 1. The wagers between which the subjects had to choose had the same actuarial value; the wagers could therefore be assumed to be close in subjective utility. Remarks by the subjects led to the suspicion that the cause of the unforeseen consistency was the subject's ability to remember his previous choices (although various masking procedures were attempted such as reversing the order in which the wagers in a pair were offered, and inserting other offers between repetitions of the identical pair of wagers). In psychophysical experiments, memory cannot have this effect since the subject is given no way of identifying the repetition of a stimulus.

To avoid the effect of memory, the same *pair* of wagers was never offered twice to a subject. The method used for testing our hypothesis under this restriction is explained in the next section.

Each subject was asked to make 319 choices; a choice consisted in a verbal response (*A* or *B*) to a stimulus card of the kind illustrated in Table 1. In 107 cases selected (with certain limitations to be mentioned later) at random, and unknown in advance to the subject, the response

TABLE 2. Money Amounts (Wins and Losses) Used in Constructing Stimulus Cards

Sequence	a	b	c	d	e	f	g
1	−17	−12	− 5	+ 2	+ 8	+17	+21
2	−20	−16	−11	− 4	+ 3	+10	+15
3	−12	− 5	+ 2	+ 9	+14	+19	+23
4	−22	−18	−14	− 9	− 2	+ 5	+12
5	−14	− 8	− 4	+ 5	+13	+20	+26
6	−36	−17	− 8	+ 2	+10	+21	+27
7	−13	− 8	− 5	− 1	+ 4	+ 7	+12
8	−35	−28	−22	−15	− 8	− 2	+ 6
9	−27	−16	− 4	+ 7	+21	+34	+47
10	− 6	+ 1	+ 8	+15	+22	+30	+34
11	−39	−25	− 9	+ 6	+23	+40	+56
12	−37	−22	− 6	+ 5	+21	+38	+54
13	− 7	− 4	− 1	+ 3	+ 6	+ 8	+11
14	−14	− 9	− 6	− 2	+ 3	+ 6	+11
15	− 6	+ 2	+12	+21	+29	+36	+42
16	−24	−20	−14	− 7	+ 1	+ 8	+13
17	−31	−17	− 5	+ 8	+21	+33	+46
18	−11	− 3	+ 4	+12	+19	+24	+28
19	−17	− 6	+ 5	+13	+24	+31	+38

of the subject was followed by playing off the wager selected, and the subject lost or won the appropriate amount of money.

The 319 stimulus cards were designed as follows. Every card displayed four figures (positive or negative) representing a possible outcome consisting of losing or winning the amount of money shown. On the left were two nonsense syllables (WUH and XEQ; ZOJ and ZEJ; QUJ and QUG) which stood for chance events. The events were created by the subject tossing a die with one nonsense syllable on three faces and another nonsense syllable on the other three faces. In an effort to offset recency and memory effects three different dice were used. The two right-hand columns, marked A and B, represent the wagers between which the subject was to choose.

For testing hypotheses concerning the existence of an even-chance wager utility function, it was necessary to ascertain whether the events created by the three dice were even-chance events. In practice, this was tested indirectly by assuming, for any money amounts m and n (in cents):

$$P(mEn, nEm) = \tfrac{1}{2} \text{ if and only if } P(mEn, n - 1\,E\,m) > \tfrac{1}{2}$$

$$\text{and } P(mEn, n + 1\,E\,m) < \tfrac{1}{2}.$$

Previous experiments had shown that, given this modified interpretation, subjects generally accepted the nonsense-syllable dice as generating even-chance events; therefore we tested each die only a few t:mes with each subject [11, p. 56 and Table 1, p. 57].   In all, 12 stimulus cards were used to test the dice; three additional cards were added to this group to familiarize the subject with other sorts of choices.

The remaining cards were intended to test the transitivity of alternatives and of intervals (Conditions 1 and 4).   Thirty-eight sequences of seven money amounts were chosen such that the money amounts, in the light of previous experiments [3, 11], would be approximately evenly spaced in utility for most subjects.   Table 2 gives the first 19 sequences; the other 19 sequences were produced from the first by reversing the signs (thus wins become losses and vice versa).   This symmetry provides a simple guarantee that the actuarial value of the complete set of wagers is zero; why this is desirable will be explained below.   Eight cards were made for each septuple of money amounts, yielding $8 \times 38 = 304$ cards in all.   Using the letters at the top of Table 2, the eight cards showed the following patterns:

	1	2	3	4	5	6	7	8
	a b	c d	a b	b c	a c	d e	b c	b d
	d c	f e	f e	e d	f d	g b	g f	g e

It will be observed that the triads 3, 4, 5 and 2, 7, 8 each contain just three alternatives (wagers, represented as columns), and thus may be used to test the transitivity of alternatives.   Triads 1, 2, 3 and 4, 6, 7 each compare, in effect, three intervals (represented by rows), and thus may be used to test the transitivity of intervals.   Because of this overlap between triples, we have achieved some economy in the number of observations: the total of 304 cards yields 76 triples designed to test the transitivity of alternatives and 76 triples designed to test the transitivity of intervals.

The assignment of one of the three dice to a specific card was random. Because certain wagers (not cards) were repeated once, the column (A or B) on which a wager appeared was randomized; the row (top or bottom) assigned to an outcome in a wager was also randomized.   Finally, the order in which the cards appeared was randomized, except that the 15 cards, used for learning and to test that the dice created even-chance events, preceded all others; and all three cards from a given triple appeared during the same session.

We may now make explicit two rules employed in limiting the offers appearing on the stimulus cards. No sure-thing alternatives were allowed on the ground that these might distort the results should there exist a specific utility or disutility of gambling. The second rule is intended to eliminate cases of absolute preference. In any given triple of cards, there are six distinct outcomes. Let us assign the numbers $1, 2, \cdots, 6$ to the six outcomes in order of monetary value; the number assigned to an outcome denotes its rank. The rule is this: on any given card, the sum of the ranks of the two outcomes in one wager must be equal to the sum of the ranks of the two outcomes in the other wager. Since the outcomes are chosen to be approximately evenly spaced in utility, the rule is designed to insure that two wagers that are compared shall not differ too strongly in expected utility. In application, no two wagers on one card differed by more than $4\frac{1}{2}$ cents in actuarial value. When the transitivity of intervals is tested for six outcomes, the two rules just mentioned limit the pairs of wagers to be compared to exactly three.

Of the 17 subjects 6 were women and 11 were men. Subjects were tested individually. Each subject came to three sessions, spaced a few days apart; two sessions were never on the same day for a given subject, nor more than five days apart. A session lasted between 35 and 55 minutes. Subjects were asked not to discuss the experiment during the testing; none of them had any detailed knowledge of game theory or decision theory.

At the beginning of the first session, a subject was shown the three nonsense-syllable dice and the game he was to play was explained. The subject was given $2 credit (in chips) and told that this was his stake for the three sessions. At the end of the three sessions, his chips would be redeemed in cash; if he had won, he would receive $2 plus his winnings; losses would come out of the $2; greater losses would have to be paid out of his own pocket.

The first 15 stimulus cards have been described; of these, 12 tested whether the subject accepted the dice as creating even-chance events, and three were for learning purposes. In effect, every subject did accept the dice as "fair." All of the first 15 cards were played off. After the subject gave his response by choosing wager A or B, he put the indicated die in a leather cup, shook, and rolled. Depending on the outcome, the experimenter then collected from or paid out to the subject the appropriate number of chips. The rest of the first session consisted in responses to 88 more stimulus cards testing the two sorts of transitivity. Of these, 25 choices were played off; the subject did not, of course, know whether a card would be played until after he had made his choice. The cumulative expected win for a subject who always chose the wager with the higher actuarial value was +44 cents for the 25 cards which were played off. Subjects were urged to take as long as they wished to make a decision.

During the second session the subject was asked to make 112 decisions; of these, 36 were played off. The cumulative expected win for the actuarial chooser was +39 cents.

The last session called for 104 decisions of which 31 with an expected win of +55 cents were played off. During this last session, the experimenter could play off additional wagers to increase the winnings of an unlucky subject.

As mentioned above, the actuarial value of the total of all wagers offered was zero. Since the wagers between which a subject was to choose seldom had exactly the same actuarial value, a consistent "actuarial chooser" could have expected to win if every choice had been played off. The cards chosen for playing had a small positive actuarial value for the "random chooser" and a higher actuarial value for the actuarial chooser. The hope was that the average subject with average luck would slowly increase the sum at his disposal; its size would not vary enough to influence choices substantially. It may be doubted whether this hope was entirely realized. In any case, for many subjects the sum at their disposal changed fairly radically during the play, and verbal comments by subjects suggested that this influenced choices. The highest total win (for all three sessions) was $4.87 (including the original $2 stake); the least fortunate subject received a few cents less than $2. However, several subjects had their winnings "artificially" increased during the last session by the experimenter naming for playoff certain cards on which both wagers had high positive actuarial value; unknown to the subject, it had been decided in advance that no subject would average less than $1 an hour for his time.

STATISTICAL DECISION RULES

Transitivity Regions. Consider the three related probabilities p_1, p_2, p_3 as defined for the statement of Conditions 3(a) and (b), or as defined for the statement of Conditions 7(a) and (b). Let us denote by $p^i = \langle p_1{}^i, p_2{}^i, p_3{}^i \rangle$ the ith ordered triple of probabilities so defined. p^i is a point in the unit cube U, since each component of p is between 0 and 1.

We now define two subregions of U:

Region W: p^i obeys Condition 3(a) [or 7(a)] (region of weak transitivity).

Region S: p^i obeys Condition 3(b) [or 7(b)] (region of strong transitivity).

Obviously, region S is included in region W. The hypothesis pairs to be tested may be stated:

Hypothesis H_w: For all i, p^i is in W.
Hypothesis H_w^0: There exists an i such that p^i is in $U - W$.

Hypothesis H_s: For all i, p^i is in S.
Hypothesis H_s^0: There exists an i such that p^i is in $U - S$.

Note that each of the hypotheses has two empirical interpretations; one concerns stochastic transitivity of alternatives, the other stochastic transitivity of utility intervals. We need not distinguish between the two interpretations in discussing the method of statistical testing.

Since a given choice was presented to a subject only once, it was impossible to estimate the probability triples p^i from observed frequencies. Corresponding to a given p^i, we made one observation consisting of the three responses of a subject to a triple of related stimulus cards. Suppose, for the sake of simplicity of exposition, that the pairs of wagers on a related triple of stimulus cards are arranged in the order suggested by the definitions of p_1, p_2, p_3 (pp. 240, 247); this has been done for the triples of cards shown in Table 1. Then if the subject chooses column A on the first card, there is greater likelihood that $p_1 > \frac{1}{2}$ than that $p_1 < \frac{1}{2}$; if he chooses column A on the third card, there is greater likelihood that $p_3 > \frac{1}{2}$ than that $p_3 < \frac{1}{2}$. An *observation* is an ordered triple of responses; there are just eight possible observations:

$$O_1 = \langle A, A, A \rangle \qquad O_5 = \langle B, A, A \rangle$$

$$O_2 = \langle A, A, B \rangle \qquad O_6 = \langle B, A, B \rangle$$

$$O_3 = \langle A, B, A \rangle \qquad O_7 = \langle B, B, A \rangle$$

$$O_4 = \langle A, B, B \rangle \qquad O_8 = \langle B, B, B \rangle$$

In a nonstochastic theory, observations O_1 and O_8 would be cases of intransitivity. In a stochastic theory, they merely strengthen the evidence in favor of (stochastic) intransitivity. To avoid confusion we call such observations *cyclical* because, e.g., $\langle A, A, A \rangle$ means that a certain wager a was chosen in preference to b, b to c, and c in preference to a, thus forming a cycle.

In its strict formulation, our problem is analogous to the following simpler (one- instead of three-dimensional) problem: "Test the hypothesis that each coin made by a certain coin-making machine has a bias, not necessarily an equally strong one for all coins, in favor of falling heads. You are permitted to take a finite number of coins and to toss each coin just once." Each coin of this example corresponds to a triple of choices from three pairs of our wagers. The parameter space is, respectively, the unit interval $(0, 1)$ or the unit cube U. The interval $(\frac{1}{2}, 1)$ which contains the probability of a biased coin falling heads corresponds to our transitivity region W (or S) which contains all probability triples if the subject satisfies the transitivity condition. Should this formulation be accepted, then, out of the infinite set of potential observations (coins, triples of choices) it would suffice for a single one to be outside of a specified region (the bias interval for coins, the transitivity region for response triples) to rule out the hypothesis in question. But such a fact cannot be ascertained empirically from a finite number of observations. The problem becomes accessible to empirical test if it is reformulated as follows: "A coin-making machine is characterized by an unknown probability distribution of the chance variable p (probability of a coin falling heads); one is permitted to toss coins, each only once, in order to get evidence about the distribution of p." The chance variable p corresponds, in the theory of stochastic choice, to the triple: $\langle p_1, p_2, p_3 \rangle$ defined above.

For example, one might test the following hypothesis about the distribution of p: the proportion of coins (or of triples of wagers) whose p falls into a specified region is at least 95 per cent. This approach has been used in a later study, by H. D. Block and J. Marschak [20]; with regions like S, this statistical problem is rather complicated. In the present study, we chose a simpler though more arbitrary approach by adding the following assumption: p is uniformly distributed about an unknown region which is either the whole space of possible p's (the unit cube, in our case) or a specified region (such as W or S). We have thus two pairs of alternative hypotheses:

H_w: p^i is distributed uniformly over W, and $\text{Prob}(p^i \epsilon W) = 1$.
H_0: p^i is distributed uniformly over U, and $\text{Prob}(p^i \epsilon U) = 1$.

H_s: p^i is distributed uniformly over S, and $\text{Prob}(p^i \epsilon S) = 1$.
H_0: p^i is distributed uniformly over U, and $\text{Prob}(p^i \epsilon U) = 1$.

It turns out that for testing the statistically reformulated hypotheses, all that matters (the "sufficient statistic") is the number of cyclical observations. Computations yield the following probabilities of a cyclical observation:

Probability of a Cyclical Observation

If H_0 is true	$\frac{20}{80}$ or 25.00%
If H_w is true	$\frac{15}{80}$ or 18.75%
If H_s is true	$\frac{11}{80}$ or 13.75%

The reasoning leading to the first figure (25 per cent) is obvious: if p^i is distributed uniformly over the unit cube, each of the eight possible observations $O_1, \cdots, O_8$ is equiprobable. Since two of these are cyclical, the probability that a given observation is cyclical if H_0 is true is $\frac{1}{4}$. The other two figures ($\frac{15}{80}$ and $\frac{11}{80}$) were obtained [7] by integrating over the specified region (W or S, respectively) the expression

$$p_1 p_2 p_3 + (1 - p_1)(1 - p_2)(1 - p_3)$$

(i.e., the probability that O_1 or O_8 will occur), and dividing by the volume of that region.

The *decision rule* used was this (we state it for H_w; that for H_s is analogous). Accept H_w if the number r of cyclical observations is less than c, where c (a number obtainable from tables of binomial distribution) is such that $\text{Prob}(r < c$, when H_0 is true$) = \text{Prob}(r \geq c$, when H_w is true). The two probabilities just written are, respectively, that of committing the error of accepting H_w when H_0 is true, and that of committing the error of accepting H_0 when H_w is true. By making them equal, we make the larger of the two error probabilities a minimum. The significance level of test is equal to both of them. If instead of this "minimax" principle that takes into account both kinds of error, we had followed the custom of merely "testing the null hypothesis," the decision could have been made, given our number of observations, with a much lower probability of errors of Type I (called "significance level"). The latter would then have been defined as the probability of rejecting H_0 when it is true. However, the nature of the problem forces us to treat the null hypothesis and its alternative symmetrically.

In the present experiment we made on each subject a total of 76 observations for each hypothesis; 26 observations for each hypothesis were made during the last session. Applying our computations and decision rule to these figures, we obtain:

[7] With the help of Karol Valpreda Walsh and Robert C. Mercer, which we gratefully acknowledge.

Number of Observations

Decision Rules	$n = 76$ (All Sessions)		$n = 26$ (Session III)	
Accept H_w if r is less than:	17		6	
Significance level:		24%		35%
Accept H_s if r is less than:	15		5	
Significance level:		10%		23%

TABLE 3.   Number of Cyclical Observations for Each Subject

	Testing Transitivity of Alternatives				Testing Transitivity of Intervals			
Sessions	I	II	III	Total	I	II	III	Total
Number of triples offered	22	28	26	76	22	28	26	76
Expected Number Under Uniform Distribution Over the Region of:	Number of Cyclical Observations							
Unit cube	5.50	7.00	6.50	19.00	5.50	7.00	6.50	19.00
Weak transitivity	4.13	5.25	4.88	14.25	4.13	5.25	4.88	14.25
Strong transitivity	3.03	3.85	3.58	10.45	3.03	3.85	3.58	10.45
Subject								
A	4	0	0	4	0	0	1	1
B	3	5	2	10	1	6	3	10
C	5	3	3	11	6	5	5	16
D	4	7	0	11	4	5	2	11
E	1	0	0	1	0	3	3	6
F	3	6	0	9	5	10	2	17
G	2	1	2	5	3	0	0	3
H	2	1	1	4	4	2	1	7
I	1	2	1	4	3	3	0	6
J	2	9	5	16	3	3	6	12
K	4	2	2	8	3	5	3	11
L	1	1	0	2	1	1	0	2
M	2	2	1	5	7	5	1	13
N	6	3	7	16	2	0	3	5
O	4	2	1	7	3	2	0	5
P	1	3	3	7	2	1	3	6
Q	7	5	2	14	1	4	2	7
Average no. of cyclical observations	3.06	3.06	1.76	7.88	2.82	3.24	2.06	8.12
Proportion of cyclical observations	13.9%	10.9%	6.8%	10.4%	12.8%	11.6%	7.9%	10.7%

One obtains, of course, much lower significance levels if one is permitted to regard the responses of all subjects as belonging to the same statistical population, thus increasing the sample size by the factor of 17 (the number of subjects). Using the normal distribution formula, one can compute the decision rules at which the probabilities of errors of both kinds are equal. The rules are, for samples of this magnitude: reject H_w if and only if the proportion of cyclical observations is larger than 21.7 per cent; reject H_s if and only if this proportion is larger than 18.7 per cent (compare these figures with the last line of Table 3). The significance levels are as follows: for Session III, 0.055 for H_w and 0.001 for H_s; for the total of all sessions, 0.003 for H_w and negligible for H_s.

Finally, we observe that, if the proportion of cyclical observations falls very much below the probability indicated above for weak or strong transitivity, we shall presume that the assumption of uniform distribution over the (weak or strong) transitivity region is to be corrected: we shall have to assign lower weights to those points of the region that lie near its boundaries other than the facets of the unit cube.

As another and possibly preferable way of exploiting the information more fully, Herman Chernoff and Roy Radner [8] suggested computing the likelihood ratio for each pair of hypotheses and each possible set of observations. Let $P_0(r, n)$ be the probability that, out of n responses, exactly r are cyclical if H_0 is true. With a corresponding notation for the cases when H_w or H_s are true, we can use the ratios

$$L_w(r, n) = P_w(r, n)/P_0(r, n) \qquad \text{and} \qquad L_s(r, n) = P_s(r, n)/P_0(r, n)$$

to convey the confidence that one may attach, on the basis of observations, to the hypothesis H_w or H_s, each against the hypothesis H_0. Using the binomial distribution formulas, one derives from the probabilities of cyclical observations ($\frac{20}{80}$ for H_0, $\frac{15}{80}$ for H_w and $\frac{11}{80}$ for H_s), the two likelihood ratios

$$L_w(r, n) = (\tfrac{9}{13})^r(\tfrac{13}{12})^n \qquad \text{and} \qquad L_s(r, n) = (\tfrac{11}{23})^r(\tfrac{23}{20})^n$$

These numbers are tabulated in Table 4, for $n = 76$ and $n = 26$ (with r ranging from 0 to respectively 17 and 7), and can be used to interpret, subject by subject, the results shown in Table 3 for the total of observations and for Session III: [9]

[8] In an oral communication.

[9] Again, if we regard all subjects as belonging to the same statistical population, the likelihood ratios are naturally much higher; they are of the order of many thousands, for both H_w and H_s, even if the proportion of cyclical observations is as high as 15 per cent.

TABLE 4.   Likelihood Ratios (Approximate)

No. of Cyclical Responses: $r =$	H_w Against H_0		H_s Against H_0	
	$n = 76$	$n = 26$	$n = 76$	$n = 26$
0	430	8.0	40,000	38
1	300	5.5	20,000	18
2	210	3.8	9,300	8.7
3	140	2.7	4,500	4.1
4	100	1.8	2,100	2.0
5	69	1.3	1,000	0.9
6	49	0.9	490	0.5
7	33	0.6	240	0.2
8	23	0.4	110	0.1
9	16		54	
10	11		26	
11	7.6		12	
12	5.3		5.9	
13	3.6		2.8	
14	2.5		1.3	
15	1.7		0.6	
16	1.2		0.3	
17	0.8		0.1	

RESULTS OF EXPERIMENT

Table 3 summarizes the main experimental findings.   For a large majority of subjects, the number of cyclical responses falls far below the expected frequency under strong transitivity (both of alternatives and of intervals).   Under the null hypothesis, one out of four triples could, on the average, be expected to be cyclical; this would result in 38 cyclical responses for the total of 152 triples, or 19 for the 76 triples which tested each of the two varieties of transitivity.   The highest total number of cyclical responses for any subject was 28 (subject J), while subject F had the highest number of cyclical responses (17) for a set of 76 triples.   The expected numbers of cyclical responses in 76 triples for H_w and H_s are 14.25 and 10.45 respectively.   Two subjects (J and N) in the case of transitivity of alternatives, and two subjects (C and F) in the case of the transitivity of intervals, exceeded the number of cyclical responses expected on the assumption that H_w is true.   The *average* number of cyclical responses for all subjects on the 76 triples testing transi-

TABLE 5. All Sessions (76 Triads); Distribution of Subjects by the Number of Cyclical Observations (Correlation Coefficient = 0.49)

Column groups (No. of Cyclical Observations for Intervals): columns 1–13 = **Accept Strong and Weak Transitivity**; columns 14–17 = **Accept Weak Transitivity Only**.

Row groups (No. of Cyclical Observations for Alternatives): rows 1–14 = **Accept Strong and Weak Transitivity**; rows 15–17 = **Accept Weak Transitivity Only**.

No. of Cyclical Observations for Alternatives	1	2	3	4	5	6	7	8	9	10	11	12	13	14	15	16	17	No. of Subjects
1						E												1
2		L																1
3																		0
4	A					I	H											3
5			G										M					2
6																		0
7					O	P												2
8											K							1
9										B								1
10											D							1
11																C	F	2
12																		0
13																		0
14							Q											1
15																		0
16					N							J						2
17																		0
No. of subjects	1	1	1	0	2	3	2	0	0	1	2	1	1	0	0	1	1	

Column totals: **Accept Strong and Weak Transitivity** (cols 1–13). **Accept Weak Transitivity Only** (cols 14–17): 0 0 1 1.

tivity of alternatives is 10.4; the average on the 76 triples testing transitivity of intervals is 10.7. These figures are close to the prediction of 10.45 cyclical responses if strong transitivity holds.

The last line of Table 3 should be related to what was said about using the responses of *all* subjects as a sample from the same population (p. 257). On this basis (and under the assumptions of the foregoing section regarding *a priori* distribution), weak as well as strong transitivity, for both alternatives and intervals, should be accepted at a quite low (i.e., strict) significance level.[10]

Table 5 applies the decision rules (p. 256) to each subject (using the results from all sessions). For all subjects, Hypothesis H_w of weak transitivity had to be accepted with respect both to alternatives and to intervals (though at a very modest, i.e., high, significance level). For all but two subjects, strong transitivity had to be accepted (at a significance level of 10 per cent), but the two subjects were not the same for alternatives and for intervals. The correlation of 0.49 between behavior with respect to alternatives and behavior with respect to intervals is just significant at the 5 per cent level for 17 observation pairs; however, it should not be judged significant at that level if one considers the fact that some of the data were used in two ways as described on p. 250.

An interesting feature of the data displayed in Table 3 is the change in the proportion of cyclical observations from session to session. Although not always evident for individual subjects, when the results for all subjects are averaged there is a systematic decrease in the percentage of cyclical observations from session to session both for alternatives and for intervals. During the first session, the over-all proportion of cycles is 13.4 per cent; during the second session, 10.5 per cent; during the third 7.4 per cent.

For the third session, the decision rule indicates that the null hypothesis must be accepted for one subject (N) for transitivity of alternatives, and for one subject (J) for transitivity of intervals. There is also one subject in each category (subjects J and C respectively) for whom weak but not strong transitivity must be accepted. In every other case the hypothesis of strong transitivity may be accepted.

During the three sessions, there was an increase in the correlation between performance with respect to alternatives and performance with respect to intervals, as follows:

---

[10] The size of the sample used for the *joint* test of transitivity of alternatives *and* of intervals is somewhat reduced by the overlapping between the sets of cards used for these two tests separately (see p. 250); this raises the significance level somewhat.

Session	I	II	III	Total
Correlation	0.00	0.52	0.58	0.49

The change from I to II is significant at the 5 per cent level.

DISCUSSION

Assuming that a utility function of money unique up to a linear transformation exists for a subject, it is possible to make some rough inferences from the data concerning the shape of the utility curve (a curve which plots utility against the money amount of the basic alternatives).

TABLE 6.   Responses for Each Subject According to Actuarial Value and Dispersion (Total Number of Wagers = 304)

Subject	Actuarial Responses	Pairs of Wagers of Unequal Actuarial Value — Counteractuarial Responses — Dispersion Chosen High	Low	Total	Pairs of Wagers of Equal Actuarial Value — Dispersion Chosen High	Low	All Pairs of Wagers — Dispersion Chosen High	Low
A	227	10	12	22	11	44	134	170
B	149	75	25	100	41	14	213	91
C	162	54	33	87	37	18	184	120
D	165	75	9	84	43	12	234	70
E	174	45	30	75	29	26	168	135
F	161	73	15	88	41	14	223	81
G	149	79	21	100	43	12	225	79
H	175	65	9	74	46	9	225	79
I	200	36	13	49	34	21	181	123
J	162	50	37	87	27	28	164	140
K	167	54	28	82	34	21	184	120
L	182	15	52	67	18	37	103	201
M	136	49	64	113	28	27	137	167
N	160	53	36	89	37	18	177	127
O	216	12	21	33	12	43	127	177
P	165	23	61	84	18	37	104	200
Q	145	58	46	104	34	21	169	135

Table 6 classifies the responses of each subject to the 304 cards used to test transitivity. On 249 cards the two wagers had different actuarial values; the second and fifth columns in Table 6 show in how many cases the subject chose the wager with the higher *actuarial value* ("actuarial responses") and in how many cases the subject chose the wager with the lower actuarial value ("counteractuarial responses"). On every card, one wager involved both the highest and the lowest money amount, whereas the other wager involved outcomes of intermediate money value; see p. 251. Responses may therefore be classified according as the subjects chose the wager with the greater or the lesser *dispersion* (the dispersion of an even-chance wager is the difference in money value between the two outcomes). The second and third columns of figures in Table 6 show how often the counteractuarial choices favored high or low dispersion. Fifty-five cards showed wagers of equal actuarial value; these responses are classified to indicate whether the high or the low dispersion wager was chosen. In evaluating the figures in Table 6, it is necessary to know that of the 249 cards with wagers of unequal actuarial value, 124 paired the higher actuarial value with the higher dispersion and 125 paired the higher actuarial value with the lower dispersion.

A subject for whom utility was linear in money and with absolute preferences between all pairs of wagers offered would always choose the wager with the higher actuarial value. There is no subject who did this. Subjects *A* and *O* come closest with 22 and 33 counteractuarial answers. Both these subjects show some preference for low dispersion when they depart from the actuarial choice.

We may call a subject *conservative* who, when departing from the actuarial answer, more often than not chose the wager with the lower dispersion, for such a subject would, from an insurance point of view, be paying for the privilege of taking the smaller risk. In the same way we may call a subject *venturesome* who, when departing from the actuarial answer, more often than not chose the wager with the higher dispersion. Using this criterion, five subjects were conservative and twelve were venturesome. In the light of previous experimental results with college students [3, 11], the percentage of venturesome subjects is perhaps surprising. Part of the explanation may lie in the fact that the subjects were volunteers and knew, before they volunteered, that the experiment involved some financial risk.

A subject who invariably chose the higher or the lower dispersion would yield no cyclical observations (no pair of wagers showed the same dispersion, since this would lead to absolute preference), whereas the consistent actuarial chooser would be certain to show no more than six cyclical triads of responses (there were six triples of cards where each pair of wagers had the same actuarial value). It is therefore an interesting question to what extent the results obtained were caused by actuarial, conservative, or venturesome strategies (conscious or otherwise) on the part of the subjects. Table 6 makes it obvious that no subject consistently followed any of the three policies. Comparison of Tables 3 and 6 brings out the fact that the four subjects with the largest number of cyclical observations (subjects C, D, F, and J) include none of the five subjects with the largest number of counteractuarial responses. On the other hand, subject L, with the lowest number (4) of cyclical triples, seems to owe this score in part to a conservative taste for low dispersion wagers, whereas subject A, with only five cyclical triples, has the fewest counteractuarial responses.

We may also ask whether the frequency of cyclical observations

TABLE 7.   Actuarial Characteristics of Triples Offered and the
Frequency of Cyclical Observations

		Number of Observations			
Character of Triples Offered *		Total	Cyclical	Non-cyclical	Percentage of Cyclical in Total
A	$d = 0$ on all three cards	102	17	85	16.7
B	$0 < d \leq \frac{1}{2}¢$ on all three cards	272	59	213	21.7
(A, B)	$0 \leq d \leq \frac{1}{2}¢$ on all three cards	(374)	(76)	(298)	(20.3)
C	$d \geq 1¢$ on all three cards	442	49	393	11.1
D	All other triples	1,768	147	1,621	8.3
(C, D)	$d > \frac{1}{2}¢$ on at least one of the three cards	(2,210)	(196)	(2,014)	(9.3)
	Total	2,584	272	2,312	10.5

Variation of Frequency Between Groups	χ^2	P	Significant?
A against B	1.3	>0.25	No
C against D	3.2	>0.05	Hardly
(A, B) against C	13.7	<0.005	Yes
(A, B) against (C, D)	43	<0.005	Yes

* d = difference between the actuarial values of the two wagers on a card.

depends on the size of the differences in the actuarial values of each pair of wagers. One would expect cyclical observations to occur relatively more often in cases where these differences are small and thus provide no guidance, or only a weak one, for the choice between two wagers and the ranking of three wagers. In Table 7, four groups—A, B, C, D—of triples are defined, the number of observations (i.e., the number of triples times 17, the number of subjects) is entered for each group, and the frequency of cyclical versus noncyclical observations is given. A finer grouping of triples was precluded by sample size limitations. In fact, the distinction between groups A and B proved to be statistically insignificant (and hence the unexpectedly *lower* percentage of cyclical observations in group A compared with group B is not statistically significant). Significant and interesting results are obtained by comparing group (A, B) (which is the union of A and B and thus consists of all triples with actuarial differences not exceeding $\frac{1}{2}$ cent on any card) either with group C (actuarial differences not smaller than 1 cent on any card) or with the composite group (C, D) (actuarial difference exceeds $\frac{1}{2}$ cent on at least one card). These comparisons tend to confirm the hypothesis that small actuarial differences favor the occurrence of cyclical choices.

It may be asked whether the decrease in the proportion of cyclical observations from session to session was accompanied by an increase in the proportion of actuarial responses. The following figures show that it was.

	Sessions		
	I	II	III
Number of cards with wagers of different actuarial value	1,241	1,598	1,394
Number of actuarial choices	810	1,106	979
Percentage	65.3	69.2	70.2
Number of triples	748	952	884
Number of noncyclical observations	648	845	819
Percentage	86.6	89.5	92.6

The increase in the proportion of actuarial choices was statistically significant ($P < 0.05$) from Session I to Session II and definitely not significant ($P > 0.50$) from Session II to Session III. On the other hand, the proportion of noncyclical observations increased highly significantly ($P < 0.01$) from Session II to Session III, although it did not increase significantly ($P > 0.2$) from Session I to Session II. This suggests that, to the extent to which there was an increase in noncyclical observations, it should not be explained by the increase in actuarial choices. However, a more detailed analysis would be necessary to clarify this point.[11]

In the table just given, the proportion of noncyclical observations to the total number of triples of cards is, in each of the three sessions, consistently higher than the proportion of actuarial choices to the total number of cards. A formal test shows the difference between the proportions to be statistically highly significant. Thus, considering all subjects to belong to the same population, the probability that a subject's response to a triad of cards will be noncyclical is higher than the probability that his response to a single card will be actuarial.

Broadly speaking, the present experiment shows that in its context decisions are better explained by certain implications of a stochastic decision theory than by the assumption that choices are made at random. The interest of this result would be impugned if the same data could be as well or better explained by alternative hypotheses. For this reason, we have been considering the plausibility of the claim that, to the extent that subjects avoided cyclical triads of responses (and hence tended to verify the hypotheses under test), this was caused by the more or less consistent employment of actuarial, venturesome, or conservative policies by the subjects. In Table 8 we attempt a direct comparison of three alternative theories as predictors of certain observed choices.

Assume that a related triple of cards was always arranged in the "normal form," shown in Table 1, and that the three cards were presented to the subject in order from left to right. If a subject chose one left and one right column for the first two cards, the hypotheses H_w (or H_s) as well as H_0 would predict equal probabilities of choice for each wager on the third card. The interesting cases arise when the left column or the right column is chosen on both the first two cards; then the hypotheses H_w and H_s will give the higher probability of choice to the opposite column on the third card (for example, if column A is chosen on each of the first two cards, column B is more apt to be chosen on the third card if the hypotheses are true).

The first two columns of figures in Table 8 show how often the subject chose the more probable wager on the third card for those cases where both of the first two choices were wager A or wager B. The third and fourth columns show how often, for the same cards for which results are

[11] We are grateful to R. Rosett for computations and suggestions.

given in the first two columns, the subject chose the wager with the higher actuarial value. The total number of predictions is lower because some cards had two wagers with equal actuarial values. The last two columns show, for the same cards again, how often the subject chose in accord with his general tendency to favor low or high dispersion wagers. This tendency was determined from the figures in Table 6, showing how often the counteractuarial responses of the subject favored low or high dispersion.

At the bottom of Table 8, the three theories are compared with respect to the percentage of correct predictions. The expected utility theory is superior to the other two with 81.6 per cent correct predictions; the actuarial theory is slightly better than the dispersion theory with 72.2 per

TABLE 8. Comparison of Expected Utility, Actuarial, and Dispersion
Theories as Predictors

Subject	Expected Utility Theory		Actuarial Theory		Dispersion Theory	
	Correct	Incorrect	Correct	Incorrect	Correct	Incorrect
A	84	5	74	5	56	33
B	63	20	39	29	60	23
C	46	27	42	20	44	29
D	86	22	69	24	84	24
E	76	7	56	19	50	33
F	80	26	68	28	74	32
G	86	8	47	33	80	14
H	100	11	74	22	92	19
I	71	10	66	8	50	31
J	49	28	43	25	42	35
K	52	20	43	17	48	25
L	83	4	60	17	64	23
M	57	18	43	25	50	25
N	63	21	53	22	59	25
O	76	12	69	8	57	31
P	70	13	52	24	68	15
Q	70	21	41	35	48	43
Totals	1213	273	939	361	1026	460
Percentage correct	81.6		72.2		69.0	

cent correct predictions as compared to 69.0 per cent correct predictions.

Each of the differences between these proportions (taken pairwise) is statistically significant ($P < 0.01$). It is also worth noting that for every individual subject, the expected utility theory predicted better than the dispersion theory; however, the actuarial theory was very slightly superior to the expected utility theory for two subjects (subjects C and J).

A remark is called for concerning the marked decrease in the proportion of cyclical observations from session to session. It seems attractive to call this a learning phenomenon. However, what was learned was certainly not connected with specific cards, wagers, money amounts, or triples of cards, for none of these was repeated in two sessions (specific cards and triples were not repeated even in the same session). The evidence indicates that the subjective probability of the chance events was firmly established from the start. We may say that the subject learned transitive behavior or that he learned to maximize expected utility (at least in the sense of our stochastic definitions of these terms). There is also evidence that some subjects learned to make actuarial choices. The matter seems worthy of fuller study, both theoretical and experimental.

SUMMARY

The experiment was designed to test whether certain conditions hold which are necessary for the existence of a utility function over the set of money wagers as well as over the set of money amounts. Seventeen subjects were tested individually in three sessions each. Every choice involved a risk since subjects did not know in advance which choices would be played off, i.e., would result in actually paying (or receiving) money. The main results may be summarized as follows:

1. For all subjects, the number of intransitive triads of responses (called "cyclical observations") was, as required by the hypotheses, less than the number expected by chance.

2. A statistical test, based on responses to nonrepeated choice situations, indicates the acceptance, for all subjects, of the hypotheses of weak stochastic transitivity of alternatives and weak stochastic transitivity of utility intervals.

3. For 15 subjects in each case, the acceptance of the hypotheses of strong stochastic transitivity of alternatives and of intervals is indicated.

4. Both in testing the transitivity of alternatives and the transitivity

of intervals, there was a systematic decrease in the number of cyclical responses from session to session.

5. A comparison shows the superior accuracy of a stochastic theory of decision in predicting certain choices as compared to two alternative theories. On the whole, the evidence does not appear to support the claim that the low number of cyclical observations can be wholly explained by simple policies based on the actuarial values of wagers or on the degree of risk (dispersion).

REFERENCES

1. von Neumann, J., and O. Morgenstern, *Theory of Games and Economic Behavior,* 2nd ed. Princeton, Princeton University Press, 1947.
2. Savage, L. J., *Foundations of Statistics,* New York, John Wiley and Sons, 1951.
3. Mosteller, F., and P. Nogee, "An Experimental Measurement of Utility," *Journal of Political Economy,* **59,** 1951, pp. 371–404.
4. Edwards, Ward, Articles on probability preferences, *American Journal of Psychology,* **66,** 1953, pp. 345–364; **67,** 1954, pp. 56–67; **67,** 1954, pp. 68–95.
5. Papandreou, Andreas G., with the collaboration of O. H. Sauerlander, O. H. Brownlee, L. Hurwicz, and W. Franklyn, "A Test of a Stochastic Theory of Choice," *University of California Publications in Economics,* **16,** No. 1, 1957, pp. 1–18.
6. Fechner, Gustav Theodor, *Elemente der Psychophysik,* Leipzig, 1859 and 1889.
7. Marschak, Jacob, "Norms and Habits of Decision Making Under Certainty," *Mathematical Models of Human Behavior—Proceedings of a Symposium,* Dunlap and Associates, Stamford, Conn., 1955.
8. Luce, R. Duncan, "A Probabilistic Theory of Utility," *Econometrica,* **26,** 1958, pp. 193–224.
9. Luce, R. Duncan, and Howard Raiffa, *Games and Decisions,* New York, John Wiley and Sons, 1957 (Appendix I, "A Probabilistic Theory of Utility," pp. 371–384).
10. Guilford, J. P., *Psychometric Methods,* New York, 1954.
11. Davidson, Donald, Patrick Suppes, and Sidney Siegel, *Decision Making, An Experimental Approach,* Stanford University Press, 1957.
12. Suppes, P., and M. Winet, "An Axiomatization of Utility Based on the Notion of Utility Differences," *Management Science,* **I,** 1955, pp. 259–270.
13. Alt, Franz, "Ueber die Messbarkeit des Nutzens," *Zeitschrift fuer Nationalœkonomie,* **7,** No. 2, 1936, pp. 161–169.
14. Suppes, P., "A Set of Axioms for Paired Comparisons" (dittoed), Center for Behavioral Sciences, 1956.
15. Debreu, Gerard, "Stochastic Choice and Cardinal Utility," *Econometrica,* **26,** 1958, pp. 440–444.
16. Scott, Dana, and P. Suppes, "Foundational Aspects of Theories of Measurement," *Journal of Symbolic Logic,* **23,** 1958.
17. Vail, Stephan, "A Stochastic Model for Utilities," Seminar on the Application of Mathematics to the Social Sciences, Ann Arbor, University of Michigan, 1953 (dittoed).

18. Ramsey, Frank P., *The Foundations of Mathematics and Other Logical Essays*, London, Routledge & Kegan Paul, 1931.
19. Debreu, Gerard, "Cardinal Utility for Even-Chance Mixtures of Sure Prospects," *Review of Economic Studies*, **26,** 1958–1959.
20. Block, H. D., and Jacob Marschak, "Random Orderings and Stochastic Theories of Responses," Cowles Foundation Discussion Paper No. 66, 1959 (mimeographed).

INDEX